GW00836306

Brigitte Klesse · Hans Mayr

# European Glass
# from 1500–1800

The Ernesto Wolf Collection

Kremayr & Scheriau

© 1987 by Brigitte Klesse und Hans Mayr
Published by Kremayr & Scheriau, Vienna
Layout: Hans Mayr
Lithography: Beissner & Co., Vienna
Printed in Austria by Mechitharisten-Druckerei, Vienna
Bound by G. + G., Hollabrunn
Translation: Perran Wood
ISBN 3 218 00465 9

# Foreward

Even in the formative years of my childhood, I had an enthusiasm for all things of beauty. In those early years, it did not matter whether that beauty resided in poetry, literature, or the pictorial arts, and it was not until my eighteenth year that the visual perception of beauty assumed an overhelming importance for me. This concern for the esthetic beauty of objects soon became an essential consideration in my initial activities as a collector. I early resolved, therefore, to acquire only those objects which held the qualities inherent in masterpieces of art, and, as a collector, I have ever since sought every opportunity to achieve this goal.

My interests have always been diversified. Although this catalogue on decorated glass of the Renaissance and Baroque eras provides a partial insight into my special interest in glass, which covers the entire history of glassmaking from its beginning in Mesopotamia and Egypt, I have as well for many years pursued the collecting of printed volumes which delineate the history of the illustrated book, seeking works with original paintings and graphics. I have placed my emphasis primarily on the acquiring of a very few important illuminated manuscripts of the Middle Ages and particularly illustrated books of the 15th and early 16th centuries. In the 19th and 20th centuries, the focus has been on works which illustrate the artistry of painters since Manet and Lautrec until the present day. The extreme diversity of my collecting endeavors can perhaps best be seen in the variety of objects which have fascinated me, ranging from antique lace from the Renaissance and Baroque periods to ritual spoons from Africa.

In the realm of ancient art, I have acquired single pieces of Cycladic origin, archaic objects from the Near East, works of pre-Columbian art, early Islamic ceramics, and bronze objects of the Etruscans, from Luristan, as well as from the Middle Ages. My collections also include old jewelry, paintings, sculpture, and old and modern masters. Aside from a fascination with objects, which I have been fortunate in being able to collect, I have since the 1950s and the 1960s taken an active role in the area of the public arts, serving as one of the directors of the São Paulo Biennial and of the city's newly formed Museum for Modern Arts. My sponsorship of living Brazilian artists has also enabled me to form one of the best collections of contemporary arts of Brazil. In 1958 I married the sculptor Liuba, and we have continued to add to the collections following our combined interests.

The collection of European glass, which is only partly reflected in this volume, began many years ago. It was begun by my father, Alfred Wolf, in Stuttgart, Germany, in the 1920s, and he was particularly fortunate in having as his extraordinary advisor the noted Gustav Pazaurek, then Director of the Kunstgewerbemuseum of Stuttgart. Unfortunately, the economic crisis of the later 1920s and later the emigration of my father and his family forced him to discontinue his collecting activities. Thus it was not until after 1945 that I was able to resume with him the development of our glass collection in New York. By that time, trouble with his heart precluded his active interest in adding to the collection, but I could always count on my father's advice and financial support to enrich our collection with the most important glasses.

Thanks to a close friendship with the most prominent dealers in the field of glass – Sami Rosenberg, Leopold Blumka, and Julius Carlebach – I was very often given the opportunity to be the first to see pieces which appeared on the market in the early years after the Second World War. As a result, I was able to purchase the most beautiful objects which were then available. It is interesting to note that very few of the glasses which appear in this catalogue were added to my collection during the past two decades, for the majority of the most significant pieces for sale during these years would not have added any additional value to the collection, particularly as I was not disposed to pay the absurd prices being asked for them.

The breadth and richness of the beauty and artistry of the glass added to the collection in the 1920s and immediately after the Second World War have, therefore, directed my collecting interests into areas of glass which will broaden the scope of this collection. For the past twenty-five years I have concentrated my glass collecting on very early Middle Eastern, Hellenistic, Roman, Merovingian, and Islamic objects. By 1990, I hope to exhibit a collection of these more ancient objects. This collection should equal the quality of the European objects which can be viewed in this volume. I also intend to publish a separate catalog of the undecorated glasses from the Gothic and Renaissance periods in my collection.

The creation of this beautiful catalogue would not have been possible except for the help of two colleagues in particular. I would like, therefore, to express my appreciation, first of all, to Frau Professor Dr. Brigitte Klesse, who has in recent years dedicated all of her free time to the work of compiling this catalog. I think that I may say without reservation that never before has a catalog of a private collection been prepared with such thorough scholarly research. Thus her efforts will no doubt be rewarded by the recognition of her work as one of the most important technical publications in the literature of this highly specialized field.

I am also most grateful to Professor Hans Mayr who is responsible for the photographs of the objects and for the layout of this volume. Without the help of these two able individuals, this permanent record of the objects from my collection which are being exhibited in the United States and Europe would not be possible.

Ernesto Wolf

# Preface

It is not often that an exhibition or publication produces genuine surprises. However, glass historians will be delighted by their first view of the Wolf Collection, as it includes a number of masterpieces long thought to have disappeared. Ernesto Wolf astounded his fellow enthusiasts and historians at the 1982 International Glass Conference at Corning, when, Glass for the first time, he showed them photographs of the highlights of his collection. It was the first glimpse of glasses, recorded in the literature of fifty, sixty, or a hundred years ago, and subsequently thought to have succumbed to the vicissitudes of two world wars, now reappearing in all their glory. A few notable examples will suffice to convince art historians of the importance of the Wolf Collection.

In 1894, on a visit in Cologne, Gustav Pazaurek saw an interesting and particularly richly-decorated *Zwischengold* beaker inscribed "P. Pacificius Kliegel" (cat. no. 206). First published by him in 1898 as a signed example, it has remained the key piece in determining the origins of this group of delicate glasses. As the whereabouts of this beaker was unknown for over eighty years, it had been impossible to confirm or challenge his contention that the name, "Kliegel" represented a signature. The old Pazaurek interpretation was only recently refuted by Jarmila Brožová when she studied the latest photographs from Mr Wolf, as part of her detailed researches into the identity of the Franciscan monk. Nonetheless, one of the most important pieces in this group had at last resurfaced.

A similar fate befell the only recorded, fully-signed and dated, piece by the highly-gifted Thuringian glass engraver Andreas Friedrich Sang (cat. no. 151). Robert Schmidt, Christian Scherer and Gustav Pazaurek in their published works all mentioned the flask, which was still at that time in the collection of the Dukes of Anhalt-Köthen at Schloss Dessau. This flask was in fact merely a cover to a goblet, commissioned by Duke August Ludwig of Anhalt-Köthen in 1729 to commemorate the first completed year of his reign. What a happy coincidence then to find this flask reunited with its original goblet in the Wolf Collection. Once again the richest and finest example of this artist's *œuvre* can be included in the mainstream of historical research.

No less exciting has been the reappearance of the Augustus Rex goblet (cat. no. 142), unique within the context of the art of *Hochschnitt* decoration on glass. When Robert Schmidt knew the piece it was in the collection of Prof. K. von Bardeleben in Jena. Influenced by certain features such as the lid in the form of an electoral cap, and the carving of the crowned cypher on stem and finial, he attributed the piece to Gottfried Spiller. Later he altered his opinion in favor of Gottfried Gondelach, after seeing a signed example of this artist's work in the Mühsam Collection in Berlin. Pazaurek, who did not always agree with Schmidt, supported this attribution in his seminal monograph on Gondelach, although he did emphasize its atypical qualities. It was only in 1937 that Hans von Schlieben had the good fortune to find the bill from the Dresden glasshouse for this goblet. At last a correct attribution was possible, although this could not be verified as the goblet was now thought to have been lost. Even as recently as the 1960s Franz-Adrian Dreier relied on the theories of Schmidt and Pazaurek, although now that the goblet can be compared to its description in the bill of 1731, the extraordinary attributes of the Dresden glasshouse at the court of Augustus the Strong are confirmed once and for all.

From the early 1920s, when Robert Schmidt and Walter Bernt last saw it at Schloss Dessau, the signed goblet with a rendering of Daniel in the lions' den by Hermann Schwinger (cat. no. 70) was also lost to the view of the glass connoisseur. This was all the more regrettable as the relatively small number of signed pieces by him reveal him to have been by far the most gifted of the second generation of Nuremberg engravers. This was also one of his earliest works, which, with the exception of the 'St. Christopher' goblet formerly in the Mühsam Collection, had been long neglected by scholars. The Wolf Collection, which also includes the incomparable portrait goblet of the Emperor Leopold I (cat. no. 71), illustrates the complete artistic development of this metic's talents. These talents were unfortunately cut short by his untimely death at forty-three.

From the nineteenth-century collection of Breslau commercial councillor and town clerk Theodor Wiskott, and unknown to the great glass historians Robert Schmidt and Gustav Pazaurek, come more jewels of the glass engraver's art which were hidden away for many years. On the one hand there is a Nuremberg baluster goblet with the exceptionally fine portrait of the Würtemburg Prince-Bishop, Gottfried von Guttenberg (cat. no. 72), which throws a new light on late Nuremberg portraiture. On the other, there is an exquisite signed work by the highly-cultivated Berlin glass-engraver Elias Rosbach, embellished with an allegory of Happiness and Transience (cat. no. 137), which was previously known only in the form of a dull workshop copy in Görlitz. Those who are familiar with Rosbach's signed *œuvre* and its fluctuations in quality, will be delighted to encounter a work which so vividly communicates the joy of artistic creation.

Robert Schmidt, in his 'Brandenburgische Gläser,' drew attention to a *Hochschnitt* and *Tiefschnitt* goblet, at that time in the Gotisches Haus in Wörlitz, as being one of the finest early works of the Prussian Court Glasshouse engraver Gottfried Spiller (cat. no. 128). After the dispersal of the collection of the Dukes of Anhalt-Dessau in the 1920s, only Pazaurek returned to this piece in his researches. From the same collection we also find the Halloren *Humpen* (cat. no. 52) discussed by Robert Schmidt in his Handbook on Glass, and the rare and historically important glass with a view of Schloss Coswig on the Elbe (cat. no. 51). It shows the castle as it appeared in 1676 during a period of alterations lasting for a decade from 1667, a stage unrecorded in any other contemporary view. Unappreciated in 1916 when it appeared in the auction catalogue of the renowned Stuttgart collecter Philipp Schwarz, the elegant cold-decorated vase from Hall-in-Tyrol undeservedly sank into oblivion, although a rare example from the group of outstanding blue-tinted vessels produced in this glassmaking center.

From the Wolf Collection one could single out rows of these glasses which had taken an important place in contemporary glass research around the time of the First World War and subsequently disappeared without trace. The few which have been selected from different periods and regions confirm the importance and variety of this collection. A careful study of the exhibition catalogue will show that, with the exception of English glass, all the important glassmaking centers are represented by major examples. The collection is particularly strong in Venetian glass of the sixteenth century, Bohemian-Silesian seventeenth and eighteenth-century engraved wares, and seventeenth- and eighteenth-century glasses decorated with the diamond-point in the Netherlands.

For a number of reasons, this idiosyncratic collection remained out of the public eye from the twenties until 1956, when a small part of it was exhibited in Zurich. The worsening political situation prior to the outbreak of the Second World War had led to the removal of many works of art from Germany. The reappearance of the Wolf Collection in 1956 acted as a catalyst in the revival of glass scholarship after a long period of inactivity. As a result, historians such as Robert Charleston and Astone Gasparetto were able to include a number of particularly fine examples of Venetian art in their contemporary studies. These included the enameled and gilt beaker found in Damascus (cat. no. 1), the richly-decorated Pucci pilgrim flask (cat. no. 5), and its pendant in agate glass (cat. no. 4). In the meantime, there had been favorable opportunities, (particularly upon the dispersal of the Friedrich Neuburg Collection) to enrich and round off the collection. And so it falls to another generation to present the result of more than sixty years of discriminating collecting.

We should like to say how honored we were to be entrusted with the cataloguing of this outstanding collection. Our warmest thanks go to Ernesto and Liuba Wolf, not least for their unfailing cooperation and understanding.

Without the sympathetic cooperation of the owners of important glass collections, both here and abroad, it would have been impossible to complete these four years of research. Finally, to all colleagues and friends in the glass world who have given either their professional advice, made available the support of their organizations, or met the many demands for photographs, our most sincere thanks:

Jürgen Arndt, Der Heroldsausschuß der Deutschen Wappenrolle, Berlin
Jörn Bahns, Kurpfälzisches Museum, Heidelberg
Maria Theresia Balboni Brizza, Museo Poldi Pezzoli, Milan
Margrit Bauer, Museum für Kunsthandwerk, Frankfurt a. M.
Sabine Baumgärtner, Stuttgart
Erwin Baumgartner, Basel
B. J. R. Blench, Art Gallery & Museum, Kelvingrove, Glasgow
Helmut L. Bosch, Munich
Halina Brožková, Kunstgewerbemuseum, Prague
Eva Brües, Städtisches Museum, Schloss Rheydt, Mönchengladbach
Karl Brunnarius, Obershagen
Robert J. Charleston, Whittington, Cheltenham
Felix Czeike, Wiener Stadt- und Landesarchiv, Vienna
Rudolf Distelberger, Kunsthistorisches Museum, Vienna
Olga Drahotová, Kunstgewerbemuseum, Prague
Franz-Adrian Dreier, Staatliche Museen Preußischer Kulturbesitz, Kunstgewerbemuseum, Berlin (West)
Jean Favière, Musées Château de Rohan, Strasbourg
Gisela Förschner, Historisches Museum, Frankfurt a. M.
A. W. Gerlagh, Gemeentearchief, Amsterdam
Burkhardt Göres, Staatliche Museen zu Berlin (East), Kunstgewerbemuseum, Schloss Köpenick
Rita Gründig, Staatliche Galerie Moritzburg, Halle
B. Haak, Historisches Museum, Amsterdam
Gisela Haase, Staatliche Kunstsammlungen Dresden, Museum für Kunsthandwerk, Schloss Pillnitz
Hans Haase, Herzog-August-Bibliothek, Wolfenbüttel
P. Christian Haidinger, Benedictine Monastery, Kremsmünster
Sabine Hesse, Württembergisches Landesmuseum, Stuttgart
Helga Hilschenz-Mlynek, Kestner-Museum, Hanover
Jutta Hörning, Kunstsammlungen zu Weimar
Ingeborg Hohferber, Staatliches Museum, Schwerin
Helmut Jungwirth, Kunsthistorisches Museum, Vienna

9

Ingeborg Krueger, Rheinisches Landesmuseum, Bonn

Joachim Kruse, Kunstsammlungen der Veste Coburg

Frides Laméris, Amsterdam

Dwight P. Lanmon, The Corning Museum of Glass, Corning, N. Y.

Manfred Leithe-Jasper, Kunsthistorisches Museum, Vienna

J. V. G. Mallet, Victoria and Albert Museum, London

Jessie McNab, The Metropolitan Museum of Art, New York

Ursula Mende, Germanisches Nationalmuseum, Nuremberg

Joachim Menzhausen, Grünes Gewölbe, Dresden

Ottfried Neubecker, Wappen-Herold, Stuttgart

Ludwig Neustifter, Österreiches Museum für angewandte Kunst, Vienna

Waltraud Neuwirth, Österreichisches Museum für angewandte Kunst, Vienna

Miroslava Nováková, Staatliches Denkmalpflegeamt, Brno

Annaliese Ohm, Museum für Kunsthandwerk, Frankfurt a. M.

Irmgard Peter, Historisches Museum, Basel

Ilona Petzold, Museum des Kunsthandwerks, Leipzig

Joseph Philippe, Liège

A. Piechocki; Stadtarchiv, Halle

Franz Xaver Portenländer, Historisches Museum der Pfalz, Speyer

Helmut Ricke, Kunstmuseum, Düsseldorf

Helmut Rischert, Stadtarchiv, Augsburg

Pieter C. Ritsema van Eck, Rijksmuseum, Amsterdam

Rainer Rückert, Bayerisches Nationalmuseum, Munich

Axel von Saldern, Museum für Kunst und Gewerbe, Hamburg

Ekkehard Schmidberger, Staatliche Kunstsammlungen, Kassel

Annegrit Schmitt, Staatliche Graphische Sammlung, Munich

Jenny Schneider, Schweizerisches Landesmuseum, Zurich

Irene Stahl, Nuremberg

Rosemarie Stratmann-Döhler, Badisches Landesmuseum, Karlsruhe

Franz Swoboda, Städtisches Reiss-Museum, Mannheim

Hugh Tait, British Museum, London

Christina Thon, Kunstbibliothek, Staatliche Museen Preußischer Kulturbesitz, Berlin

Hans-Peter Trenschel, Mainfränkisches Museum, Würzburg

Marianne Uggla, Nationalmuseum, Stockholm

A. Westers, Haags Gemeentemuseum, the Hague

Leonie von Wilckens, Germanisches Nationalmuseum, Nuremberg

Inge Woisetschläger, Landesmuseum Joanneum, Graz

M. L. Wurfbain, Stedelijk Museum "De Lakenhal," Leiden

It is my sincere hope that all those who have donated their time and effort to the production of this volume will feel that the great artistic value of the collection fully justifies their generous cooperation.

Brigitte Klesse and Hans Mayr
São Paulo, August 1986

10

# Considerations on the Major Works of the Ernesto Wolf Collection

# Venetian and Façon de Venise Glass – Enameled Decoration

It is appropriate that this introduction should begin with colored, enameled Venetian glasses, the first great highpoint in the history of European glass production. This section includes not only glasses decorated with enamels, a technique originating in the Middle East, but also those glasses of part or completely colored glass. Experiments in the use of colors, whether integral in the glass, as in the case of agate, combed, or filigree glass, or annealed onto the surface of the glass, resulted in the discovery and perfection of the water-clear decolorized *cristallo* so advantageous to the Venetian glass trade in the second half of the fifteenth century.[1] So we begin this survey of the Wolf Collection, which includes all the most important stylistic phases in glass production, with Venetian glass.

Only a handful of glasses from the Wolf Collection came to be internationally known through the Exhibition "Viertausend Jahre Glas" in the Kunstgewerbe Museum in Zurich thirty years ago. Among them was an interesting Venetian beaker with gilt and enamel decoration, to which Robert Charleston has referred more recently in connection with the question of Venetian exports to the Near East in the fifteenth and sixteenth centuries[2] (cat. no. 1, fig. 1). The sides of the beaker are decorated with molded gilt reticulated ribs ("nipt-diamond-waies") interspersed with lily of the valley

Fig. 1

Fig. 2

Fig. 3

13

rosettes in green, rust-brown, white, and sky blue, in each case with a yellow central dot. Beneath the gilt rim runs a continuous leaf meander with three corresponding rosettes. When compared with an almost identical example in The Corning Museum of Glass there emerges a distinct group of glasses, decorated with dot rosettes instead of lily of the valley. They must all have originated from the same workshop.[3] Like the Wolf example, most of them are heavily corroded and flaking, supporting the tradition that they were found in a Jewish cemetery in or near Damascus. Only the British Museum example in London[4] and that in the Museo Poldi Pezzoli, Milan, would seem to retain the original clarity of the *cristallo*[5] (fig. 2). The case for a Venetian provenance is reinforced not only by the clarity of the glass, but also by the fact that a goblet, preserved at Corning, N. Y., has a bowl which conforms in every way to this beaker, supported on a foot of trumpet form[6] (fig. 3). Before 1480, proof that Venetian glass was indeed exported to the Near East is preserved in a documentary commission of an official at the court of the Mamluke Sultan Kait-Bey (1468–1496).[7] Charleston and Gasparetto both mention the lily of the valley motif on a mosque lamp inscribed with Kait-Bey's name in the Cairo Museum and known for some time to be a piece of occidental origin.[8] Documents indicating exports to the sultan's court once again suggest Venice as being the most likely center of production. Finally, a mosque lamp recently acquired by the Düsseldorf Kunstmuseum, formerly in the collection of Ernst Ascher in Paris, is also decorated with these flowers and could well have been made in response to a similar order.[9]

A possible Spanish origin has been put forward for this group, as the lily of the valley motif is found on Catalan glasses of this period. However, A. Gasparetto has argued that the molded "nipped diamond" pattern was already to be found throughout the Middle East on glasses of the late

Roman and Sassanian periods and could well have been adopted by Venetian glassmakers in the production of export wares for the Near East in the late fifteenth century.[10]

Extended in a shallow concave form, the decorative motifs appear again on a footed bowl (cat. no. 2), except that here the lily of the valley motif has been replaced by alternating, strong red and blue disks, framed in white dots. The gilt, ribbed decoration has lost its true honeycomb pattern and assumed the shape of a radiating star on which the spots of color appear as regular accents.

As with the reticulated rib pattern, other Islamic elements frequently surface in fifteenth- and sixteenth-century Venetian glass. At this time, the artistic handling of gold and enamel was influenced by the prominence of the Middle East in these techniques. Traces of these Eastern influences were later absorbed into all aspects of the Venetian applied arts. The Islamic influence on style also spread to other European countries, for example, the use of arabesque ornament in Renaissance decoration. It is interesting to note that in this context, Venetian Glass played an important pioneering role. This is demonstrated by a glass in the Wolf Collection (cat. no. 3, fig. 4). This glass, the bowl of a goblet, of which the foot (probably of trumpet form) is now unfortunately missing, is decorated with a multi-colored, endless-knot motif and infilled with Islamic-inspired, stylized leaves. An early prototype of the moresque, which was to overwhelm the European decorative vocabulary a quarter of a century later, can already by seen in the use of geometric and foliate forms, which were so typical of thirteenth- and fourteenth-century Islamic art. From the form of the few existing examples of this type of unusual decoration, among which is a goblet in the Museum für Kunsthandwerk in Frankfurt a. M.,[11] and a bowl in the Württembergisches Landesmuseum in Stuttgart[12] (fig. 6), one can judge that this type of decoration was not produced much later than the end of the fifteenth century. In the case of the Stuttgart bowl, it is interesting to note that on the rim, underneath a knotted border, there is a second border which echoes the decoration on the Damascus beaker (cat. no. 1), consisting of rosettes punctuating a continuous green wreath. Perhaps a specific workshop or group of painters was responsible for producing this Islamic-style decoration, which was predominantly aimed at the Middle Eastern export market. In contrast to the decoration on the beakers, glasses with moresque-style, knot-ornamentation are painted with a striking, opaque black, which is found nowhere else in the Venetian color palette. These pieces may well have been the work of one hand. The fact that this color on the Wolf glass is a little drier in tone than on others, has doubtless to do with differences of temperature in the muffle kiln, and it is of no consequence when considering the homogeneity of this group.

The coat-of-arms was also a popular motif in Venetian glass decoration. Together with beakers,

Fig. 4

Fig. 6

Fig. 5

15

Fig. 7

goblets and bowls with armorials, pilgrim flasks played a particular role (cat. no. 5, fig. 7, detail). The flattened, globular body offered an ideal decorative surface which was probably first exploited toward the end of the fifteenth century, as can be seen on the famous Bentivoglio/Sforza armorial flask, which probably celebrates the marriage of Alessandro Bentivoglio to Ippolita Sforza in 1492.[13] The example in the Wolf Collection is painted with the arms of the Pucci family surmounted by a cardinal's hat, and relates to either Lorenzo Pucci (1458–1531) raised to the cardinalship in 1513, or Antonio (1485–1544), raised to the same rank in 1531.[14] The shield is surrounded by a green laurel wreath. The details are picked out in gold and outlined in white, and repeated at the handle joints and under the rim. In strong contrast to the red of the Cardinal's hat, the clear black-and-white of the moor's head shield and the gold and blue scrolls, large areas of the green enamel are rubbed off, almost in the manner of decoration executed in cold or very low-fired enamels. Matt olive green appears very

seldom in the Venetian tradition and reminds one more of the later *façon de Venise* glasses from Hall-in-Tyrol or Innsbruck. On the other hand, the glass and form, as well as the overall decorative motifs are unmistakably Italian. Cold-painted decoration only appears on Venetian glass towards the end of the golden age of enameling, that is, somewhere between the first and second quarters of the sixteenth century. On the question of date, one must consider the later Pucci cardinal as the more likely owner of the flask.

Armorial decoration was also popular on shallow bowls, as can be seen from the Medici example in this collection (cat. no. 6, fig. 8). The flat reserve in the center of the bowl lends itself to the display of a coat-of-arms. As there are a considerable number of examples bearing the Medici arms, which relate either to Pope Leo X (1513–1521)[15] or Pope Clement VII (1523–1534), there must have been a considerable service, indicating that they were not just used for display but also at the table, perhaps for fruit and sweetmeats. The fact that there are minor differences in the execution of the arms, such as circular or trefoil key handles, sometimes suspended above and sometimes partly obscured by the field (fig. 9, detail of a parallel from the Kunstmuseum, Düsseldorf), points to the possibility of replacements at a later date. This could suggest additions to the service during the reign of the second Medici pope, though it is not possible to determine which "type" of shield refers to which papacy, as there would have been no major heraldic changes within the short timespan between the two reigns.

Instead of armorial blazons, the central panel on dishes and platters was also decorated with single animals within a round medallion, usually depicted on a bright-green, grassy mound beneath yellow sun rays (cat. no. 10, fig. 7). Among the many examples of secular animals such as heron, roe deer, lion, and stag, it is rare to find examples

16

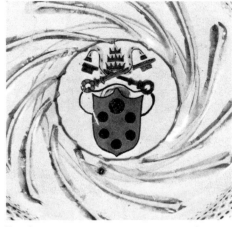

Fig. 8                    Fig. 9                    Fig. 10

of animals as Christian symbols, such as the Lamb of God on the tazza in the Wolf Collection. In most cases these zoological pieces are decorated with gilt scale borders embellished with enamel dots, and the under sides have either radial or wrythen gadroons, perhaps designed to improve the server's grip.

By the beginning of the sixteenth century, the preference for *cristallo* was overtaking the demand for colored glass, which, until the end of the fifteenth century had predominated as the base for enameling, as can be seen from the previous examples. From this period of changing taste we have two particularly fine amethyst-tinted bowls in the Wolf Collection (cat. nos. 9 and 10). The one on high trumpet foot must be considered a product of the early sixteenth century in view of the nobility of its proportions and sparing use of ornament. It is decorated with gilt vertical ribs and a band of scales embellished with sky-blue dots (cat. no. 10). On the other hand the bowl decorated with the head of a youth in classical style in the center of the interior roundel (cat. no. 9, fig. 11) is very much in the late fifteenth-century tradition of *coppe nuziali*,[16] cups with idealized portraits of the male or female partner, presented as a gesture of friendship or betrothal. This classi-

Fig. 11

Fig. 12

cally-idealized youthful portrait with purple robe highlighted in gold and green laurel wreath on the imbricated golden hair, may not be a direct allusion, but its particularly fine painting is entirely within the style of this tradition. The decorative treatment on the outer wall of the bowl is also interesting, consisting of a wide border of grotesques with opposed pairs of seahorses alternating with the Islamic palmette on a gilt and white-dot ground. This particularly rich type of decoration

is only found on a few examples of beakers and goblets dating from the second half of the fifteenth-century, most of them being in the more common deep blue, the density of which compliments the brilliance of the gilded foliate ornament.[17] Finally, this bowl must be placed in a group of colored glasses of similar form, painted with a variety of subjects within the central medallion. They are often decorated with portraits, and embellished on the outside with dotted scale

Fig. 13

Fig. 14

Fig. 15

Fig. 16

borders.[18] A similar bowl, painted with a bust of St. Anthony of Padua is in the Museo Poldi Pezzoli in Milan (fig. 12). It is possible that all these pieces originated from the same workshop.

In comparison with the examples of Venetian glass discussed so far, a pair of blue-tinted gilt and cold-painted carafes seem very unusual (cat. no. 27, figs. 13 and 14). There is of course a time-span difference of a half to three-quarters of a century. This is confirmed not only by the shape, but also by the painted scenes placed below the spouts, which are after Bible illustrations by Bernard Salomon, first published by Jean de Tournes in Lyon in 1553/4. One is decorated with a rendering of the Baptism of Christ, John the Baptist kneeling beside Him with arm outstretched toward the nimbus surrounding the Holy Dove (figs. 13 and 15 after Matthew 3, 13–17). The shoulder is decorated with a pierced heart and the letters "SS." The other depicts the warrior and Israelite hero Gideon, with sword and shield brandished in his struggle against the Midianites (figs. 14 and 16, after Judges 7, 16–23) and the shoulder is marked "AA."[19] The narrow-shouldered, thin-blooded figures of the original printed source have been transformed by the glass painter into muscular, three-dimensional "men-of-action," achieving in the realistic modeling of flesh and careful gilt imbrication an astonishing sureness of touch never found in the medium of enamel. There is evidence in the painting of an artistic training which is not to be found even in the best decoration on Venetian glass of the late fifteenth century. The grotesques which flank each scene are also exceptional, and are rendered with a lightness of touch and a sense of fantasy (fig. 17). One is reminded here of decoration on maiolica of the period, perhaps wares painted in the workshop of the families of Fontana and Patanazzi in Urbino. Here one also finds biblical scenes after Bernard Salomon combined with dragon and bird grotesques, and there is a convincing parallel, a basin in the Victoria and Albert Museum[20] (fig. 18, under side). It is nonetheless difficult to prove these connections. It is hardly

Fig. 17

Fig. 18

Fig. 19                          Fig. 21                          Fig. 22

likely that we are dealing here with a one-off example from Hall, Innsbruck, or even further north, as these centers were not yet known for the production of such motifs in their cold-painted wares. On stylistic grounds, the excellence of the painting points to Italy, possibly Tuscany or Umbria, while the rather carelessly blown glass suggests a center other than Venice.

The question of the function of these carafes is just as unresolved as that of their origin.[21] The fact that they are a pair would suggest they were designed to be used during the Mass for wine and water. However, it is explicitly stated in Roman Missals and Charles Borromeo's *Instructiones fabricae ecclesiae* that colorless vessels were to be used in order to avoid confusing the two liquids. In the case of opaque vessels, it was stipulated that they were to be clearly marked with the letters "A" and "V" or the corresponding symbol of fish and grape. The fact that these carafes only

partially obey this rule precludes their being considered as part of the paraphenalia for the Mass.

If, on the other hand, one accepts the letters 'AA' and 'SS' as standing for *Aqua* and *Spiritus Sanctus*, it is possible that they were baptismal vessels.

The Council of Trent (1546) and the *Rituale Romanum* (1614), in justification of the ritual of Baptism and particularly infant baptism, quoted the Vulgate: "Nisi quis renatus fuerit ex aqua et Spiritu Sancto, non potest introire in regnum Dei."[22] While the Baptism of Christ on one of the carafes appears to support this theory, the appearance of Gideon on the other carafe does not at first seem to be linked with baptism. However, although no rendering of the history of Gideon as a prefiguration of the Baptism of Christ has been recorded in the Iconography, the successful trial by water of Gideon's three hundred warriors (Judges 7, 2–7) could be linked with the rite of

20

Fig. 20                                          Fig. 23

baptism, in the way that a Christian becomes one of the chosen when annointed with water.[23]

Since the fourteenth-century *Superfusio*, only one carafe, and matching basin to catch the water, had been deemed necessary for the ritual of baptism. According to liturgical stipulations, the remaining baptismal vessels, for the annointing with oil and chrism, were to be of metal and fitted with catches. This would naturally discount the Gideon carafe. One wonders whether two similar carafes could have been ordered for a single occasion, such as a domestic christening for two candidates, as the cold-painted decoration would scarcely have survived frequent use.

If the origins of these carafes are to be sought in a narrow area around Venice, the powerful proportions and smoky-tinted glass of the covered goblet decorated in cold paint with the arms of the Nuremberg family of Pfinzing (cat. no. 28, fig. 19) immediately suggest an origin north of the Alps. Indeed, this type of *façon de Venise* goblet is a typical product of Hall-in-Tyrol and Innsbruck.[24] Typical, too, is the limited palette: iron-red, olive-

green, and black, a little silver, as well as the dominant element of gold. As it happens, there is another very similar goblet decorated with the Pfinzing arms[25] which was at Schloss Henfenfeld, the family seat near Nuremberg, until the beginning of this century. The Henfenfeld goblet is almost a twin to the Wolf goblet, except that the finial of the cover is mounted with a silver warrior of typical Nuremberg workmanship.[26] Using Pfinzing family manuscript sources, the genealogical tables of Jacob Scheurl,[27] and other contemporary sources, the coat-of-arms dated 1594 can be identified, without doubt, as that of "Carolus Pfinzing"[28] (fig. 20). It must be noted that the painter of the Wolf goblet inadvertantly reversed the charges on the field, perhaps giving a clue as to why this goblet became separated from the others at Henfenfeld. All of them, incidentally, are decorated by the same hand with the same colors and in the same technique. Karl (Carl) Pfinzing von Henfenfeld (Gründlach, Reutlass and Letten) was born on 14 September 1578, the son of Hans (Johannes) Pfinzing (1546–1582). He was a barrister and lay-assessor in the land court in Nuremberg, and died on the 27 June 1629.[29] He is por-

Fig. 24

Fig. 25

trayed with his wife, Clara Holzschuherin, whom he married on 17 September 1599, on a tall, cylindrical glass of the Henfenfeld group, which also bears his well-known coat-of-arms. His monogram "KP" appears above the coat of arms. This is flanked by the date (partly rubbed) "1601"[30] (fig. 21). It is possible that this glass celebrates the birth that year of the first of his five children, Clara Magdalena. Another Henfenfeld glass is of particular interest here. This depicts a man offering a *Humpen* as a toast, set beneath a slightly different version of the Pfinzing arms, and once again the monogram "KP," this time in better condition[31] (fig. 22). Even a superficial comparison between the arms as depicted in the genealogical reference works and those on the glasses indicates a most unusual stylistic similarity (figs. 19 and 20). If one takes only the figures on the Pfinzing glasses (figs. 21 and 22) and compares them with another page of the Scheurl genealogies (published 1594) depicting the figures of Sigismund Bonifaz Ebner and his wife, as well as his coat-of-arms[32] (fig. 23), the question arises as to

whether the painter of such Nuremberg genealogical tables and the painter of the glasses was not one and the same. That the use of watercolor on vellum produces a more spirited effect reflects the limitations of the lacquer medium. Eric Meyer-Heisig, perhaps influenced by Robert Schmidt,[33] had already suggested when he published the Henfenfeld glasses that they could have been decorated by a Nuremberg *Hausmaler*.[34] In view of the close trade links between Nuremberg and the Tyrol[35] the artists would certainly have been familiar with the type of cold painting practiced there. Contrary to Schmidt's and Meyer-Heisig's further assumption that the blank glasses came from a Franconian glasshouse, a Tyrolean provenance would seem more likely in view of the early date and smoky tint of the Pfinzing glasses.

A cold-painted *Stangenglas* (cat. no. 29, fig. 24) which is placed at the end of this section, not because of its form, which is conventional, but because of its idiosyncratic decoration and clear decolorized metal. It came from a glassmaking cen-

22

ter where *façon de Venise* techniques were also practiced, as will be seen in a similar example. The striking motif on this *Humpen* is a cherub in the form of an applied gilt prunt in the form of a human face, flanked by a pair of painted black and gold wings and sketchy body, these motifs being separated by vertical pairs of free-playing rings which run through applied scroll hasps. Unfortunately, only one of the rings is still complete. The reverse bears a diamond-engraved inscription arranged on several lines alluding to one "Friedrich Sundtmann," and "Mattheus Frisse," as well as the date "1664." By chance, this unusual winged cherub motif is also found on a dainty goblet with double-knopped stem, exhibited at the Westböhmischen Museum in Pilsen[36] in 1984[37] (fig. 25). The conical bowl with everted base displays the enameled motif of the Brazen Serpent flanked by two applied cherub masks with gilt wings, while the rim is decorated with gilt-line borders embellished with rows of dots. In view of the fact that the cherub-mask prunts are so similar to those on the Wolf *Humpen*, appear so seldom as a decorative element, and must have been applied before the glass cooled, it would seem highly likely they were both produced at one glassmaking center. This type of goblet has parallels with finds from excavations of Bohemian glasshouse sites of the sixteenth and seventeenth centuries, where it has been proved without doubt that they produced glass *à la façon de Venise*.[38] The exact locale in Bohemia remains difficult to pinpoint more precisely. The goblet with small cherubs was found in Pilsen itself, at the "Dominikancka 2," which throws no further light on its origin as all large towns tended to obtain articles and luxury goods from various sources. In view of the fact that the Wolf *Humpen* bears an inscription in diamond point, it is tempting to think of Southwest Bohemia, in particular the Wilhelmsberg glasshouse where there is documentary confirmation of the use of the diamond in conjunction with cold-painted decoration[39] as well as the use of high-fired enamels.[40]

Notes to Chapter on Venetian and *Façon de Venise* Enameled Decoration Glass

[1] In this connection see the latest summary of these developments in Franz Adrian Dreier "Glasveredelung in Venedig," in: exhibition catalogue, *3000 Jahre Glaskunst*, Lucerne 1981, pp. 144–152.

[2] R. J. Charleston, "The Import of Venetian Glass into the Near-East: 15th–16th Century," in: *Annales du 3e Congrès des Journées Internationales du Verre*, Liège 1965, p. 161, fig. 49; Idem, "Types of Glass Imported into the Near East and some Fresh Examples: 15th–16th Century," in: *Festschrift für Peter Wilhelm Meister zum 65. Geburtstag*, Editor: A. Ohm and H. Reber, Hamburg 1975, p. 245.

[3] Compare with parallel examples and variants mentioned in the footnote to cat. no. 1.

[4] Tait 1979, no. I, col. pl.

[5] *Bulletin de l'Association Internationale pour l'Histoire du Verre*, no. 9, Liège 1981–83, p. 58, fig. 2; G. Mariacher/E. Roffia, *I vetri in Museo Poldi Pezzoli. Ceramiche-vetri. Mobili e arredi*, Milan 1983, no. 37, pl. 37.

[6] Fig. 3 shows the goblet in Corning, The Corning Museum of Glass (see Strauss, no. 88, col. pl.; Perrot 1958, no. 5, ill.).

[7] Charleston 1965, p. 159.

[8] Gasparetto 1958, p. 84, fig. 42; Charleston 1965, pp. 159–160.

[9] Charleston 1965, p. 160; H. Ricke, "Neue Räume – neue Gläser," in *Kunst und Antiquitäten*, 1985, no. 4, pp. 50–51, col. pl. 9.

10    A. Gasparetto, "Matrici e aspetti della vetraria veneziana e veneta medievale," in: *JGS 21*, 1979, pp. 90–91, fig. 32.

11    Ohm 1973, no. 115, ill.; see also the variants listed in footnote to cat. no. 3.

12    Inv. no. 11965.

13    Gasparetto 1958, p. 83, fig. 21.

14    In connection with the identification of the arms, for which we are indebted to R. J. Charleston, see the notes to cat. no. 5.

15    Compare with parallel examples mentioned in notes to cat. no. 6.

16    Schmidt 1911 V. E., pp. 265–268, fig. 9–11; Gasparetto 1958, pp. 81–82. fig. 21 *quinq.*, 25, 32–36; Venice 1982, no. 65, 70, 73, 98–100, ill.

17    Compare for example with Tait 1979, no. 19, ill.

18    See notes to cat. no. 9.

19    Figs. 15 and 16 are reproduced from a 1558 edition in the Kunstbibliothek, Staatliche Museen Preußischer Kulturbesitz, Berlin (Inv. no. Gris 1515 Kl).

20    A bowl from the Fontana workshop with the arms of Cardinal Inigo d'Avalos e Aquino, which is painted on the front panel with the meeting of Abraham with Melchisedek, and the reverse with God appearing before Noah ( fig. 18), both scenes after illustrations by Bernard Salomon (VAM 8: 1864: Bernard Rackham, *Catalogue of Italian Maiolica*, Victoria and Albert Museum, London 1977 [2nd ed.], no. 845).

21    My thanks to Eva Neuroth, Cologne, who thoroughly researched this point (letter of 13 March 1986).

22    Cited from: Jean Charles Didier, *Le baptême des enfants dans la tradition de l'église*, Tournai/Paris/Rome/New York 1959, p. 187.

23    Father Walter Schulten, director of the Erzbischöfliches Diözesanmuseum, Cologne, has suggested this interesting interpretation.

24    See Egg 1962, figs. 37–39.

25    Now in the Germanisches Nationalmuseum, Nuremberg. Published by Erich Meyer-Heisig, "Die Sammlung deutscher Gläser im Germanischen Nationalmuseum zu Nürnberg," in: *Glastechnische Berichte* 26, 4, 1953, pp. 85–86.

26    Germanisches Nationalmuseum, Nuremberg, Inv. no. Gl 157.

27    *Geschlechterbuch* of the Pfinzing Family, manuscript, Nuremberg about 1680 (Germanisches Nationalmuseum, Nuremberg, Library, no. 4836a); Jakob Scheurl (1577–1623), *Stammbuch*, manuscript, entries 1592–1601 (ibid. no. 128 793).

28    J. Scheurl's *Stammbuch*, op. cit. fol. 103.

29    Joh. Gottfried Biedermann, *Geschlechtsregister des hochadeligen Patriziats in Nürnberg*, Nuremberg 1740, vol. 6, pl. 409.

30    Germanisches Nationalmuseum, Nuremberg, Inv. no. Gl 161.

31    Ibid., Inv. no. Gl 156.

32    Jakob Scheurl's *Stammbuch*, op. cit., fol. 100v and 101r. Karl Pfinzing's wife was first married to Hans Ebner; in this respect Sigismund Bonifaz Ebner was perhaps a brother-in-law, or some such contemporary connection.

33    Schmidt 1922, pp. 222–223.

34    Op. cit. 1953 (note 25), p. 86.

35    Hampe mentions a whole list of "glasern" who dealt with "Venetian glass" and "Glass from Hall-in-Tyrol" in his work *Altnürnberger Kunstglas* (1919).

36    Exhibition *České sklo ze sbírek západočeského Muzea v Plzni*, Pilsen, Summer 1984.

37    This glass unfortunately is not illustrated in the exhibition catalog. It was described in the exhibition as "late 16th century." Whether this dating was based on the archeological evidence is not clear. In M. E.'s view, an early 17th century date for this glass is equally possible.

38    Karel Hetteš, in: JGS 5, 1963, pp. 39–53, and Dagmar Hejdová, ibid. 23, 1981, pp. 18–33.

39    Schmidt 1922, p. 224; F. Mareš, *České sklo*, Prague 1893, p. 170.

40    The surface of the Pilsen goblet is completely iridescent, which makes it difficult to comment on the possible method of painting. The colors are dull, brittle, and blackened in the manner of cold painting, although they may originally have been high-fired enamels.

# Diamond-engraved Venetian and Façon de Venise Glasses

Once again, it is to the Venetians that we owe the rediscovery of a fascinating and charming form of decoration on glass; the artistic scratching of patterns on the glass with the diamond. This technique, complementing as it does the delicacy of the glass itself, soon became popular in other parts of Europe. Disseminated by itinerant Italians, as well as the Venetian technique of glassmaking, any stylistic differences are so small as to make attribution very difficult.

Among the small group of important diamond-engraved glasses, of definite Venetian origin, one in the Wolf Collection holds a unique place (cat. no. 30, fig. 26). It is a plate whose decoration is divided into three zones of diamond-engraved ornament by gilt bands. In the central medallion stands a symbolic female figure in flowing robes

Fig. 27

Fig. 26

Fig. 28

looking at herself in a hand-mirror and flanked by flowering plants. This is surrounded by a band of dense festoons tied with ribbons, while on the outer rim there is a border of grotesques in the form of opposed dolphins. The central figure may have been intended as an allegory of *Prudentia*, but as no other comparable piece is recorded which might have facilitated the pinpointing of the engraved source, the symbolic interpretation remains open to question. The mirror may have been intended as a symbol of Vanity, one of the Vices, or as a symbol of Sight (*Visus*), one of the Five Senses. The interpretation as *Prudentia* may stand for the time being, particularly as it is noticeable that slightly later, enameled glasses were most often decorated with allegories of the Virtues north of the Alps.

Stylistically this plate can be quite easily pinpointed thanks to two stylistic elements. Both the gilt bands and the grotesques and festoons frieze clearly link it to plates bearing the arms and insignia of the Medici Pope Pius IV (1559–1565).[1] Again grotesques are employed, as on the example in the Musée du Verre in Liège (fig. 27), in particular opposed mermaids and putti with fishtails with cornucopiae, as well as small dragons and birds. Comparable motifs are found on two further plates in Corning and New York (fig. 28), which are identical, (as opposed to the small variations on the Papal series), and decorated in the center with the arms of Medici and Orsini. The arms are possibly those of Paolo Giordano Orsini (1541–1585) who married Isabella, daughter of Cosimo I de' Medici, later Grand Duke of Tuscany, in 1558. As Guelphs, the Orsini were for centuries faithful papal servants and military leaders. Pope Pius IV created Paulo Giordano Duke of Bracciano, and in 1566 he commanded the army of Pius V against the Turks. It would seem probable that Pius IV, a lover of luxurious Venetian glass, would have commissioned the same artist to decorate a series of glasses as a present for his

worthy commander. The Orsini service must have originated before 1576, the year of Isabella de' Medici's death. It lacks the gilt bands, thus giving a decoratively plainer appearance. Stylistically, the similarities in the diamond engraving are so strong that all these diamond-engraved pieces may be attributed to a common workshop without hesitation.

Diamond-engraving in Venice is thought to have originated with Vincenzo di Angelo dal Gallo, who, although working from around 1534, was only granted a privilege from the Venetian Senate in 1549,[2] a period quite close to the date of the series of armorial dishes. Even when privileges tend to aggravate professional rivalry, their validity is justified by the commissions for the Holy See given to the grantee or at least to his workshop in those first decades. In this respect it is possible that all these diamond-engraved wares mentioned here, including the plate in the Wolf Collection, may be connected with Vincenzo di Angelo dal Gallo.

Fig. 29

Recently Detlef Heikamp, in his *Studien zur Mediceischen Glaskunst*,[3] has tentatively connected the examples engraved with the arms of Orsini and Medici with the products of the Tuscan glasshouses of the Medici, certainly at first glance a convincing hypothesis. The axial symmetry of the grotesque borders on this group of plates, which adds tectonic strength to the decorative system, could be considered a Tuscan, rather than Venetian creative feature. For the Florentines, the element of draughtsmanship in diamond engraving must have been that much more important than for the Venetians. It is strange, however, that neither in the countless design drawings produced for the Medici glasshouses (published in detail by Heikamp), nor in the archives, does diamond engraving play any role. On the contrary, it can be seen that, although artists at the Grand Ducal Court in Florence produced a rich harvest of fantastic forms, the driving force must have been the glassblower, engaged anew season after season from Venice. It is therefore not possible at present to change the attribution of this group of plates unequivocally from Venice to Florence.

Until now, we have dealt with a composition of ordered decorative elements systematically arranged. On the other hand, floral and foliate motifs are often handled in a completely informal and almost playful manner. A tall elegant tazza and a low credence dish from this collection display the opposite extremes of this stylistic tendency (cat. no. 31 and 32). Joined by slim baluster and knop stem, the shallow bowl and conical foot of the tazza are engraved with a seemingly irregular arrangement of etiolated stylized flower-sprays and scrolls (fig. 29). Closer inspection reveals four strong, decorative accents beneath the rim in the form of three large, multi-petalled flowers and a coat-of-arms with a "demi-rampant dragon in chief."

Here the Italian engraver has mistakenly interpreted the panther of the Austrian noble family of Starhemberg as a dragon.[4] The tazza was perhaps made for by Erasmus von Starhemberg (1493–1560) who took part in the liberation of Vienna from the besieging Turks in 1529. The close trade links between Austria and Italy meant

Fig. 30

Fig. 31

Fig. 32                              Fig. 33                              Fig. 34

that Venetian glass was very popular north of the Alps. A characteristic of the flower decoration is the interplay between large, stylized floral motifs and meandering, leafy tendrils which seem to colonize all available surface areas.

On the other hand, the decoration on the credence (fig. 30) is less dynamic as a result of the greater surface area. As the center is defined by the applied chain of blue trails, only the outer rim remains available for decorative purposes, in this case a dense, foliate circlet with incidental flowerheads, a lion and birds which are at first almost camoflaged among the obovate leaves and berried tendrils. This is the other style of foliate decoration, interspersed with small figures, typical of Venetian diamond engraving of the late sixteenth-century. A bowl with decoration in close agreement, and bearing the arms and name of *Maria Magdalena Chieregata* (a Vicenzan family) which was at one time in the Berlin Schlossmuseum, supports the argument for a Venetian attribution.[5]

The combination of these two decorative el-

ements, that is, the large flowerheads and intricate, foliate scrolls, are frequently found on the same Venetian glass, carefully differentiated, as can be seen on the water bucket in the Wolf Collection (cat. no. 34, fig. 31). Naturally, the two types of floral decoration are used in so many combinations and with such fantasy that it is not always possible to distinguish among them. It is easier to distinguish genuine pieces of Venetian glass from derivative *façon de Venise* versions from Spanish and north Alpine glasshouses, once their characteristics have been fully grasped (e. g., cat. no. 33).

Among the glass produced north of the Alps, that of the Tyrolean glasshouses of Hall and Innsbruck has been demonstrated by Erich Egg to be particularly idiosyncratic in form and decoration[6] with its well-known use of gilding and cold-painting combined with diamond engraving. As with early Venetian enameled glasses, here the best work was effected on a colored body, as in the case of the translucent, sapphire-blue, covered goblet in the Wolf Collection (cat. no. 35, fig. 32). This artistic stimulus was first felt in the Court Glass-

28

house, founded by Archduke Ferdinand of the Tyrol at Innsbruck. In Venice, on the other hand, colored glass had long been supplanted by the star-bright *cristallo*. Likewise the blue of the Wolf goblet is replaced on a few rare occasions by a strong emerald green. Against this background, the red, green, and brown areas, framed by gilding like precious jewels or semi-precious stones, achieve as brilliant an impression as the lacy effects of the diamond decoration. Moreover, this vase-like goblet on its tall, mold-blown stem must be judged one of the most refined of glass forms, which complements the subtleties of the glass itself. At this point it is interesting to compare the essentially well-balanced Venetian prototype[7] and its variants, where the body is of an extended egg shape, and separated from the foot only by a knop, as opposed to a hollow baluster (fig. 33). By means of these subtle nuances a completely different impression is created.[8] As opposed to the harmonious form of the Venetian prototype, the profile and polarities of color of the Wolf goblet are tenser and richer in their dynamic contrasts. These are relatively uncommon within the Venetian canon of form, but they are more typical of the Mannerist influences on northern artists in the sixteenth century.

The same Mannerist elegance of form is achieved on a tazza with tall, mold-blown stem from the Innsbruck glasshouse (cat. no. 36, fig. 34). The wafer-thin glass is only embellished with an applied filigree band creating a central medallion from which emanates the radially-emphasized engraving. A characteristic idiom of the Innsbruck glasshouse is the treatment of the acanthus leaves, their exact outlines given weight and repose when infilled with parallel lines. Here a logical system is brought into play in the decorative ornament which outstrips the rigid Italian grotesques and has little to do with the rampant Venetian floral ornament, found to a certain extent on the Starhemberg tazza (fig. 29).

The foliate scrolls on a small bowl and cover in the Wolf Collection (as yet without parallel), are

Fig. 35

Fig. 36

29

Fig. 37        Fig. 39        Fig. 40

also strongly symmetrical, but include very different floral and foliate motifs (cat. no. 37, fig. 35). Particularly noticeable here is the consistent use of the double line, which emphasizes the beautifully controlled regularity of the linear curves. Such an abstract decorative structure could hardly have been the work of a Venetian metic. There are slight similarities within the engraved borders on a hurricane lamp which bears the arms of Cardinal Christoph von Madrutz, Bishop of Trent and Brixen (1543–1567), and now in the Bayerisches Nationalmuseum[9] (fig. 36 detail). Here the double-line motif is found only at the edge of the lively, encircling frieze of scrolls, and it is in strong contrast to it. Here too, the symmetrical foliate details have reached a degree of stylization entirely divorced from their origins in nature. Rainer Rückert attributes the lamp to a decorating workshop in the Innsbruck Court glasshouse. Perhaps only here on the frontiers of Northern and Southern Europe could such contrasting artistic styles flourish side by side.

It is therefore conceivable that the covered bowl in the Wolf Collection had its origins here as well. It is noticeable among *façon de Venise* glasses from the Tyrol that, despite the richness of artistic invention, there are few important figural examples. One must hesitate therefore before attributing the tall, cylindrical *Humpen* decorated with mounted electors in diamond engraving to either Hall or Innsbruck, although apparently typical of products from this center (cat. no. 38, fig. 37).[10] The sides are divided into two encircling decorative zones embellished with scrolls inscribed with drinking toasts and depicting the Emperor with the Imperial Eagle (*Reichsadler*) and six mounted electors – the Emperor in his capacity as King of Bohemia in place of the missing temporal elector. The printed source was obviously Jost Amman's illustrations of the *Ritterliche Reutterkunst*[11] (fig. 38), which the engraver has then simplified. Of interest is a *Humpen* in the Kestner Museum, Hanover which bears many similarities to this *Humpen*[12] (fig. 39). The placing and delineation of the riders, even down to the engraving of the horses, as well as the orthography of the inscrip-

30

Fig. 41

Fig. 38 ↑

Fig. 42 ↓

tions, and the arrangement of the long scrolls, points to their origins in the same workshop, if not from the same hand. There is only slight variation in the lily of the valley and stiff-leaf borders, as well as in the decorative border and ornamental infill. The Hanover goblet is of broader cylindrical form, with applied foot ring, which allows space for pendant palmettes between the riders. This type of *Humpen* is definitely of Bohemian origin, which facilitates the pinpointing of the Wolf glass. Finally there is an Electors' *Humpen* of the same form in the Prague Kunstgewerbemuseum, on which the same riders are separated by an inserted vertical panel. This *Humpen* also strengthens the case for a Bohemian provenance for the Wolf example.[13] Even an Electors' *Humpen*, of earlier and slimmer form, in the Kunsthistorisches Museum in Vienna, whose diamond-engraved decoration is most closely based on the Amman original, particularly in the figure of the Emperor, is probably Bohemian rather than Tyrolean[14] (figs. 40 and 41, detail).

Also bearing the same date of 1607 as the Electors' *Humpen* is another goblet, in form only closely related to the broad, cylindrical, Bohemian type of vessel with applied, flattened foot ring (cat. no. 39, fig. 42). On its sides the broad central zone is engraved with a long, drinking inscription and standing, allegorical figures of *Prudentia* and *Caritas*, whose engraved source has not as yet been identified. They bear a marked resemblance to those glasses on which diamond engraving is combined with cold-painted details, and are based on allegorical prints from the circle of Virgil Solis and Jost Amman.[15] The sureness of touch and the high standard of draughtsmanship indicate an accomplished artist, who perhaps did not wish to be bound by any prototype, but wished rather to add something of his own. Of particular importance when discussing the centers where diamond engraving was produced is the combination of this form of engraved decoration with enameled blue and white dots and lily of the valley flowerhead borders around the upper and lower rims. At the upper rim they border a gilt band, now unfortunately completely rubbed, which is absolutely typ-

Fig. 43

ical of decoration found on Bohemian *Humpen* of the late sixteenth-century and the entire seventeenth-century. Even if the lily of the valley motif is not exclusive to Bohemia, it excludes the possiblity of a Tyrolean origin, where this motif was unknown. The appearance here of the rare combination of lily of the valley with diamond engraving may help to solve the question of the origin of the so-called "Silesian" group of diamond-engraved *Humpen*,[15] as on the whole they are comparable with the Wolf *Humpen* in quality and style.

If the *Caritas-Prudentia Humpen* has diverted us from glass produced under Venetian influence, this section ends with a glass which is without doubt the product of a Netherlands or German glasshouse working in the Venetian style (cat. no. 40, fig. 43). The diamond engraving is again the most marked feature of this extraordinarily thin-walled glass. The engraving is of the *Reichsadler* with crown and Imperial insignia clasped in its talons. The inscription on the reverse leaves us in no doubt that it is dedicated to Leopold I, offers him a toast, and is dated 1666. As opposed to the strongly stylized examples of a hundred years earlier from Hall and Innsbruck, the Imperial emblems here are executed in a glib and almost naturalistically charming manner which is stylistically in keeping with the third quarter of the seventeenth-century. The only diamond engraver of this generation known to us by name is Peter Wolf, who was based in the Rhineland.[16] However, there are not sufficient comparable stylistic criteria linking this glass with his work. Since glasses of this type from Netherlands' glass centers were marketed over a wide area, and at the same time the engraving shows no Netherlandish characteristics, the glass could have been decorated in western, central, or southern Germany, or in Bohemia. The reference to Leopold I is of interest in being particularly rare on this type of wing-stemmed goblet. It will be remembered that his father Ferdinand III, barely a decade earlier, summoned the engraver George Schwanhardt to Regensburg to demonstrate his engraving abilities, not that this glass has any connection with Schwanhardt's style or the Nuremberg school of engraving.

It seems more likely that the months-long festivities attendant on the marriage of the Emperor Leopold I to the Spanish Infanta Margaretha Theresia in 1666, attracted glass artists to the splendor of the Viennese court, where they would have received the occasional commission.

Notes to Chapter on Diamond-engraved Venetian and *Façon de Venise* Glasses.

1   See comparable pieces listed under cat. no. 30.

2   Gasparetto 1958, p. 96; Dreier 1981, p. 150.

3   Detlef Heikamp, "Studien zur Mediceischen Glaskunst – Archivalien, Entwurfszeichnungen, Gläser und Scherben," (no. 1/2, vol. XXX, *Mitteilungen des Kunsthistorischen Instituts in Florenz*), Florence, 1986, pp. 188–189, 319–320, fig. 86.

4   Arms identified by Ottfried Neubecker, Stuttgart/Wiesbaden (see cat. no. 31). Actually it is noticeable that the Starhemberg panther does take on rather draconian characteristics in German armorial representations over the centuries (see Siebmacher, *Niederösterr. Ständ. Adel*, vol. IV, 4, I, pls. 83–84).

5   Schmidt 1922, p. 102, fig. 63; see also the variants in the notes to cat. no. 32, as well as the comprehensive references in Rückert 1982, I, notes to no. 97.

6   Egg 1962, pp. 52–57.

7   Compare with an example in the Museo Poldi Pezzoli (Mariacher/Roffia 1983, no. 57, pl. 59).

8   Compare with corresponding variants in Egg 1962, figs. 25, 28, 31, as well as Heikamp, 1986, note 3, pp. 172–173, figs. 37 and 38. Fig. 33 is from the R. Strasser Collection in Pelham Manor, N. Y.

9   Rückert 1982, I, no. 135, pl. 34.

10   Egg 1962, figs. 62, 63, 64, 67, 68.

11   Published in 1584 in Frankfurt a. M.; the illustrations here are taken from a copy in the Kunstbibliothek, Staatliche Museen Preußischer Kulturbesitz, Berlin.

12   Mosel 1979, no. 271.

13   Vávra 1954, fig. 133. Bohemian enameled *Humpen* were also produced in this shape.

14   Heinrich Klapsia, "Ein diamantgerissener Kurfürstenpokal aus der Haller Glashütte," in: *Pantheon* 32, 1944, pp. 125–128.

15   See Schmidt 1922, p. 224; a brief summary and list of the most important references by Axel von Saldern in: Klesse/Saldern 1978, notes to no. 284.

16   Schmidt 1911, pp. 822–823; idem 1922, p. 230; see also notes to cat. no. 40.

# Glasses with Enamel Decoration

Not only did the techniques of producing glass *à la façon de Venise* spread north of the Alps, to Hall-in-Tyrol and Innsbruck among other places, but with them the sixteenth-century Venetian technique of enameling as well. Here this colorful mode of decoration took on a more intense and enduring resonance than in Italy, where by 1520, it had almost died out. Northern drinking habits encouraged the production of a large drinking vessel, foremost among them the *Humpen*, whose greater surface area was ideal for enameling. As opposed to the Venetian miniature effects in enamel (see cat. nos. 7 and 9), there was of course a danger that an enlarged area for decoration would result in oversimplification and coarseness. This was compensated for in most cases by the liveliness and appeal of the strong fresh colors themselves.

Among the earliest enameled glasses from the German-speaking lands in the Wolf Collection are two examples, both dated 1572, a tankard painted with the Risen Christ (cat. no. 41, fig. 44), and a *Reichsadler Humpen* (cat. no. 42, fig. 47). The type of tall elegant tankard with its applied rings to foot and neck, and slender handle, was popular only for about three generations between 1570 and 1650. Unlike other forms of drinking vessels, it seems to have been particularly popular as a vehicle for religious subjects. The figure of the Risen Christ with right hand raised in blessing, and the left supporting the crucifixion banner over his shoulder, has marked similarities with a glass dated 1576 in the Fritz and Mary Biemann collection in Zurich (fig. 45). The face with dark beard in three-quarter profile, the yellow rays of the nimbus, as well as the proportions of the body and

Fig. 44

Fig. 46

Fig. 45

the use of linear shading, the knotted loin cloth and the stiffly-drawn rust-brown cloak with contrasting crosshatched lining agree so closely in every detail that a common origin may be assumed. The painter of the Wolf glass has of course misinterpreted the centuries-old tradition of portraying the open sarcophagus to symbolize the Resurrection, and has invented his own peculiar version. On the question of origin, a useful comparison can be made with a fragment of a glass panel with the same subject, and dated 1620, which was unearthed during excavations of the Reiditz glasshouse in north-eastern Bohemia[1] (fig. 46). Although the style of painting is less assured, as is appropriate to the difference in date, the similarities are still obvious.[2] The Reiditz glasshouse near Gablonz was owned by the Schürer family from the 1570s until 1609, when it passed into the control of the Preissler family; its fortunes were thus in the hands of two numerous and famous glass-making families, originally of Saxon origin, who therefore maintained a wide circle of contacts beyond their local borders.

Another interesting factor which supports a provenance from the Schürer/Preissler glasshouse is that examples of this type of tankard are also found in cobalt-blue glass.[3] Recently Olga Drahotovà has discussed the production of blue-tinted glass in the sixteenth-and early seventeenth-century in the Schürer and Preissler glasshouses in the Saxon and Bohemian areas of the Erzgebirge, which was a center rich in cobalt.[4] This factor, together with the iconographical similarities, strengthens the attribution of the Wolf and Biemann tankards to the region of the Erzgebirge, and to the Bohemian rather than the Saxon part.

The second glass dated 1572 in this collection, the *Reichsadlerhumpen* (cat. no. 42, fig. 47), is one of the earliest examples of the motif used to test the skills of an apprentice, thus appearing more frequently than any other motif. [5] The earliest recorded dated example is that of 1571 in the British Museum[6] (fig. 48). Following that, there are four surviving *Reichsadler* glasses dated 1572 including the Wolf glass: one in the Focke-Museum, Bremen[7] (fig. 49), the British Museum example,[8] and a flask in the Los Angeles County Museum.[9] Common to all these early *Reichsadler* glasses is the crucifixion on the bird's breast and the treatment of the tail feathers which extend right down to the basal ring like pairs of fins. On all of them, Christ's loincloth is knotted on the right hip, and the nail is driven through the left foot placed over the right, contrary to all engraved prototypes.[10] At the same time there are small variations of detail in the shading of the body, the halo, the treatment of the grain of the cross, and the eagle's feathers, as well as the style and form of the inscriptions. The example in the Focke-Museum, Bremen, is closest in detail to the Wolf glass, except that the Wolf glass lacks the motif of the Brazen Serpent on the reverse, which is another feature of these early *Reichsadler* glasses. It could perhaps be argued that the slimmer proportions of the Wolf glass do not allow room for it between the symbolic flying sparks and the pinions which meet on the reverse. Of no great importance either, are the color variations on these five glasses of 1571/2; for instance the eagle on the Wolf glass is painted in brown rather than black and the cross varies between red, green, or yellow.

Sabine Baumgärtner has pointed out a connection between the British Museum *Reichsadlerhumpen* (fig. 48) and three very similar variants from the 1570s, all of which are inscribed on the reverse under the Brazen Serpent with the monogram "GP," [11] and she has suggested convincingly that it is the house mark of Georg Preissler's Marienberg glasshouse. This would imply that the *Reichsadler* motif was not only painted in north Bohemia, but also in Saxony at an early date, and opens up the possibility that the Wolf glass, stylistically related as it is, may also be of Saxon origin.

Fig. 47           Fig. 48           Fig. 49

In favor of this attribution is the gray-green tint of the glass and a certain casual execution of the outlines.

On the other hand the enamel decoration on the second *Reichsadlerhumpen* in the Wolf Collection, ten years later in date (cat. no. 43) has been handled with greater precision. The glass is grayish in tone and the *Reichsadler* motif, although taken from the same source as the 1572 *Humpen*, is noticeably more elegant, disciplined, and anatomically more accurate. The eagle has been positioned in such a way that there is plenty of room for the spreading pointed tail feathers to form a well-proportioned triangular composition and still leave space at the base of the glass. This difference in quality between two versions of more or less the same motif can only be explained when the 1582 *Reichsadlerhumpen* is seen as originating from a region where enamelers had had more experience in this technique, which can only apply to Bohemia. Olga Drahotová has pointed out that as early as 1561 Archduke Ferdinand of the Tyrol,

at that time the Governor in Prague, ordered "etlich glasswerkh zum ausprennen nach vorgelegten Mustern" (some glasses be decorated after particular patterns). This is without doubt the "earliest report of enamel glass production in Bohemia,"[12] which would imply that there was an extended period of experimentation, and that the Bohemian painter would have been more experienced than his Saxon counterpart.

As has already been mentioned, the extent of the exchange of technical and artistic information between the glass-making centers on the borders of Saxony and Bohemia, in the areas of the Erzgebirge and adjacent Isergebirge, and North Bohemia in general, can be judged in the context of the blue-tinted glasses.[13] Among these in the Wolf Collection are a footed beaker and a tankard mounted in pewter dated 1598 and 1605, decorated with hunting scenes of hounds chasing a fox and hares (cat. nos. 45 and 46, fig. 50). There is also an undated colorless-glass tankard in this collection painted with a stag hunt which belongs to

37

the same group (cat. no. 47, fig. 51). The graphic source for all three pieces was plainly the woodcuts from Jost Amman's *Thier-Büchlein*, published in 1592, and which, unlike the earlier hunting scenes by Virgil Solis, are divided into types of animals, "Greyhound," "Hare," "Fox" or "Stag"[14] (figs. 53 and 54), thus from the outset suggesting the various possible combinations open to the painter. The astonishing number of parallel examples, all stylistically identical and based on the same source, suggests that they are all from a specific glasshouse and painters' atelier. Particularly noticeable for its Bohemian character is the type of goblet with high, conical foot and shoulder collars below the bell bowl, to which, with great dexterity, the glassmaker has added rings held by applied, scrolled hasps. A particularly good example, also probably from Bohemia, and as yet unpublished, is in the Biemann collection in Zurich (fig. 52). Conditions in Bohemia at that time were ideal for the making of the glass itself and its decoration, as is confirmed by fragments retrieved from glasshouse excavations in Bohemia.[15]

A tall *Stangenglas* in the Wolf Collection, of el-

Fig. 50

Fig. 52

Fig. 51

Fig. 53

Fig. 54

Fig. 55                              Fig. 56                              Fig. 57

egant form and marked gray-tinted glass, dates from around 1560–1580 and is a typical example of the popularity of armorial decoration on glass throughout the German lands (cat. no. 48, fig. 55). With the aid of the gilt inscriptions the arms are identified as those of the Augsburg families of Biller and Zeilner, although no marriage between a Lorenz Biller and Barbara Zeilner is recorded in the marriage records of the Augsburg City Archives which date back to 1563,[16] so that the dating of this glass has to be based on what seems stylistically possible. A possible clue to the lack of documentary evidence in Augsburg is the Italianate name "Lorenzo" (in place of the German Lorenz). The marriage could have taken place while on a long sojourn in Italy, as was common among South German merchants at that time,[17] with resultant lack of documentary evidence in Augsburg, particularly as there is no record of a "Lorenz" Biller in the sixteenth century, while this name appears frequently in the seventeenth and eighteenth century.

The smoke-tinted glass speaks without doubt for an origin in one of the *façon de Venise* glasshouses

of the Tyrol, or the Bavarian or Bohemian Forest. As many of the arms on these early German armorial *Stangen*-glasses are those of Southern German families, Ludwig Fuchs, followed by Axel von Saldern, have plumped for a South German provenance,[18] while Rainer Rückert supports the case for Hall-in-Tyrol;[19] at the present the argument for one or other origin must remain tentative. From Theodor Hampe's researches into sixteenth-century archival sources, we learn of the many painters on glass in Nuremberg alone. He argues convincingly that they were not just decorators of panels, but vessels as well,[20] which suggests that these glasses were not just produced in one center. While their origin remains unresolved, the terms "alpine region," "Bohemian" or "South German" must continue to serve, the Biller/Zeilner glass belonging without doubt under the latter heading.

The next glass, an armorial *Humpen* dated 1591 (cat. no. 49, fig. 56) was commissioned for the castle at Dessau by Duke Johann Georg I von Anhalt-Dessau (1567–1618), and is painted on one side with the arms of Anhalt, and on the other with the arms of his first wife, Dorothee, daughter of Count Albert von Mansfeld-Arnstein, who died in 1594. Two similar *Humpen* with this prince's arms are in the Bayerisches Nationalmuseum in Munich[21] and in the Städtisches Reiss-Museum at Mannheim.[22] While the Munich glass is painted with the Anhalt arms alone, and a vase of flowers on the reverse, the Mannheim example dated 1611 is painted with the arms of both Anhalt and the Pfalz, from whence came Johann Georg I's second wife (fig. 57). There is also an elaborate toast inscribed on the reverse, which gives no clue however as to owner or donor. The metal of all three glasses is, atypicall for Bohemia, of greenish yellow tint, strongly seeded, and the form is relatively tall and slim. Also unusual is the decorative treatment of the the flattened foot ring,

Fig. 58

which was gilded overall (now completely rubbed) and embellished with two or three rows of colored enamel dots. Further examples, in glass of the same tones, are mainly decorated with armorials of the various branches of the House of Saxony. Another group of very similar armorial *Humpen*, but in clearer glass, have, according to the latest research, been attributed to the Saxon glasshouses of the Erzgebirge,[23] thus pinpointing the origins of the Wolf example as well.

Another Saxon *Humpen* of even taller proportions, dated 1601, provides an example of an armorial glass in its most developed form. It is painted on one side with the arms of Halle and on the other with a rider in smart, contemporary dress on a leaping horse, flanked by inscribed toasts (cat. no. 50, fig. 58). It is particularly interesting to note here the small, covered armorial *Humpen* which the rider holds up for inspection in his right hand. Thanks to the help of the director of the Halle town archives,[24] the arms and flanking initials "CH" have been identified as those of "the old established Halle family of Herold," and the monogram as being that of the councillor Carl Herold (1574–1637).

From 30 August to 5 September 1601 a *gemein Land- und Spahn-Vogelschießen* (a kind of clay-pigeon shoot) was organized at Halle in which Carl Herold is listed as a participant among the three hundred and thirty others from fifty Saxon and Thuringian towns. It is amusing to read the detailed contemporary description of this extensive folk festival.[25] In the *Verzeichnis der von der Ritterschaft, der Städte, Herren und Schützen, welche bei diesem Landschiessen persönlich gegenwärtig gewesen* (list of knights, towns, gentlemen, and marksmen who were present at this shooting contest in person), Carl Herold is listed among the seventy-five participants from the town of Halle. At the end of this shoot he was among the winners who "die Gewinne der sechs Spähnen zu 2 Thalern haben empfangen ... Diesen

40

Herren und Schützen ist sämmtlich und einem jeden insonderheit zu seinem empfangenen Gewinn ein darzugehöriges gemaltes Fähnlein, von roth und weissen Kartäken verehret" (received two thalers for each hit ... these gentlemen and marksmen received as a particular honor with each win, a little flag in red and white).[26] The finale of the rough-shooting contest was very lavish, "... die ganze anwesende Armbrustschützen-Gesellschaft ... (ist im Festzug) ... in eines ehrenvesten hochweisen Rahts Waage angelanget, und hat vielwohlgedachter Raht, als man dahin aufm Saal kommen, den anwesenden Herren und Schützen, inmaßen sie vormals und anfangs freundlichen und solenni modo und oratione mit Anziehung ihre gebürenden Ehrentitel empfangen ... zum höchsten durch ihrer Syndicum bedanken ... auch ferner ... bey einem freundlichen Abendtrunk zu verharren freundlich bitten und ersuchen lassen." (the whole company of crossbowmen ... [in procession] ... proceeded in an official transport to the hall, where, on their arrival,

they were cordially greeted with due regard for their honorable titles ... thanked by the head of their syndic ... and asked in friendly fashion to remain for an evening's drink). After the guests had returned thanks for this "sonderlich rühmliche Munificenz und günstige Affection eines ehrbaren Rahts" (great and famous munificence and benevolent affection of an honorable council) they "männiglich ... Rheinischen Wein, Torgischen Bier, Kuchen, Confect und andern nach aller Möglichkeit und zu allen Gnügen fürgetragen und gespeiset, ... und (ist) nach genommenen frölichen Trunk und Abschied auf kommenden Morgen in Gottes Geleit wieder nach Haus verreiset" (drank and ate in manly fashion at every opportunity and with enjoyment ... Rhine wines, Torgau beer, cakes, sweetmeats, and other appropriate things ... and after happy toasts and farewells until the morrow, made their way home in the sight of God).[27] It was no doubt to commemorate this exceptional event, at which Carl Herold played the dual role of councillor and marksman, that he

Fig. 60

Fig. 59

commissioned this fine *Humpen,* now preserved in the Wolf Collection.

Finally, mention must be made of a very fine example among the enameled *Humpen* in this collection. It dates from 1676, and has a bird's eye view of Schloss Coswig in Anhalt on one side and an inscribed toast on the other (cat. no. 51, fig. 59). As Schloss Coswig was destroyed in the War of the Schmalkald League in 1547, rebuilt from 1555, and modernized with extensions between 1667 and 1677,[28] the version on the *Humpen* is first-hand documentary evidence of an exact stage in the alterations, then nearing completion. The "U" shaped castle, built around a central courtyard, is clearly shown, the corners embellished with gables in Renaissance style, as well as the staircase tower, a relic of the old castle. It is interesting that the ground-plan is still basically Renaissance in style with a central courtyard and a low terrace (no longer in existence), connecting the massive side pavillions, and flanking the river Elbe. The castle, at a similar stage in its modernization, but without the central fountain in the courtyard, is

depicted in an engraving by Johann Christoph Beckmann in his *Historie Des Fürstenthums Anhalt, von dessen Alten Einwohnern und einigen annoch verhandenen Alten Monumenten ...* which appeared in Zerbst in 1710 [29] (fig. 60, detail). The differences between the two views of the castle of 1676 and 1710 clearly indicate that the version on the *Humpen* is indeed an accurate, rather than artistic view of the state of the building in the 1660s and 1670s, and is documentary evidence of a precise stage in the rebuilding reached in 1676, as no other recorded evidence exists.

Views of specific buildings enameled on glass were not very common during this period. The few surviving parallel examples are of Saxon origin, and depict the castle at Dresden and Schloss Hartenfels at Torgau, both dated 1688.[30] The somewhat brighter palette, the less disciplined composition, and the luxurious decorative detail set them apart stylistically from the Wolf *Humpen.* Furthermore they are painted with the arms of the Elector of Saxony and inscriptions which distinguish them as *Hofkellerei* glasses for Dres-

Fig. 61

Fig. 62

Fig. 64

# Nuremberg and South German Engraved Glasses

The high point of the Wolf Collection is without doubt the representative group of glasses, embellished with wheel engraving, from each of the well-known German centers of production. Historically we begin our discussions in Nuremberg, to which city the art of engraving on glass was transplanted from the Court of the Emperor Rudolph II in Prague in the first quarter of the seventeenth-century.

The second generation of Nuremberg engravers is particularly well represented in this collection. There are two signed glasses by Hermann Schwinger, for instance, certainly the most gifted of this group. One is a goblet with hollow-baluster stem, the bowl engraved with Daniel in the Lions' Den (cat. no. 70, fig. 80, detail), a reversed version of a composition by Matthäus Merian from the third part of his illustrations to the Bible published in 1627[1] (fig. 81). In view of the broader field at his disposal, the engraver has dispersed the elements of the original, at the same time extending the perspective of the backdrop of arched ruins by means of arcades. In the original print

the prophet sits, withdrawn and bowed, surrounded by vault-like caves open only to the sky, whereas Schwinger places him in a more spacious den, seated with head raised. The smaller format has likewise forced Schwinger to dispense with the background figures of King Darius and his false advisors sealing off the entrance to the den with stones. The figure of Daniel, with a more modern haircut, appears younger and rather more stylish, which is in keeping with the artistic taste of Schwinger's generation. The scene on the reverse is as yet unexplained, and it shows one of the elect with a bowl in his hand, being born aloft by an angel in flowing robes. It might have represented some wish of the patron. In keeping with the Nuremburg preference for continuing the decoration right round the bowl, unless enclosed by medallions, Schwinger has connected these scenes with a landscape with a harvesting scene.

Of all the glasses definitely by Schwinger, (and Meyer-Heisig's work published twenty-five years ago included fifteen signed pieces)[2] the Wolf goblet, and the well-known 'St. Christopher' goblet

Fig. 80

Fig. 81

Fig. 83                                    Fig. 82                                    Fig. 84

dated 1669,[3] once in the Mühsam Collection, are the only two examples with religious themes. It is not only the iconographical, but also the stylistic similarities which suggest that the Wolf goblet probably dates from around the same period. Robert Schmidt, who knew the glass when it was still at Dessau, was of the same opinion.[4] Not just the slimmer proportions of the figures, but also the exclusive use of wheel-engraving, left unpolished, suggests an early date, whereas a decade later this artist favored the use of polished detail to create artistic effects with greater contrasts.

This becomes obvious when dealing with the second goblet by Schwinger engraved with the portrait of the Emperor Leopold I (cat. no. 71, fig. 82). Here the polished detail of the monarch's full-bottomed wig is beautifully contrasted with the matt laurel wreath, stiff jabot, cuirass and sash. Thus the florid details of Leopold's face are minimised by offsetting them against a sumptuous frame. Likewise on the reverse, the polished engraving of the *Reichsadler* and Imperial insignia is contrasted with the matt background, heightening the precise and luxurious effect. Among the many versions of Leopold's likeness, in paintings, prints, and on medals and coins, the three-quarter profile is in the minority. Heinrich Raab in Nuremberg,[5] and Peter Schenk in Amsterdam executed very similar portraits (fig. 83, detail, and

84), of which Schwinger could have been aware, although there are deviations in the narrow-shouldered stance, the stiff lines of the jabot, and the less pleasing treatment of the sash.

How much better, though, is the glass-engraver's portrait, than the original engraver's, in catching the essential character of this great yet reluctant monarch, who in 1680 wrote to his confessor Father Marco d'Aviano: "Wahrlich, ich würde lieber in einer Wüsteneinsamkeit leben als in meiner Hofburg. Aber da mir Gott diese Last auf meine Schultern geladen hat, so hoffe ich, er wird mir auch die Kraft geben, sie zu tragen" (Truly, I would rather live in the loneliness of a desert than in my Hofburg. However, as God has placed this burden on my shoulders, He will give me the strength to bear it).[6] The *Cristallschneider* (crystal engraver) as he calls himself in the signature, has managed to convey the combined art-loving and ascetic qualities of the Emperor's character through the nuances of polished and matt detail. Few glass engravers achieved such masterly effects in portraiture as Hermann Schwinger in the last years of his life. The portrait of the Nuremberg patrician Gabriel Nützel on a signed goblet dated 1682 in Munich shows evidence of the same psychological insight,[7] suggesting that the Wolf goblet might also have been executed in the same year, the last year of his life.

56

Fig. 85                          Fig. 86                          Fig. 87

Another portrait goblet in the Wolf Collection, which comes close to Schwinger's achievements in this field, is at the same time somewhat drier and more prosaic in style (cat. no. 72, fig. 82, detail). The portrtait is of Johann Gottfried von Guttenberg (1645–1698), from 1684 until his death, Prince Bishop of Wurzburg. The engraved source used here was possibly a print by the court and university engraver Johann Salver(1670–1738), which was included in a number of portrait series – for instance the *Philosophia Herbipolensis aeternae Episcoporum, S. R. I. Principum, et Franciae Orientalis Ducum memoriae devota ...* by Anton Reinhard Franz Höffling which was published in 1712[8] (fig. 86, detail). The reverse is embellished with the mirror monogram, arms, and insignia of Johann von Guttenberg. The sitter's dates pinpoint the date of the glass to between 1684 and 1698, a period after the deaths of both the famous engraver portraitists Georg Schwanhardt the Elder (died 1667) and Hermann Schwinger (died 1683). In view of Salver's dates the portrait must have been engraved towards the end of Guttenberg's life. It is interesting to note that the scrollwork frame and flanking pendant fruits appear in almost identical guise on the Heidelberg goblet with a portrait and arms of the *Deutschherrenmeister* Johann Caspar von Ampringen dated 1665, and generally accepted as the work of the elder Schwanhardt[9] (fig. 87, detail). The Ampringen portrait, as opposed to the earlier portraits of Gustav Adolph or the Emperor Ferdinand III[10] includes more of the body, set in a wider frame, thus heightening the impact of the sitter's personality in a novel way. The master of the Guttenberg goblet, who must have known the Ampringen forerunner well, in view of the details already mentioned, has by comparison increased the size of format and concentrated details of the face to create a powerful portrait, thus enabling him to dispense with any flanking motifs. Here also the older style of encircling inscription has been replaced by a mirror monogram. In view of the similarities with the work of Schwanhardt the Elder, the only metic who could have engraved the Guttenberg goblet among the recorded glass engravers of the second half of the seventeenth-century, is his son Heinrich Schwanhardt (died 1693), who is recorded as surpassing almost all other engravers, as well as his father in drawing and perspective skills.[11] The unusually precise delineation of the portrait, somewhat drier in style than Schwinger's, also supports this attribution, although, in view of the lack of signed glasses, it must obviously remain hypothetical. A stylistic comparison with other portrait glasses attributed to Heinrich Schwanhardt, one, for instance, somewhat similar at Schloss Pommersfelden,[12] unfortunately does not contribute to a strengthening of this attribution.

Fig. 88

Fig. 89

Fig. 90

The next glass is evidently at a considerable artistic remove from the Guttenberg goblet and the work of Hermann Schwinger. It is a goblet on a hollow-baluster stem with a portrait of the Emperor Leopold I in profile to dexter within a bound laurel wreath by Johann Wolfgang Schmidt (cat. no. 73, figs. 88 and 93, details). In view of the profile effect and the quite unrealistic addition of the hand with marshal's baton, it is possible that this portrait is based on a coin or medallic original. In this context a thaler of 1693 from the Nuremberg Mint could be considered, on the grounds of the stylization of the physiognomy and the wreath crowning the full-bottomed wig, even though on the glass the profile has been reversed[13] (fig. 89). On the other hand the portrait could be based on a medal by Philipp Heinrich Müller struck to commemorate the marriage of the Emperor with Eleonore von Pfalz-Neuburg in 1679.[14] The metic would seem to have confined himself to the simplified form of the coin which certainly would have been more accessible to him. At the same time he was satisfied with a relatively schematic version of the subject. Compared to the delicate modelling of the face in Schwinger's psychologically controlled interpretations, the unmistakable Habsburg profile is coarsely structured. The streotyped handling of the wig is reminiscent of the unimaginative handling of trees, indicated by parallel lines, characteristic of Schmidt's landscapes.[15] That this is Schmidt's work is confirmed by a goblet engraved with a stylistically comparable profile portrait of Margrave Ludwig Wilhelm of Baden in a private collection in Upper Franconia, which bears the Schmidt monogram "I. W. S."[16] The source here was also a medal by P. H. Müller of 1693.[17] Strengthening this attribution is a goblet dated 1690 with a portrait of Maximilian II Emanuel of Bavaria from the Strauss Collection, now in The Corning Museum of Glass,[18] (fig. 90, detail). Two further glasses which agree in form and decoration with the Wolf goblet, are in the Strasser Collection in Pelham Manor, New York[19] and in the Bayerisches Nationalmuseum, in Munich[20] (figs. 91 and 92, detail). In both cases the reverse is engraved with the *Reichsadler* with a small polished lens on its breast (fig. 93). A certain uniformity and carelessness is due perhaps to the frequent repetition of the same theme. At one time there was a goblet in the Schiftan Collection with a portrait of Leopold based on the same source, but executed with greater elegance and depth of detail, and possibly by Heinrich Schwanhardt, which could have influenced Schmidt.[21]

Although portraits cannot be considered his strong point, Johann Wolfgang Schmidt still engraved an astonishing number, including later emperors. His real preference was for the well-

Fig. 91

Fig. 92

Fig. 93

known battle scenes, at which he excelled. A beaker in the Wolf Collection with a bold representation of a cavalry skirmish (cat. no. 74, fig. 94) ties in with other examples of this theme from his early career, for instance the goblet with a mounted battle scene signed and dated 1678 (not 1679!), the bowl of which is happily still preserved in the Berlin Kunstgewerbemuseum, Schloss Köpenick[22] (fig. 95, detail). In contrast to other engravers, there is a marked stylistic difference in Schmidt's *œuvre* between his early and later output. Its progressive simplification, hasty execution, and coarsening of detail becomes increasingly obvious. In the case of the cavalry battle theme there was a tendency towards stereotyped forms. On the Berlin glass, the unusual anatomical treatment of the horses with their exag-

gerated rumps and swollen joints, is less obvious. The unbalanced proportions of the horses, with their heavy bodies, small heads, and etiolated limbs, not yet noticeable on the Berlin glass, is much more obvious on the later signed beaker in the Württembergisches Landesmuseum, Stuttgart, engraved with a portrait of Charles VI[23] (fig. 96, detail). A certain transition of styles is to be found in the engraving of the cavalry clash on the signed Prince Eugene beaker, once in the Mühsam Collection, and now in Chicago.[24] Similarly the fussy treatment of the mantling on the crest of Wolf beaker reappears in Schmidt's later work. This is seen on the cartouches enclosing a portrait medallion of Joseph I on the Düsseldorf beaker, and the goblet in Weimar,[25] neither of which can be dated earlier than 1705. The Wolf

Fig. 94

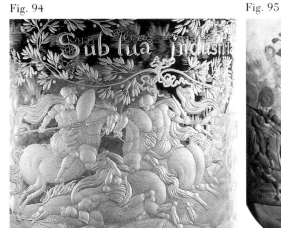

Fig. 95

Fig. 96

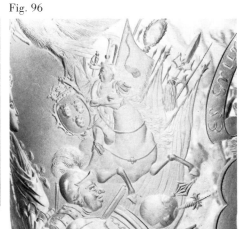

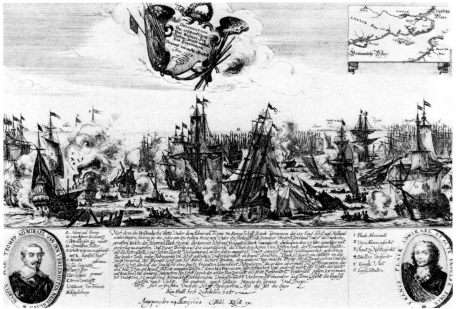

Fig. 97                                              Fig. 98

glass, dated around 1700–1705, was therefore still engraved within the reign of Leopold I, and its inscription "sub tua industria" echoes the inscription on the other glasses, "Consilio et industria". Finally it must remain conjectural as to whether the increasing technical weaknesses were the result of his waning abilities, or the work of apprentices employed to cope with the pressure of commissions.

Rather than the cavalry scenes with large figures, which required intensive application to anatomical details, Schmidt devoted himself to the depiction of battle scenes composed of small figures. A tall, baluster goblet in this collection is engraved on one side with a female figure with a palm frond and a bunch of fruit within a large medallion as an allegory of Peace, with the inscription "Jam Bellum deinde Pax," while the reverse displays one of his typical battle scenes (cat. no. 75). Flanked by high trees with characteristically-engraved leafage, the horses push and jostle under the smoke of battle, their riders depicted only as "stick men" with fluttering pennants and raised weapons. No other glass engraver achieved such strong dynamic effects in such a small space as

Schmidt did in these battle scenes. The routine engraving on this goblet suggests a late work around the turn of the century.

There is a further baluster goblet, possibly only a little earlier in date, engraved with a naval battle, where similar tense and dynamic effects are achieved (cat. no. 76, fig. 97, detail). The battle encircling the bowl, takes place far out to sea with no sign of any safe coastline. Polished smoke clouds obscure the thick tangle of masts and ragged sails, punctuated by cannonades, and exploding, burning and sinking ships. Amid the confusion there is no sign of any clear victor. With astonishing dexterity the metic uses the medium of various degrees of polished and matt engraving, contrasting the modeled and linear elements, to convey the drama of the subject. As large naval battles were an important element in seventeenth-century European history and politics, it is possible that the engraver had a specific incident in mind. However this must remain conjectural in view of the lack of armorial clues. From Jacques Callot's "Battle of the Four Galleys" of 1617[26] or his engraving of the blockade of the Citadel of St. Martin on the Île de Ré, as well as that of La

60

Rochelle in 1631[27] to the broadsheets later in the century depicting the many naval battles between the Dutch and English[28] (fig. 98, detail), there would have been many examples for Schmidt to choose from. A definite source has not yet been discovered.

The same applies to a ruby-glass tumbler engraved with the same subject, and without doubt Schmidt's work (cat. no. 77). On one side is a battle scene with small mounted figures, and on the other a sea battle, here with fewer ships involved, and both scenes within oval frames comprising palm fronds. Both engagements are depicted with great care and attention to detail, which suggests

panels, where classical armor has been used on one side and period armor on the other. Particularly conspicuous is the noticeably deeper and thereby more dynamic engraving, made possible by the thicker walls of the ruby-glass tumbler, and less evident on the more delicate baluster goblets.

J. W. Schmidt was not the only one to apply his art to ruby-glass vessels, imported to Nuremberg during the last quarter of the seventeenth century, perhaps from Hans Christoph Fidler's glassworks in Munich, or from Freising. Other contemporaries, among them probably Heinrich Schwanhardt, developed an entirely new and far more

Fig. 99          Fig. 100          Fig. 101

that it was engraved at an early date. The technical and artistic qualities are reminiscent throughout of the Berlin goblet dated 1678 (fig. 95). At the same time, the battle reek above the cavalry fight is not only more tensely coiled on the less translucent ruby-glass surface, but also more deeply gouged out of the sides than on the baluster goblets. Likewise the smoke of the cannonade in the naval engagement rises in thick coils to fill a large part of the medallion and obscure the ships in the background. As opposed to the style of his later work, the artist here avoids any repetitive stereotyping of details. This also applies to the trophies which decorate the side

sculptural technique when engraving on the much heavier ruby glass. A ruby-glass tankard in the Wolf Collection, with silver-gilt mounts by Tobias Baur, is decorated with the figure of Cupid with bow and quiver flying away with a heart, leaving three other hearts on an altar and surmounted by the motto *Un seul me suffit*, a popular love emblem which is repeated with astonishing frequency, and with great charm, either by the same engraver or his workshop[29] (cat. no. 78, fig. 99). Other tankards, comparable in many aspects, but with a variety of silver mounts are to be found in the Schloss Museum, Arnstadt (fig. 100, detail) and on the art market.[30] The motif comes

61

from the widely-circulated emblem book by Daniel de la Feuille, first published in Amsterdam in 1691, and which was published in Augsburg in five German editions between 1693 and 1703 under the title *Emblematische Gemüths-Vergnügung bey Betrachtung ... der curieusesten und er-*

from there), "Hier unverdrossen" (here indefatigable), "Wird wohlgenossen" (will be well satisfied), one with a demesne with wheatfields, the gardens of a manor house, and two children with a bowl inscribed "25" (cat. no. 82, fig. 102). Here the references obviously refer to the twenty-fifth

Fig. 202

Fig. 203

Fig. 204

*götzlichsten Sinn-Bildern ...*[31] (fig. 101). A large number of ruby-glass tankards and tumblers were decorated by the same hand with *Sinn-Bildern* (symbols) taken from the same book of emblems. A smaller tumbler of 1686, once in the Berlin Schlossmuseum, belonging to this group, but uncharacteristically not of ruby glass, was attributed by Robert Schmidt to Heinrich Schwanhardt.[32] As no signed work by this artist has come to light, no definitive attribution can be made. What is important, however, is that the Nuremberg engraver of these glasses, with his considerable capabilities, was one of the most delightful and skilled practitioners of his generation working around the turn of the century.

Finally two colorless glass beakers deserve to be mentioned. One, cylindrical in form, is decorated with three symbolic scenes in oval frame beneath the inscription "Von dort entsprossen" (it springs

anniversary of a successful squire. He was probably a member of the Imhoff family[33] as the original cover, unfortunately broken, was mounted with the Imhoff arms in gilt metal as a finial. The base is engraved with a laurel wreath from which radiate six chess pieces[34] (fig. 103), king, queen, two bishops, a castle and a pawn, suggesting that the person for whom this glass was commissioned, was a lover of the game. The chess pieces are stylized in the manner of the time, as depicted in the most important chess work of the seventeenth-century, *Das Schach- oder König-Spiel*, published under the psuedonym Gustavus Selenus by Duke August II of Brunswick-Lüneburg in 1616.[35] For the identification of the individual pieces, an illustration of the Duke himself at play (fig. 104, detail) is important, but unfortunately we can get no closer than this to the identity of the owner or the engraver.

62

Fig. 205

Fig. 206

With the second beaker we are on slightly more favorable ground in making an attribution on the basis of style. The decoration consists of two elements in a most unusual combination; below, a continuous landscape with small figures of a hunter and the herdsman-god Mercury playing the shawm with cows in the background; above, large luxuriant swags of fruit tied with ribbons (cat. no. 83, fig. 105, detail). Noticeable is the combination of swags of fruit accentuated with large flowerheads, contrasting with the delicate veining on the leaves, a detail which has only been associated so far with the work of Paulus Eder.[36] Among the few signed glasses by this metic, there is a beaker in a private collection where similar contrasts are employed, i.e., large overlapping leaves with fine overlaid details, framing small delicate landscapes with tiny figures (fig. 106, detail), stylistic characteristics typical of Eder's work. However, while both display the same use of contrasted scale, the decoration on the Wolf beaker does not achieve the same artistic force of the master, suggesting that it was a product of a close assistant working in Eder's workshop.

Notes to Chapter on Nuremberg and South German Engraved Glasses.

1 The print in fig. 81 was kindly made available from the Print Cabinet of the Kunstmuseum, Basel.

2 Meyer-Heisig 1963, pp. 54–61, WT 81–92.

3 Schmidt 1914, no. 81, pl. 11; Meyer-Heisig 1963, WT 83.

4 Schmidt 1922, p. 249; idem Ms 1931, pp. 193–194, no. 181.

5 The Raab engraving is in the Österreichische Nationalbibliothek, (portrait collection: Inv. no. 162, 149/5[98]) and the Schenck mezzotint in the Albertina (Inv. no. HB 50 [6], p. 76). The Schenck version was perhaps the model for the engraving by Johann Ulrich Krauss (see above, fig. 73).

6 Quoted from: Dorothy Gies McGuigan, *Familie Habsburg 1273–1918*, Vienna, 1967, p. 191.

7 Meyer-Heisig 1963, WT 89; Rückert 1982, II, no. 479, pl. 138–139.

8 Johann Salver's engraving would have been based on Höffling's portrait, now in the Mainfränkisches Museum, Wurzburg.

9 Schmidt 1922, fig. 136; Meyer-Heisig 1963, p. 45, WT 51.

10 Ibid., WT 24 and 28.

11 Schmidt 1922, p. 245; Meyer-Heisig 1963, pp. 49 onwards.

12 Ibid., WT 69 and 70.

13 The photograph of the coin (Inv. no. Mü 20614) was kindly made avilable by the Münzkabinett of the Germanisches Nationalmuseum, Nuremberg.

14 Drahotová 1972, p. 219, fig. 10.

15 The marked similarities in the use of the wheel are particularly noticeable on the Prince Eugene beaker in Chicago (Meyer-Heisig 1963, WT 144), in such details as the treatment of the wig, the wig, the eagle's plumage, and the trees in the landscape.

16 Saldern 1968, no. 173, ill.; idem 1970, pp. 103–105, figs. 1–4.

17 Ibid., pp. 103–105.

18 JGS 22, 1980, p. 107, no. 26, ill.

19 JGS 21, 1979, p. 121, no. 11, ill.

20 Meyer-Heisig 1963, WT 75; Rückert 1982, II, no. 486, pls. 144–145. Figs 91 and 92 show in the Munich goblet.

21 Auction no. 439, Dorotheum, Vienna, 27–29 February 1936, lot. no. 524, pl. XVI.

22 The bowl of the goblet with probably the best battle scene by Schmidt survived the upheaval of the war. The photo is by kind courtesy of the Kunstgewerbemuseum der Staatlichen Museen Berlin (-East), Schloß Köpenick. The date on this piece has always been incorrectly quoted as 1679 instead of 1678 (see Schmidt 1922, p. 251; Meyer-Heisig 1963, WT 142; Schade 1968, fig. 41).

23 See also Meyer-Heisig 1963, WT 145.

24 Schmidt 1914, no. 80; Meyer-Heisig 1963, WT 144.

25 Ibid., WT 146 and 147.

26 Lieure 194–197; Thomas Schröder, *Jacques Callot – das gesamte Werk*, vol. II (prints), Herrsching s. d. (about 1975, pp. 960–964).

27 Lieure 654 and 655; Schröder, op. cit., pp. 1197–1207, and pp. 1212–1221.

28 See for instance broadsheets of the naval battles of 28 February 1653 and 11–15 June 1666 (publisher Wolfgang Harms), *Deutsche illustrierte Flugblätter des 16. und 17. Jahrhunderts*, vol. II, collection of the Herzog-August-Bibliothek, Wolfenbüttel, part 2: the battle of 1653, mentioned above, appears in *Historica*, Tübingen 1980, II 335 and II 376, ill. Fig. 98 shows a detail from the above-mentioned battle of 1653.

29 See notes to cat. no. 78, and Klesse 1976, pp. 65–70, ill., for further examples, all in ruby glass, engraved by the same hand, and with emblems taken from the same source.

30 Auctioned at Sotheby's, London, 30 June 1980, lot no. 232, col. ill. A further variant was at Heide Hübner, Wurzburg, in 1987.

31 In this case the engraver used emblem no. 10 from plate 51 of this work. This copy is from the Kunstbibliothek, Staatliche Museen Preußischer Kulturbesitz. See also Henkel/Schöne, 1976, p. LXVI, no. 338.

32 Schmidt 1922, p. 246, fig. 138.

33 Unfortunately no known member of the Imhoff family can be named, despite the researches of Ursula Schmidt-Fölkersamb in the Nuremberg archives, as the motif of the manor house lacks specific details.

34 My thanks to Leonie von Wilckens of the Germanisches Nationalmuseum, Nuremberg, for pointing out the significance of these motifs as chess pieces.

35 The photograph for fig. 104 by courtesy of the Herzog-August-Bibliothek, Wolfenbüttel.

36 Meyer-Heisig 1963, WT 173 and 174.

# Bohemian and Silesian Engraved Glasses

This section begins with an anomaly, insofar as it is not a blown glass but a small portrait medallion in rock crystal (cat. no. 89, fig. 107). Although strictly-speaking an isolated case outside the scope of this section, its probable origins in the Imperial capital of Vienna are relevant when discussing the patronage by the court of glass from Bohemia and Silesia – as in the case of certain representative Nuremberg pieces. This medallion is engraved with the bust portrait of the Emperor Leopold I in profile to sinister with wreath-crowned, full-bottomed wig, lace jabot, and cuirass decorated on the shoulderpiece with a grimacing janissary's mask. Below this is the signature "I. G. SEIDLITZ" and within the mask's mouth the tiny digits "1695." Johann Georg Seidlitz was, according to Nagler,[1] a medallist from Coblenz who was particularly active in Vienna between 1699 and 1711, where he executed a series of medals for the Habsburgs and probably carved gems and cameos which have not been identified. From this dated, rock crystal medallion we can only judge this particular facet of his work, and that only from around 1695. When Michael Duchamps recently published this medal he rightly extolled its outstanding qualities: "... ce portrait de Léopold peut prendre rang parmi les grands portraits réalisés en glyptique ..." (this portrait of Leopold can be placed among the great engraved portraits).[2] He points out especially the unusual janissary's mask, incorporated into the armor, which he suggests might be connected with Leopold's image as vanquisher of the Turks. On other similar versions of Leopold's portrait, a lion mask is used, but on no other known occasion a human mask, which would suggest a personal adaptation by Seidlitz himself. This reference to the struggle against the Turks is echoed on two more-or-less contemporary medals by Philipp Heinrich Müller, which bear a double portrait of Leopold I and his son Joseph in profile to sinister. The earlier one, of oval form, commemorates the coronation of the Archduke Joseph as King of the Romans in 1690 (fig. 108), and it was issued again as an engraving in roundel form by S. Thomassin in 1693.[3] The other, with an almost identical double portrait, commemorates the withdrawal from Grosswardein in 1692 and eulogizes both Habsburgs as "TURCARUM VICTORES PERPETVI" (Victors of the Turks in perpetuity).[4] Seidlitz was obviously strongly indebted to the earlier of these two variants, and, except for the personal touch of the janissary's mask, he follows Müller in almost all details. At the same time he succeeds in enlivening the severe likeness on the medal, thanks to his talent with the engraving tool, through the luxurious treatment of the hair which curls around the face and on to the shoulders. The lively details of the jabot also agree with the medal original, and both artists have failed to include the collar of the Order of the Golden Fleece, which was customary on official Imperial portraits, particularly on medals. Leopold I was made a member of the Order in 1654, and the Archduke Joseph in 1687. Duchamp suggested that this omission might indicate that the rock-crystal medallion was incomplete. This is not possible, as his signature is conclusive proof that he viewed the piece as complete. This is also not true of Müller's medal. Moreover, there are an astonishing number of portraits of the Emperor where the collar of the Golden Fleece has been omitted, as, for example, on an engraving by Fleischmann after Johann Jacob Sandrart on which each of the two

Fig. 107

Fig. 108 ↑

Fig. 109 ↓

Habsburgs is shown in an individual medallion with allegorical figures of the four Cardinal Virtues and the crowned eagle[5] (fig. 109). Leopold is shown only with laurel wreath, but his son is idealized as a youthful Roman emperor with toga, laurel wreath, and the chain of the Golden Fleece, perhaps referring to his coronation. It is possible that this print may have inspired the medallist Müller, and it explains the Archduke's classical robes in Müller's double portrait. Seidlitz's work shows none of this tendency towards idealization, and in the unflattering realism of the Habsburg profile the influence of the Müller medal is revealed. In any event it is one of the most effective portraits of Leopold to have survived.

When we turn to blown glasses, it becomes obvious that the tradition of glass engraving, which developed at the court at Prague around 1600, quickly died out there, and it only reappeared towards the end of the seventeenth century after the development of a thicker-walled chalk glass, more suited to engraving. In this collection there is a conical beaker with quite thick walls with scenes

66

Fig. 110

Fig. 111

Fig. 112

Vom Pfauwen.

Fig. 113

in large medallion on both sides. It belongs stylistically to the circle of the only engraver of that period with a tangible artistic personality, the so-called Master of the Koula beaker (cat. no. 92, fig. 110, detail), who was active in the Riesengebirge.[6] The scene of a lady playing a lute beneath a tree in one medallion is directly related to the scene depicting the sense of hearing from the Five Senses on the Koula beaker itself (fig. 111, detail),[7] although the presence of an approaching youth does somewhat confuse the symbolic meaning. On the other hand the wide landscape perspectives, giving the figures plenty of space, create a different stylistic impact from the Koula beaker, although the small-chested rather self-conscious figures are stamped firmly in the Master's style.

As the engraving is somewhat weaker, the Wolf beaker is probably by a workshop apprentice. The treatment of the interstices between the medallions, with peacocks below luxuriant fruit trees, is a different solution to that favored by the Koula Master, and there would seem to be no comparable parallel. The birds are possibly meant as symbols. The peacock, with tail displayed to his mate, was used in a slightly different arrangement and reversed as early as 1592 by Jost Amman in his *Thier-Büchlein* as symbol of Vanity, Splendor, and Pride (fig. 113),[8] although it was also used later as a symbol of Fertility.[9] Without knowledge of the owner it is difficult, in this connection, to arrive at any exact interpretation.

However, we find definite symbolic meaning in the engraving on another goblet. Here, a child blowing bubbles provides an allegory of Vanity and Transience (cat. no. 96, fig. 114, detail). The model for this scene is a reversed version of the fourth emblem from Wolfgang Helmhard von

67

Fig. 114

QUALIS LABOR, TALIS MERCES.

Evanescentes devibrat in aëra bullas.
Saponi exiguam dum puer addit aquam:
Dum vana incautus cudit mendacia Mundus
perditur (et meritò) dum peritura colit.
Wie habt ihr das Eitel so lieb?

Fig. 115

Hohberg's *Lust- und Artzeney-Garten des Königlichen Propheten David*[10] (fig. 115), with illustrations by Georg Christoph Eimmart. The engraver has simplified the original, reducing the landscape motifs to flowering shrubs on each side, He has also polished the entire engraved surface. This tendency to adopt large simplified motifs is also apparent on the reverse, which is decorated with tulip, narcissus, and rose sprays. Here, too, all parts of the flowers are polished and only differentiated by deep veining. It is a typical example of the early Bohemian approach to engraving, which has not been preserved in any quantity.

An extension and refinement of this technique can be observed on a covered goblet engraved with children as allegories of the Four Seasons (cat. no. 97, fig. 116a–d, details). Here too the subjects are framed in medallions whose luxuriant flowers and branches echo each season. The children, each with relevant symbol of basket of flowers (Spring), sheaf of corn (Summer), bunch of grapes (Autumn), and faggots (Winter), follow closely the engraved original, the frontispiece of

Johann Ulrich Krauss's German/French edition, published in Augsburg in 1687, of the engraved works of André Félibien, published in Paris in 1665. These in their turn were based on designs for Gobelins tapestries by Charles Lebrun entitled *Les Quatres Élemens*[11] (fig. 117, detail). These small, droll figures, clad only in a sash, except for Winter in a knee-length shift, move nimbly through corresponding landscape scenes with flowering shrubs, wheatfields, vineyards, and leafless trees. It is interesting to note the frequent use of this allegorical series, which was particularly popular in this region in the first quarter of the eighteenth century.[12] The extremely competent engraver of this glass has not remained slavishly faithful to the source. On the contrary, one notes how felicitously he handles any difficulties and allows his imagination full play in the decoration of the borders and areas between the medallions. In similar fashion to the decorator of the previous glass with the allegory of Vanity (fig. 114), he also takes the trouble to polish almost all areas of the engraving, and he uses fine lines to break up the

68

Fig. 116 a          Fig. 116 b          Fig. 116 c          Fig. 116 d

Fig. 117

69

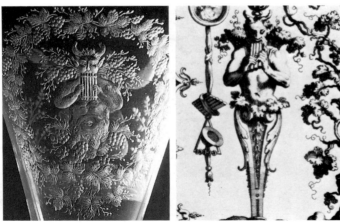
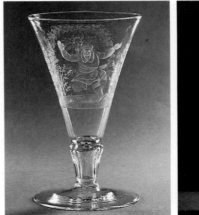

Fig. 118    Fig. 119    Fig. 120    Fig. 121

contours and other details of sprays, leaves, fruits, and flowers. Perhaps this engraver had seen this technique on glasses by the Nuremberg engravers, where the most delicate effects were achieved even down to the use of diamond point. In this example we observe early North Bohemian glass engraving of top quality, which stands comparison with similar work from other centers such as Nuremberg, Silesia, or Brandenburg.

Reminiscent of the glass mentioned above is a small goblet with funnel bowl, similarly decorated with a satyr herm playing Pan pipes, within an oval frame embellished with fruiting vine (cat. no. 98, fig. 118, detail). Here, too, the engraver has used an engraving as a model. He has taken the herm from a print by Jean Berain I, which shows the god Bacchus among fantastic figures, medallions, and cartouches[13] (fig. 119, detail). This figure is bedecked with fruiting vine spilling out of the pannier on his shoulders and hanging down to the loins. This is perfectly complemented by the wreath of fruiting vine framing it. The engraver displays a high degree of technical dexterity, not only in his effective reinterpretation, but also in the execution of all details. The motif on the other side of this glass, that of a clumsy, dancing peasant on a little island of grass, is rather puzzling (fig. 120), and it can hardly be by the same hand as the herm. By chance a whole series

of glasses has survived from a large table service, composed of similar small goblets and beakers, and decorated with comparable coarse figures of peasants, dancing, making music, or promenading. These have a well-documented provenance. Amongst them there is a goblet with wrythen stem, engraved with a peasant carrying a potted plant[14] (fig. 121). It is to be found mentioned in an inventory of Schloss Favorite, near Rastatt, which was built for the Margravine Franziska Sibylla Augusta of Baden-Baden around 1710 as a summer residence. She was the daughter of Duke Julius Franz of Sachsen-Lauenburg. She grew up mainly in the North Bohemian castle of Schlackenwerth, and she ordered all glass utensils as well as chandeliers and table glass for Schloss Favorite from her Bohemian homeland, which of course was the European center for glass production at that time.[15] The furnishing of the house was only finished in about 1720.[16] Thus, for the little Wolf collection goblet, its origin and date are pinpointed exactly. It must remain a mystery, however, who added the decorative motif on the other side, and why.

There is a definite stylistic connection between the herm crowned with fruiting vine, mentioned above, and motifs of standing bacchantes, almost overgrown with fruiting vine, placed between panels on an impressive goblet engraved with

Fig. 122

Fig. 123

Fig. 124

Fig. 125

Neptūnūs in ein Delphin.

Fig. 126

80.

Saturnus in ein Pferd.

mythological scenes (cat. no. 99, fig. 122). One almost wonders if there were a direct workshop link between both glass engravers. At first glance it is less obvious in the two main themes enclosed within wreath medallions. They represent two episodes from the loves of the gods which are seldom represented on glass (figs. 123 and 124). One depicts the affair between Chronos, in the form of a stallion, and the nymph Philyra, out of which union the famous centaur Cheiron was conceived; the other is of the nymph Melantho being carried off by Poseidon in the guise of a dolphin, who gave birth to Delphos, after whom Delphi was named.[17] Both scenes are probably from Johann Ulrich Krauss's illustrations to Ovid's *Metamor-*

*phoses* (fig. 125 and 126) of around 1694, which were based on those of Le Brun dedicated to the Dauphin in 1676.[18] They still bear signs of the influence of the Koula master, particularly in the crumpled and pleated clothing of the narrow-breasted maidens, executed almost completely in polished engraving. As opposed to the Koula beaker or the "Continents" beaker formerly in the Krug collection,[19] the engraver of the Wolf goblet, and the beaker with lute player (fig. 110) has given the figures more room, thus creating a more spacious and rythmical effect. Basically, we are dealing here with a more mature development of the Koula master's style which is paralleled in similar artistic developments in the workshop of

71

Friedrich Winter, as will be enlarged upon in due course (compare with cat. nos. 103–104, figs. 131 and 132).

A slightly later goblet and cover in this collection is definitely within the circle or workshop of the Master of the Koula beaker, its profile being of classic Bohemian type (cat. no. 100). The faceted bowl is decorated on both sides with quite small medallions within a delicately-spun web of symmetrical scrolls, one side with the monogram "TS" or "ST" beneath a coronet, the other with an allegorical figure of Happiness standing on a floating winged ball. As Rückert has rightly pointed out, the Regence ornamentation and *Laub- und Bandlwerk* (foliate scrolls) had not yet permeated the decorative vocabulary of this group of glasses.[20] The form of this type of Bohemian goblet did not make its appearance earlier than the second decade of the eighteenth century, and the many examples are decorated in a transitional style moving towards the second quarter of the eighteenth century, which was to be dominated by *Laub- und Bandlwerk* ornament.

While glasses from within the cirle of the Koula-beaker engraver bear definite signs of their origins in the Riesengebirge, that is, the border area between Bohemia and Silesia, in that either glass of Bohemian form is decorated in Silesian style, or vice versa, the next group of glasses come from the very heartland of Silesian glass production, the workshop of Friedrich Winter. As is well known, he received an exceptional privilege from Count Christoph Leopold von Schaffgotsch in 1687 to start a water-powered cutting works in Hermsdorf in the Hirschberger Tal[21] which first came into operation in 1690–91. A smoky-topaz goblet in this collection is almost certainly an experimental piece carved with the help of this new means of power (cat. no. 102, fig. 127, detail). It consists of a boat-shaped bowl connected by a screw joint to the angular-knopped stem and domed foot, and it is carved in high relief detail

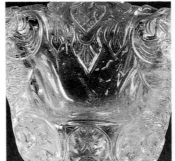 

Fig. 127                    Fig. 128

with cornucopiae, volutes, acanthus, pine-cone, and stiff-leaf motifs which appear repeatedly on his glasses (see cat. no. 103, fig. 128, detail). The clumsy proportions and inelegant outline may be a result of the original limitations of the topaz block itself, or a lack of skill and experience in this new technique. Robert Schmidt attributed this piece to Winter over fifty years ago,[22] and compared it with a very similar bowl of shell form in the Berlin Schlossmuseum, since destroyed in the war; it had a Schaffgotsch provenance and obviously came from Winter's workshop. As neither Gondelach in Kassel nor Spiller in Berlin produced anything stylistically connected with the topaz goblet in the Wolf Collection, its attribution to Winter is not seriously in doubt.

A relief-carved goblet decorated with the fir-tree motif taken from the Schaffgotsch crest, and the motto *Aucun temps ne le Change* (cat. no. 103, fig. 128) can be attributed to Winter with certainty. Characteristic of Winter glasses is the deep, funnel bowl which appears to spring from within the acanthus-carved shoulder knop, and it is to be found again on glasses decorated with large putti rather than high-relief detail, of which fine examples are in the Prague Kunstgewerbemuseum.[23] Further parallels to our goblet, the bowl, in each case decorated with a relief-carved acanthus-leaf cartouche, include a covered goblet in the Prague Kunstgewerbemuseum (fig. 130), and a goblet formerly in the Krug Collection.[24] In all three cases the basal cyst is decorated with acanthus leaves interspersed with tulip heads. Large acanthus motifs are also found on the cover of the Prague goblet, the only one which has survived complete, emphasizing the importance of the aesthetic whole in the execution of these goblets.

It is not only the acanthus motifs, but also the landscape vignettes in polished engraving with little figures, which are common to these glasses.

A landscape cartouche on this goblet with shepherds and peasants in a meadow with a hilltop castle in the background (fig. 131) can be seen as the stylistic bridge with the Koula-Beaker Master and his circle discussed earlier. The vocabulary of landscape details is very limited, and the style of the costume and hair of the figures is late seventeenth-century in feeling.[25] This is clearly seen on a small, thick-walled, double-handled bowl,

Fig. 129

Fig. 130

73

Fig. 131

Fig. 132 a

Fig. 132 b

where the acanthus leaves in high relief are restricted to an encircling frieze, and the scenes in polished engraving dominate the decorative scheme (cat. no. 104, figs. 132a and b, details). The type of hilltop castle mentioned above, the bushy crags at the edge of meadows or lakes, and small purely decorative figures occupy the landscape. The exception in this case is the woman pulling a chariot on which perches an eagle beneath lowering clouds, whose intention is probably emblematic, but whose meaning remains obscure.

It was understandable that Friedrich Winter would decorate glasses – such as the topaz goblet and rock crystal bowl – almost exclusively in relief carving in the early 1690s, with the help of

the new cutting techniques.[26] The well-balanced interplay of relief-cut and deeply-engraved areas, which appears on the Wolf goblet, was developed towards the end of the century. It is all the more astonishing that, long after Winter's death, in the twenties of the eighteenth century, the phenomenon of decorating a glass completely in relief carving made a reappearance. A goblet in this technique in this collection is decorated right around the bowl, with dancing couples and gallants and their ladies disporting themselves on the grass, while musicians in the background playing trumpets, all against a fantastic architectural backdrop with a wall fountain (cat. no. 105, figs. 133a–c, details), all in the manner of Watteau. On one side are the arms of the Silesian family of von Seidlitz beneath a baldequin supported by putti, and

Fig. 133 a

Fig. 133 b

Fig. 133 c

Fig. 140 a

Fig. 140 b

*LE CERCLE ET LE BILBOQVET*

Fig. 141

*LA MARELLE A CLOCHE-PIÉ*

Fig. 142

although again reinterpreted. This time the glass engraver has placed a goblet in his raised left hand, while with his right he reaches into a basket of fruit and flowers beside him. Even the gestures of the other children in this new interpretation seem relevant. On the reverse, the theme of children on a see-saw is taken almost exactly from "La balançoire," down to the two spectators crouching at the base (fig. 144). At the same time one of the children has been given a whirlygig,

not in the original print. Obviously the artist enjoyed not only translating charming subjects into his medium, but embellishing them with little details of his own.

That motifs of children at play were so popular with Silesian engravers is probably thanks to the influence of Friedrich Winter.[32] The use of acanthus and stiff-leaf borders in relief confirms that the engraver of this beaker was working in this tradition.

Fig. 143 a ↑ Fig. 143 c ↓  Fig. 143 b ↑ Fig. 144 ↓

*LA BALANÇOIRE*

A final goblet decorated with scenes of children is somewhat superior in the quality of the engraving to the previous two examples (cat. no. 113, figs. 145a and b, details). To begin with, the variety of motifs on the bowl, divided into four panels by vertical grooves, is astonishing. In each case animals determine and accompany the children's games: four little rascals catch a stag with the help of a hound, another talks to his dog in a courtyard, two children play with a billy goat, and three more with bowls of fruit and garlands are watched by a reclining lamb. The engraved source has only been found for the two children arm-in-arm in the last scene (fig. 145a), which is after an emblem from the *Amorum Emblemata* by Otto van Veen of 1608, representing the spiritual union of two hearts through the power of love (fig. 146). The glass engraver has omitted the children's wings in the original, so that they fit in with the other scenes on the bowl. In each case the activities of the lively children is complemented by those of the animals, and even in such

Fig. 145 a ↑                                    Fig. 145 b↓    Fig. 146 ↑                                    Fig. 147 ↓

elements as the animals' coats, the engraver displays his mastery of charming and lively detail. A footed beaker formerly in the Krug Collection engraved with two children playing at hunting in the forest[33] (fig. 147, detail) is certainly by the same hand. In this scene, one of the dog's collars is inscribed with the monogram "JW," possibly a signature. However, the "monogrammist JW" in the meantime must remain a shadowy figure.

A feature of this glass is found in almost identical form on another goblet in the Wolf Collection (cat. no. 114, figs. 148 and 151, details), where the base of the bowl is also decorated with a frieze of arched panels engraved with busts and foliate scrolls. They are matched by the same number of vertical facets on the sides of the bowl, necessitating more detailed decoration to cope with the uneven surface of the glass. On one side are the

Fig. 148     Fig. 149     Fig. 150

crowned arms of Prussia, supported by wild men on a socle, while the rest of the bowl is decorated with a garden terrace occupied by musicians, dancers, and men smoking pipes at a table. Stylistically there is no connection between these detailed crowded scenes and the scenes of children on the last-mentioned glass. In this case we can only assume that these glasses were executed in a glasshouse, either at Schreiberhau or Warmbrunn, where the glass was first prepared by a team of cutters, polishers, and apprentice engravers, who filled in small details, before it was handed over to the master engraver, who, on impulse or to order, then decorated it with figures, emblems, or coats-of-arms.

The goblet must have been intended for someone fond of music as the line of music running above the scene in a braced stave is indeed, as the inscription implies, a *Polonese*[34] (fig. 148). A central couple accompanied by a viol, cello, shawm, and horn, perform this dance with strutting gait. The Polonaise or Polish dance was first introduced at the Dresden court of Augustus the Strong in the early eighteenth century, and it reached its first high point of popularity in all circles in the second quarter of the century.[35] Dance themes with musical notation are very rare on Silesian glasses, and one suspects that the engraver himself must also have had some knowledge of written music. Two variants, also with a double line of music and a five- and six-man orchestra respectively, are in the Metropolitan Museum of Art, New York,[36] and the Museum für Kunsthandwerk in Frankfurt a. M.,[37] and are probably attributable to the same hand (fig. 150, detail). The slim and long-limbed figures of the dancers on the Wolf goblet are similar to those of the musicians on the Frankfurt and New York goblets. In their tight stockings and fashionable frock coats with pedantically exact button holes, they seem a little stiff and mannered, an impression which is heightened by the painstaking treatment of their wigs. Moreover an obvious relationship can be noted between the group of smokers on our glass, and the table of carousers on the reverse of the New York goblet (figs. 151 and 152). There is a striking connection between this motif and that of a gathering of Leipzig merchants which appears on a goblet in the Leipzig Museum für Geschichte (fig. 152).

82

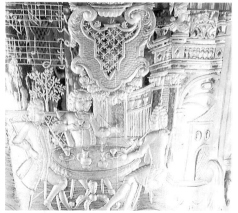

Fig. 151

Fig. 152

Fig. 153

That we are dealing here with a gathering of the Leipzig Chamber of Commerce is confirmed by the appearance on the reverse of the old stock-exchange building with its fine baroque façade of 1678–1687. Not only the rather stiff mien of the ten notables, with their accurately-rendered wigs and dress befitting their station, but also the obvious pleasure evinced by the engraver in the execution of details, such as the tiled floor, the window panes, and the enclosing frieze with monogram cartouche betray the same hand which was responsible for the three goblets with musicians. Luckily, the engraver of the Leipzig goblet is known to us from his signature. It is the only full signature on a Silesian eighteenth century glass, and it reads "Casper Gottlieb Langer in Warmbrunn d. 1749 / glaßschneider."[38] Here we are

Fig. 154

Fig. 155

Fig. 156 ↑

Fig. 157 ↓

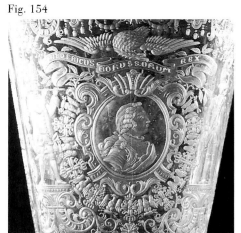

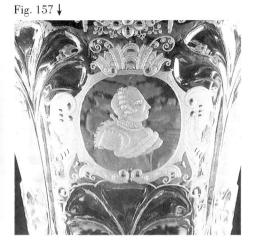

83

dealing with a contemporary of Christian Gottlieb Schneider. In view of the Prussian coat-of-arms, the Wolf glass must have been engraved after the annexation of Silesia by Prussia, while the Leipzig glass, in the stereotypical figures, and the later type of glass with relief palmettes, is probably the latest within the small group of glasses by this artist.

Another goblet in this collection (cat. no. 117, fig. 154, detail), decorated with a profile portrait of Frederick the Great, is also connected with this historical event.[39] On the thirty-first of October 1741, the Prussian king accepted the homage of the dukedom of Lower Silesia at the Town Hall in Breslau, and to commemorate this occasion a medal was struck with his profile and inscription "FRIDERICUS BORUSSORUM REX ..." and distributed a week later to all officials and persons of standing during the festivities connected with this event[40] (fig. 155). It would seem probable that the engraver actually had one of these medals to work from. A very similar portrait medallion by Johann Georg Holtzhey, struck to commemorate the battle at Prague in 1757, is put forward as the source for the Wolf goblet by Sabine Baumgärtner,[41] but is in any event too late to be connected with this glass, when the glass material itself, and the rigid ornamentation point to a date not later than 1745. The quality of the engraved detail is superb, not only in the portrait, but also the order surrounding it, and the miniature landscapes with exquisite pastoral scenes on the relief palmettes on the reverse. It is interesting to note how Christian Gottfried Schneider treats the same subject on a paper impression in the Hirschberg Museum (fig. 156), but with completely different results.[42] His bust portrait of Frederick is loosely surrounded by flags, drums, and pikes, all within a large scrollwork cartouche. This latter detail in particular suggests a later date, and perhaps Schneider used the 1757 medal as a prototype. One is struck initially by the difference in the ar-

tistic impression. The tight, densely-applied ornamentation on the Wolf goblet has completely dissolved on Schneider's example, where, as can be seen from the paper tracing,[43] there is a lighter, more graceful, and elegant approach, not least in the transformation of the Prussian eagle into a harmless spreadeagled bird. Schneider's artistic style is of course a product of his generation's taste. Most of his glasses, which we know from the paper impressions, are based on prints of the 1750s and 1760s, ten to twenty years later than the Wolf glass, and they remain true to the current rococo fashions, as Franz-Adrian Dreier has already proved so convincingly.[44] The Wolf goblet would have been executed by a highly talented engraver from Warmbrunn, probably somewhat older than Schneider.

Another goblet from this collection with a portrait of Frederick the Great can be placed between the two examples discussed above (cat. no. 118, fig. 157). The sides here are divided by four relief palmettes into vertical zones. One is decorated with the royal portrait in profile to sinister within a relatively large scrollwork cartouche, the eagle and motto being omitted. The emphasis on the piercing expression of the king's large eyes has similarities with Schneider's paper impressions (fig. 156), although this may be due to them both being based on the same graphic original. The overall impression, as well as the pastoral scenes in the upper three zones of the bowl (fig. 158, detail), indicate stylistic and iconographic similarities, but there are no specific characteristics which would justify an attribution to Christian Gottfried Schneider.

At the height of his career, this master's thematic repertoire was weighted towards genre scenes from pastoral plays, particularly popular among the upper classes of the day. In this context, a charming scene on one of Schneider's paper impressions has survived: a shepherd and his shep-

Fig. 158                    Fig. 160                    Fig. 161

herdess recline beneath a tree, while in the background a maiden approaches bearing a floral wreath with which to crown the cavalier[45] (fig. 159). By chance, a similar scene in which the gallant offers his lady a basket of fruit and flowers instead is found on two different glasses in this collection. On one, a footed beaker (cat. no. 119, fig. 160, detail), the theme is further embroidered with a shepherdess who stands beside a wall fountain. The figures are set in a park dotted with sheep. The reverse is decorated with a relief palmette embellished with delicate, miniature landscapes, and among them are a small group of trophies with two flags decorated with the Prussian eagle and "FR" monogram, which suggests a date for this glass in the pertinent years of the late 1740s.

The sides of the other beaker, comparable in form and date, are divided into four parts (cat. no. 120, fig. 161, detail). The same pastoral couple, here reversed, is otherwise occupied, the shepherdess feeding her lamb while the shepherd looks on. In the side panels, there are allegories of Peace and Justice as an embracing couple, and the four-part inscription "Es grün / und blüh / die Schlesische / Redligkeit" (Silesian honesty grows and prospers).

Fig. 159

These are possibly by a different hand. The repetition of the charming central motif on both these glasses, and the variations in the landscapes, remind one throughout of examples by Christian Gottfried Schneider, while lacking this master's vivacious technique of drawing figures and richly varied ornament. In the decoration of these two glasses in the Wolf Collection, one can see the hand of two different talented members of the same workshop team. The latter example is set apart from the other variants in the somewhat coarser and sketchier technique. Perhaps a beaker

Fig. 162 a                    Fig. 162 b                    Fig. 163

which appeared in the Munich antiques trade fifty years ago, decorated with the same motif,[46] and definitely of higher quality, was the work of Schneider himself and a prototype on which his apprentices based their versions.

A covered goblet engraved with the arms of the Silesian family of von Schweinichen takes us back to the courtly life of the times (cat. no. 121, fig. 162a and b, details). In between the coat-of-arms and owner's monogram "GSvS" decorating either side of the bowl, there are two large *haute école* riders carrying out exercises in dressage. The riders are actually represented during a particular movement of the *Gallopade.* Perhaps the owner of this glass wished to be reminded of his own dressage training. The glass engraver has used a print in original and reversed form from Johann Elias Ridinger's engraved series *Neue Reit Schul* (the new riding school) of 1734 entitled "Changieren nach rechts" (changing direction to the right) (Th. 641)[47] (fig. 163, detail). Despite the reversal and simplified stylization on the glass, the engraver has managed to catch the backward-leaning position of the rider, his riding whip transformed here into a sword. The art of dressage is seldom portrayed on glass, which is surprising as it would have been part of a gentlemen's contemporary ed-

ucation.[48] The connection, as here with a particular person or family, must be seen as a singular event.

Finally there is one other Silesian glass engraver who stands out as an interpreter of pastoral and gallant scenes. There is a goblet in the Wolf Collection decorated with the motif of a music-making couple (cat. no. 122, fig. 164a and b, details). This particular group in a park setting appears in almost identical guise on four further glasses decorated by the same hand.[49] A typical characteristic of this metic is the treatment of the fashionable clothes, whose folds seem to have a life of their own. One could argue that within this group of five glasses, the Wolf glass was probably one of the last. This is supported by the shape of the bowl which is decorated at the base with a horizontal band of foliate scrolls, as opposed to the majority of the other glasses where the engraver has kept to the older patterns. We note his use once more of little "islands" built up in layers, a characteristic of his work, with toothed projections, and bordered with trees and shrubs at the back. He had already used the compositional ploy of a central prominent tree on the beaker in the Prague Kunstgewerbemuseum[50] (fig. 165). He also makes use of this central accent on the scene on the other side of the Wolf goblet. In this case it is

86

Fig. 164 a                    Fig. 164 b                    Fig. 165

a herm of Bacchus, beneath which a gallant and his lady are seated, he showing her a nest of fledglings. The characteristic marks of this master's style are all visible within this group. From the scene on another beaker of a couple walking in a park, which has already been attributed to him on another occasion,[51] this engraver could be distinguished as the "Master of the gallants in a park." As opposed to the other five pieces, this engraver has omitted none of his most effective stylistic characteristics on the Wolf glass, his facility with the engraving tool, the lively narrative details almost treated in caricature, and the unusual richness of fantastic ornament. Certain details, such as the foliage of the trees and particular flowers and fruit, remind one strongly of Schneider's style, suggesting therefore that he might have worked for a time in Schneider's workshop, or at least come under his influence. In any case he is a particularly individual and talented example of the many anonymous glass engravers working in the Silesian tradition.

Notes to Chapter on Bohemian and Silesian Engraved Glasses.

[1] Nagler, *Allgemeines Künstlerlexikon*, vol. 16, Munich 1846, pp. 217–218. See also E. Forrer, *Biographical Dictionary of Medallists*, vol. 5, 1912, pp. 467–468.

[2] M. Duchamp, in: *Bulletin de la Société Française de Numismatique 39*, 1984, p. 467.

[3] This example is in the Bildarchiv of the Österreichische Nationalbibliothek, Vienna, (NB. 512.854 BRF). Copies of the original medal can be found in a German private collection (see exhibition cat: *Münster, Wien und die Türken, 1683–1983*, Stadtmuseum Münster, Munster 1983, cat. no. 169 B, ill.) and in the Kunsthistorisches Museum, Vienna (see Duchamp, 1984, fig. 1, p. 537).

[4] See Duchamp, op. cit. 1984, p. 536, ill. p. 537.

[5] The engraving illustrated here is in the Bildarchiv of the Österreichsche Nationalbibliothek, Vienna (Dg 162 142/5). For the missing collar of the Golden Fleece see also the illustration of the Raab engraving, fig. 83.

[6] In this connection see Olga Drahotová, "Der Kreis um den Meister des sogenannten Koula-Bechers," in: *Tschechoslowakische Glasrevue 1965*, no. 11, pp. 340–343.

[7] Further illustrations of the Koula beaker can be found in: Vávra 1954, fig. 172; Klesse 1965, p. 22, fig. 19; 1982, fig. 73.

[8] The example illustrated here is in the Library of the Germanisches Nationalmuseum, Nuremberg.

[9] See notes to cat. no. 92.

[10] The example reproduced is in the Library of the Germanisches Nationalmuseum, Nuremberg.

[11] See Henkel/Schöne 1976, p. LXI, no. 300. The example illustrated courtesy of the Library of the Germanisches Nationalmuseum, Nuremberg.

[12] See also cat. no. 202 and the examples mentioned there.

[13] The example illustrated here is in the print collection of the Kunstgewerbemuseum, Cologne.

[14] Schloß Favorite near Rastatt, Inv. no. 534.

[15] Rudolf Sillib, *Schloß Favorite und die Eremitagen der Markgräfin Franziska Sibylla Augusta von Baden-Baden*, Heidelberg 1914, p. 96.

[16] According to Rosemarie Stratmann-Döhler of the Badisches Landesmuseum, Karlsruhe, the dating of the furnishing of Schloss. Favorite can be established on other grounds, despite the lack of documentary evidence in the archives (letter of 25 February 1985).

[17] Ovid, *Metamorphoses*, book VI, verses 126 and 120.

[18] *Metamorphoses d'Ovide en Rondeaux imprimez et enrichis de figures par ordre de Sa majesté, et dediez à Monsigneur Le Dauphin. A Paris de l'Imprimerie Royale 1676* ( the preface a "Lettre de M. Le Brun à M. de Benserade," 1. Nov. 1674). Original in the Bayerische Staatsbibliothek, Munich. German edition: *Die Verwandlungen des Ovidii, In zweyhundert und sechs- und zwanzig Kupffern, In Verlegung Johann Ulrich Krauß, Kupferstechern in Augspurg* (n. d., ca. 1694), figs. 89 and 90 from the original in the Stadtbibliothek, Augsburg.

[19] Klesse 1965, pp. 22–23, figs. 18, 20, cat. no. 176; Sotheby's Krug I, no. 163, ill.

[20] Rückert 1982, II, notes to no. 771.

[21] Seydel 1919, pp. 252–253; Schmidt 1922, p. 265.

[22] Schmidt Ms 1931, pp. 274–275. A topaz goblet with similar decoration, today in the Kunstgewerbemuseum, Staatliche Museen Preußischer Kulturbesitz, Berlin, may be connected with the Winter workshop (Inv. no. 37, 20).

[23] E. g. Inv. nos. 4456, 16833; see Jiřík 1934, pl. XXVI, 58.

[24] Prague, Inv. no. 16706; Klesse 1965, no. 205, ill.; Sotheby's, Krug IV, lot. no. 818, col. pl.

[25] For similar observations concerning their clothing see: Rückert 1982, II, p. 256, notes to no. 771.

[26] Compare for example with the goblet with bowl in the form of a cornucopia: Jiřík 1934, pl. XIII; Vávra 1954, figs. 187 and 190; Schlosser 1956, fig. 103, 1965, fig. 185; Klesse 1965, p. 27, fig. 26, no. 204, ill.; Sotheby's Krug I, lot. no. 202, col. pl.

[27] Schmidt Ms 1931, pp. 276–277.

[28] In Karlsruhe, K. H. Heine Collection: Baumgärtner 1971, no. 66, ill., and in the Dr. Karl Ruhmann Collection, Vienna: Schlosser 1965, p. 74, fig. 22.

[29] Seydel 1919, p. 253 (mentioned there as "Jeremias Frister," on p. 257 corrected to "Jeremias Feister").

[30] The illustration is of the original print in the print collection, Kunstbibliothek, Staatliche Museen Preußischer Kulturbesitz, Berlin.

[31] Klesse 1973, pp. 38–40, figs. 45–46, no. 595, ill.; Sotheby's, Krug II, lot. no. 404, ill.

[32] See for example Klesse 1965, pp. 27–30, figs. 28 and 30, no. 206, ill.; Drahatová 1982, fig. 72. That Friedrich Winter's brother Martin favored this motif after entering the employ of the "great" elector can be explained on the one hand in his Silesian origins; on the other, there was already a corresponding trend in Potsdam.

[33] Klesse 1965, p. 30, fig. 32, no. 213, ill.; Sotheby's, Krug IV, lot. no. 808, ill.

[34] Thanks to the research and transcription of Prof. Heiner Spicker, Musikhochschule Cologne, the notation was found to be a genuine polonaise.

[35] In this connection see the article in: *Die Musik in Geschichte und Gegenwart*, vol. X, Cassel 1962, col. 1427–1432.

[36] Schmidt 1926, pl. 20, no. 147.

[37] Ohm 1973, no. 397, ill.

[38] Olga Drahotová last pointed out this unique Silesian signature (1982, p. 124). The photographs of the Casper Gottlieb Langer goblet were kindly provided by Ilona Petzold, Grassi-Museum, Leipzig.

[39] For further discussion see: Klesse/Saldern 1978, p. 50, figs. 108–109, no. 119, ill.

[40] Johann Christian Kundmann, *Die Heimsuchungen Gottes in Zorn und Gnade über das Herzogthum Schlesien in Müntzen*, Leipzig (n. d., ca. 1742), pp. 534, onwards, table II, D. 9; the original illustrated here is in the collection of coins, medals, and tokens, Kunsthistorisches Museum, Vienna (Inv. no. 3426 bB, diam. 32 mm, silver, 17.21 grams).

[41] Baumgärtner 1981, p. 31, figs. 17–18. Here the medal is incorrectly attributed to Adam Holtzhey. Helmut Jungwirth (Kunst-

historisches Museum, Vienna, department of coins, medals and tokens) has kindly pointed out that the siganture I. G. H. F. stands for Johann Georg Holtzhey, and that there is no mention of Adam Holtzhey in Forrer *(Biographical Dictionary of Medallists)*.

[42]  The profile portrait on the Schneider goblet is to sinister, but of course reversed on the paper impression.

[43]  In this connection see the examples published by Anna Chrzanowska, "Odbitki dekoracji skiel Christiana Gottfrieda Schneidera," in: *Roczniki Sztuki Slaskiej, II,* Wroclaw (Breslau) 1963, pp. 128 onwards, and Franz-Hadrian Dreier, *Stichvorlagen und Zeichnungen zu Gläsern Christian Gottfried Schneiders,* JGS VII, 1965, pp. 66–78.

[44]  See note no. 43.

[45]  See Dreier 1965, pp. 72–73, fig. 19, who also illustrates these three goblets, the only ones known so far, decorated with this motif (figs. 20–22).

[46]  See Bernt 1950, p. 60, pl. 70.

[47]  The illustration is reproduced from the original in the Albertina print collection, Vienna. Ridinger returned repeatedly to the theme of dressage in various series throughout his life: *Neue Reitkunst,* 1722 (23 pages); *Neue Reit Schul* 1734 (18 pages); *Die Reitschule* (6 pages), sketches 1744 (edited and published first in 1774–76); the so-called *Kleine Reitschule* 1760 (47 pages).

[48]  Compare with the small number of thematic variants: Pazaurek 1902, pp. 11–12, pl. 11c; Schmidt 1914, no. 136, ill. Saldern, 1968, no. 204, ill. All examples appear to be from the same hand as that of the beaker in the Wolf Collection.

[49]  See the variants listed under cat. no. 122.

[50]  See also Vávra 1954, fig. 203.

[51]  See Klesse/Saldern 1978, pp. 52–53, fig. 118, no. 121, ill.

## Glasses Engraved in Brandenburg

Although the group of Brandenburg glasses within this collection is not large, it includes examples of the most important aspects of the independent approach to decoration on glass in the Potsdam and Zechlin glasshouses. The foundations for this were laid on the one hand by Johann Kunckel, probably the most important German glassmaker and technician, and, on the other, certain oustandingly-talented engravers who transformed the blanks into works of art.

A small tumbler in this collection dates from the earliest days of the glasshouse, founded by the great Elector, before Kunckel's tenure which began in 1678. The sides are continuously decorated with four dancing children holding up flanking swags of fruit by means of ribbons (cat. no. 127, fig. 166). Robert Schmidt felt that a conical beaker, decorated with three very similar dancing chil-

dren in the Moritzburg Museum, Halle, was probably an early product of the Potsdam glasshouse from the mid 1670s[1] (fig. 167). These children, who appear on both glasses, with their robust, stilted little bodies, tiny pointed feet, clenched fists, thin hair, and expressionless chubby faces, are like members of the same family. They were without doubt engraved by the same hand. We know that Georg Gondelach set up a glasshouse in Oranienbaum near Dessau around 1669, and that while he was in charge of the Potsdam glasshouse, engravers were transferred from Dessau to Potsdam in the second half of the 1670s.[2] This could therefore be the hand of just such a Dessau engraver. If the Halle beaker is judged a product of Potsdam, with its thicker walls and polished frieze of circlets, a decorative feature typical of later Potsdam work, then it is possible that the Wolf tumbler, whose form is not typical of

Fig. 166

Fig. 167

Fig. 168 a                    Fig. 168 b                              Fig. 169

Potsdam glass, could have originated in the Dessau glasshouse. Finally this beaker's Anhalt provenance strengthens such a possibility. In any case, the engraver of this glass adopted not only the motif of the dancing children (found neither in Nuremberg nor Silesia) but also the idiosyncratic rounded fruit festoons typical of Berlin. In particular, Gottfried Spiller, the best-known Potsdam engraver, who was there from around 1675, seized on both motifs with delight and developed them with bravura.

The relationship between the Dessau engraver and the highly-talented Gottfried Spiller can be seen most clearly in the figures of the children on a beaker and cover with the arms of Margrave Philipp Wilhelm von Brandenburg-Schwedt (cat. no. 128, figs. 168a and b, details). His vine bedecked putti with curly hair, scantily-clad bodies, and the leftward twist to their hopping feet are features reminiscent of those of the anonymous engraver (fig. 166). However, Spiller's children are physically stronger and anatomically more accurate. They move with greater fluency, and their faces are expressively childlike. Compared with the work of his predecessors, they display a wholly original liveliness and happiness. It is still uncertain whether Spiller used a graphic source, for

instance Wolfgang Helmhard von Hohberg's Allegories of the Four Seasons as children, published as a book of emblems in Regensburg in 1675 under the title *Lust- und Artzeney-Garten der Königlichen Propheten Davids* (Pleasure and physic garden of the Prophet-King David), etched by Georg Christoph Eimmart (1638–1705),[3] (fig. 169). Despite the great similarity between the movements, especially in the case of the putto representing Autumn, no definite link can be proved. In any case it is not possible to locate any graphic prototypes for Spiller's children's scenes, rich in fantasy as they are. Spiller's progress towards a more natural interpretation, compared to that of the engraver of the other dancing children, cannot be explained only by his use of printed sources or his undoubtedly greater talent, but also by the fact that a difference of fifteen to twenty years separates the two. Through comparison with other pieces from Spiller's hand, it is possible to place the Wolf beaker in the mid 1690s.

Philipp Wilhelm assumed the title of Margrave of Brandenburg-Schwedt in 1689. The glass must have been executed between 1689 and 1698, as the armorials do not indicate his marriage, which took place in 1699 with Johanna Charlotte von Anhalt-Dessau. An almost identical beaker, en-

92

Fig. 170      Fig. 171      Fig. 172

graved with the arms of his half-brother Elector Frederick III of Brandenburg, is in Corning[4] (fig. 170). This must also have originated in the same period, that is between the beginning of his reign in 1688, and his coronation as first king of Prussia in 1701. The putti placed between the armorial and monogram medallions on the Corning glass are similar to those on the Wolf glass (figs. 171 and 168b, especially the reverse side of fig. 171, a perfect parallel with fig. 168b). A beaker in the Württembergisches Landesmuseum in Stuttgart,[5] bears the arms and monogram of the Electress Christine Eberhardine of Saxony, a member of the House of Brandenburg-Bayreuth. This beaker must have been commissioned between the year of her marriage in 1693 and that of her death in 1697 (fig. 172). Although the relief-carved details are more sparingly used on the Stuttgart beaker, it pinpoints the dating of these glasses still more exactly. A group of glasses decorated by Spiller with infant bacchanales also belongs to this period and has already been discussed by Pazaurek.[6] Among these, the best-known is the piece in the Green Vaults in Dresden,[7] and the one in the Victoria and Albert Museum in London.[8]

The thick-walled beaker, favored by Spiller for many of his finest works, was produced during the 1690s, when the typical heavy Potsdam goblet and cover was also developed. This type of glass was so successful that its popularity lasted into the twenties and thirties of the next century. A fine example, of vigorous proportions, has survived in the Wolf Collection (cat. no. 129). The obvious hand of the cutter suggests that the piece might first have been decorated in the glasshouse with facets, flutes, and stiff-leaf motifs, which distinguishes the glass as a Potsdam product, after which the bowl was decorated mainly with wheel-engraved details including figures. Four separate cartouches are flanked by scrollwork borders (*Laub- und Bandlwerk*), two of which are decorated with hunters carrying hares on staffs, one with horn-blowing huntsman, and the fourth with a mounted huntsman pursuing a stag. The style of engraving is entirely Bohemian in charac-

93

Fig. 173

Fig. 174

ter and is echoed in the swags of fruit alternating with miniature hunting scenes on the rim of the bowl and cover. Robert Schmidt refers to glass-engravers and sellers from Bohemia who were granted citizen's rights in Berlin at the beginning of the eighteenth century.[9] It is understandable therefore that there must have been a small group of typical Potsdam goblets decorated in Bohemian taste, of which only a few have survived. A goblet in Hamburg[10] and another in Cologne[11] can be dated to between 1708 and 1715 by the monogram of Frederick I of Prussia and his second wife, as well as the monogram of Queen Sophie Dorothee. On the other hand the type of decoration to be found on the Wolf goblet must date it a little later.

An equally typical, if somewhat smaller Potsdam goblet is decorated with an applied molded-glass portrait of Augustus the Strong (cat. no. 130, fig. 173, detail). The molded portrait with additional cut details is after a marble relief by the court sculptor François Coudray in the Dresden City

Library,[12] (fig. 174). It is certainly of Saxon origin as the art of molded, as a substitute for cut, reliefs was practiced in Dresden from an early date.[13] While portraits of Augustus III and his wife, Queen Maria Josepha, are often found on glass, molded glass portraits of Augustus the Strong are rare by comparison, especially as the technique of relief-carving was just beginning to blossom in his reign. It is interesting that the relief-carved portraits of Augustus the Strong on the well-known goblets[14] are also after the Coudray relief. The Saxon elector and Polish king, quite young beneath his curly wig, wears a cuirass, and is in strict profile to sinister. The engraved laurel-wreath frame and the Saxon/Polish arms on the reverse are competently executed, and they could have been engraved in Berlin or Dresden. Perhaps the glass was produced in Berlin, decorated there as well, and only the paste portrait added later in Berlin or Dresden.

In connection with the foreign influences on the products of Potsdam and Berlin, we must mention

94

Fig. 175              Fig. 176              Fig. 177

a goblet and cover which combine a Silesian form with decoration of Brandenburg type (cat. no. 132, fig. 175). The goblet is of a type commonly associated with the Silesian workshop of Friedrich Winter around 1710,[15] where the decorative vocabulary of relief stiff-leaf borders on foot, stem, base of bowl, and cover was used as frequently as in Potsdam-Berlin. This type of graceful bell-shaped bowl was only developed in Silesia at this time, and it was totally foreign to Potsdam glass-making. However, the decoration of putti supporting fruit festoons is a motif favoured by Gottfried Spiller among the early engravers at Potsdam and Elias Rosbach among the next generation.[16] The prototype for the Wolf goblet would seem to have come undoubtedly from the Spiller workshop. It is a thick-walled goblet from the Potsdam glasshouse with the arms of the Elector of Trier, Hugo, Freiherr von Orsbeck (1676–1711) and five similar putti. This goblet was on loan from a private collection to the Historisches Museum of Speyer until about 1927, when it disappeared[17] (figs. 176 and 177). The illustration published by Pazaurek shows the rear view of a putto with bent leg and arm upstretched to grasp the ribbons, in exactly the same stance as those on the Wolf goblet. The greater degree of anatomical accuracy and confidence in the outline of Spiller's example is noticeable, despite the poor quality of the illustration, and it reveals the Wolf goblet as a charming copy.

With the signed goblet by Elias Rosbach (cat. no. 137, fig. 178, detail) we are dealing with a later generation of Potsdam engravers whose style is marked by an unusual grace and elegance. The scene shows the reclining god Chronos, his scythe beside him, and a tiny figure of Fortuna with raised veil poised on a ball, balanced in his right hand. This allegorical combination of Happiness and Transience was one of the most popular emblematic subjects in the literature of the time.[18] The contemporary motto "Caduca fluxa vanitas" which is translated onto the glass in simplified form as "Zeitt und Glück hat seine Tuck" (Time and Happiness are false) is here represented by

95

Rosbach in pictorial form with rare mastery and care. The god Chronos has in this case been adapted from a similar figure often used by him elsewhere, the reclining river god. As W. Holzhausen has discovered,[19] the river-god motif was borrowed from a medal by Raimund Faltz, struck to commemorate the victory of Elector Friedrich III at the Rhine[20] (fig. 179). Thus, on the Wolf glass, the river god's trident and spouting vase have become the scythe and figure of Fortuna, and the god has been given a large pair of wings. Rosbach achieves charming contrasts here by picking out these new attributes in polished engraving in the midst of predominantly matt decoration. These small but meaningful changes are effected with brilliance and conviction. A Zechlin goblet decorated with the same subject, but weaker engraving, was in the former Kaiser-Friedrich-Museum in Görlitz[21] and was probably the work of a member of Rosbach's workshop. In view of the fact that this motif appears on a glass whose shape was already in use in Potsdam, it is possible that the Wolf goblet was produced before the glasshouse was transferred to Zechlin in 1736.

It seems almost unfitting to end this chapter with goldruby glasses, when the fame of the Potsdam glasshouse and Johann Kunckel was based on his successful production of ruby glass, unique at the time, and which he perfected with the help of a recipe by the Hamburg chemist Dr. Andreas Cassius.[22] Kunckel made it quite clear in his *Ars vitraria experimentalis* published in 1679, that he had discovered the secrets of how to make ruby glass, before any other rivals were aware of the practical difficulties. It is, however, difficult to attribute surviving ruby glasses with certainty to Potsdam when none of the forms are unmistakably from that center. A thick-walled beaker in the Wolf Collection (cat. no. 139) with interlocking rows of graduated facets might be a product of the Potsdam glasshouse. A beaker, with similar cutting, whose dark-red tone also graduates to raspberry red, was formerly in Kassel, and another is

Fig. 178

Fig. 179

96

Fig. 180                    Fig. 181

in Zurich.[23] A heavy beaker with vertical facets bearing the monogram of Johann Georg II von Anhalt (died 1693), which Robert Schmidt attributed to Brandenburg,[24] could act as a link with this group. Even though similar ruby glass was being produced in a number of Bohemian centers towards the end of the seventeenth century,[25] the proximity of the Dessau Residenz makes a Potsdam provenance more likely.

The attribution of the polygonal, mostly hexagonal, ruby-glass flasks (cat. no. 140) dating from around the turn of the century, is equally problematical. Here too, a Potsdam, Bohemian, or a central region such as Thuringia must be considered.[26] The flower cut on the base would seem to indicate a Thuringian or Franconian, rather than Potsdam, origin.

As opposed to these uncertainties, there is a glass in this collection whose form absolutely confirms its provenance (cat. no. 141, fig. 180). The deep ruby-glass goblet with its idiosyncratic ogee bowl can only have been produced in Potsdam – and this form is found on colorless-glass examples as well.[27] The profile is one of the most attractive to have been devised in the eighteenth century. It says much for the artistic sensibilities of the maker that only the supporting sections are embellished with carved detail, while the clear, tensely-curved outlines of the bowl are accentuated by being left plain, allowing the deep red of the glass to make its greatest impact. A parallel example in the Österreichisches Museum für angewandte Kunst in Vienna [28] (fig. 181) creates a similar impression. Although this type of goblet was developed only after Kunckel's death, it is a convincing example of the creative power generated by his discovery a generation earlier.

Notes to Chapter on Glasses Engraved in Brandenburg.

[1]    Schmidt 1914 B. G., p. 69, text ill. 19. As the glass engravers who decorated the glasses produced by the Potsdam glasshouse resided in Berlin, these glasses are described in the catalogue as "Potsdam-Berlin," and "Zechlin-Berlin" (once the glasshouse had moved from Potsdam to Zechlin in 1736).

[2]    Ibid., pp. 68–69. Among those working in the Potsdam glasshouse for instance is a record of a glass-engraver with the christian name Anton, and one Christoph Tille, both from Dessau.

[3]    The example illustrated is in the Germanisches Nationalmuseum library, Nuremberg.

[4]    Charleston 1980, no. 62, col. pl.

[5]    Pazaurek 1927, fig. 28.

[6]    Ibid., p. 48.

[7]    Schmidt 1914 B. G., pl. 8.

[8]    Ibid., pl. 7, nos. 2 and 3.

[9]    Ibid., p. 92.

[10]    Ibid., pl. 27, no. 2.

[11]    Ibid., pl. 27, no. 1; Cologne 1963, no. 344, and 1973, no. 411, ill.

[12]    Erna von Watzdorf, Johann Melchior Dinglinger, Der Goldschmied des deutschen Barock, vol. I, Berlin 1962, fig. 287; Baumgärtner 1977, p. 63.

[13]    Ibid., p. 63.

[14]    Ibid., p. 62, fig. 50; Haase 1975, nos. 74 and 74a, ill.; further examples mentioned in: Von Schlieben 1937, no. 16, p. 179 (not illustrated).

[15]    See examples in: Vávra 1954, pl. 77, fig. 189; Ohm 1973, no. 385, ill.; Klesse 1973, p. 30, no. 563, ill.; Klesse/Saldern 1978, no. 108, ill.

[16]    Rosbach's graceful children are not really stylistically connected with those on this goblet (for example Schmidt 1914 B. G., pl. 33, nos. 1 and 3, pl. 34, no. 2).

[17]    Pazaurek 1927, pp. 50–52, fig. 30–31.

[18]    See for example Gottfried Kirchner, Fortuna in Dichtung und Emblematik des Barock, Stuttgart 1970, pp. 33 onwards.

[19]    Walter Holzhausen, in: Kunstwanderer, Nov. 1930, p. 79, ill.

[20] The example illustrated is in silver (weight 85.6 grams) and in the Kunsthistorisches Museum, Vienna (department of medals, coins and tokens). My thanks to Helmut Jungwirth for his collegial help.

[21] Schmidt 1914 B. G., pl. 37, no. 1. According to information (letter of 5 August 1986) from the Städtische Kunstsammlungen, Görlitz, this glass disappeared during the war.

[22] Ibid., p. 61.

[23] Klesse/Saldern 1978, p. 40, fig. 81, no. 137, col. ill.

[24] 1914 B. G., p. 80, text ill. 28.

[25] Drahotová 1973, pp. 8–11, ill.; in connection with a ruby-glass carafe, entirely decorated with cut circlets, in the James A. de Rothschild Collection, Waddesdon Manor, R. J. Charleston argues for a Bohemian origin, of all the possible contemporary centers under consideration (1977, pp. 212, 214–215, col. pl.). Without the help of signatures, arms, or archival evidence of one or another center, the question of origin with regard to these ruby glasses can hardly be determined categorically.

[26] See the parallel examples and variants mentioned in the notes to cat. no. 140.

[27] See for example Schmidt 1914 B. G., pl. 33, nos. 1 and 3, pl. 34, no. 1, pl. 37, no. 2; Klesse 1965, no. 273, ill.; Sotheby's, Krug II, lot no. 383, ill.

[28] Schlosser 1956, fig. 143; 1965, fig. 230.

# Engraved Glasses from Central Germany

## Saxony

By far the most interesting and well-documented glass in the Wolf Collection, is the relief-carved goblet and cover executed for the Saxon elector and Polish king Augustus the Strong (cat. no. 142, fig. 182, detail). Not only the high quality of the original design, but the masterly and consistent use of relief-cut details suggest its princely origins. The bill, sent by the clerk Adam Heinrich Rauhe on 10 December 1731 to Augustus the Strong, confirms that this goblet was made in the Dresden glasshouse. The bill includes such an accurate description of the glass that it must be quoted here in full: "... 1 gross stark Gesundheitsglass, unten am Fusse mit Muscheln, am Knopff A. R. in Triangel, darüber die Königl. Crone, am Kelch unten mit Muscheln und auf einer Seite das Pohl. und Sächss. Wappen, welche 2 Adler halten, unten am Wappen das goldene Fliess, auf der anderen Seite der Pohl. Orden, der Deckel präsentiert einen Churgutt (Kurhut), auf welchn A. R. in Triangel, worüber die kgl. Crone, alles mit doppelt erhobener Arbeit ...110 Thlr."[1] (A large impressive toasting goblet, the foot with scallops, the knop with AR repeated thrice, above it the royal crown, the base of the bowl with scallops and the Polish and Saxon arms held by two eagles, below the arms the Golden Fleece, on the reverse with Polish order, the cover is an elector's hat, above which AR is repeated thrice and the royal crown, all in double relief work ... 110 thaler). Hans von Schlieben first discovered this bill in the Dresden archives and connected it with this glass, at that time in the K. von Bardeleben Collection in Jena, and he expressed the opinion that

Fig. 182

Fig. 183

the "kunstsinnige König August der Starke" (the art-loving monarch Augustus the Strong) must have had a personal hand in the design. Twenty-three years before, Robert Schmidt commented, "The extraordinary idea of using the theme of the elector's hat for the cover, and combining the crown knops with the repeated initials A. R., must have come from the client who ordered this goblet."[2] At that time he attributed the goblet to Gottfried Spiller and the prince who commissioned it as King Frederick I of Prussia. When he published the first signed relief-carved goblet by Franz Gondelach it seemed more likely to him that "... the fine goblet and cover in the Bardeleben Collection should be placed amongst the works of Franz Gondelach, ... although there are still small stylistic discrepencies, which, at the moment I not in a position to clarify."[3]

This cautious attribution was followed by Pazaurek who was also impressed by the "witty decoration" of this "fantastic and original covered goblet," but at the same time expressing the reservation that "... the overall impression is so successful, that of the master glass engravers known to us today, only F. Gondelach, certainly not G. Spiller, can be considered, if not as the actual engraver, then as the mastermind behind its execution."[4] Pazaurek's additional reference to the richly-mounted, rock-crystal goblet in the Green Vaults in Dresden, with cover finial in the form of a three-dimensional crown and "AR" monogram reminiscent of the Wolf glass, would strengthen the attribution of both pieces to Gondelach[5] (fig. 183, detail). At least it lends support to the idea that this type of finial was already familiar as a decorative conceit from the time of the Elector of Saxony's elevation to the Polish throne in 1697.

Perhaps, as Joachim Menzhausen has also suggested,[6] the rock-crystal goblet with similar decoration in the Green Vaults is actually by Gondelach himself. It is possible that he was working at an early date in Dresden, in view of "4 Fläschgen von Christallinen Glaß geschnitten" (four small flasks of cut crystalline glass), in the shape of small pilgrim flasks with engraved allegorical figures which stand on the base of Johann Melchior Dinglinger's "Goldenes Kaffeezeug," commissioned by Augustus the Strong for the Green Vaults, completed in 1701, and described as "Rosoglio-Flaschen."[7] No glass engraver other than Gondelach could have effected such elegant curved lappets in relief on the sides, allowing space for the projecting medallion frames enclosing engraved allegorical scenes. On purely stylistic grounds, these flasks, with their three-dimensional treatment, can only have been designed and executed by Franz Gondelach. We cannot consider engravers in either Brandenburg or Silesia. It would be understandable if Gondelach's impressive rock-crystal goblet with "AR" knop delivered to Augustus the Strong had encouraged further commissions, such as the Wolf goblet.

The motif of the crown knop or crown cover was certainly not a complete novelty at that time, being incorporated in Potsdam glasses in the 1680s, as Stengel has already noted.[8] The motif was used by Martin Winter and Gottfried Spiller on goblets for the first king of Prussia, Frederick I, and his son Frederick William I, again with fanciful variations.[9] Unfortunately we have only written records to give us some idea of the earliest examples of this type of glass.

Finally there is evidence of another goblet which could have been a prototype for the 1731 goblet. It was presented by Frederick William I to Augustus the Strong at the *Chur-Sächsisches Lager,* his camp at Mühlberg in 1730. The Brunswick Resident at the Berlin court, Wilhelm Stratemann, describes it in his diplomatic despatches as a tall "Pokal, worauf ein großer Grenadier und des Königs von Pohlen Initial Buchstaben AR mit

Fig. 184 a                    Fig. 185 a                    Fig. 186

Fig. 184 b

Fig. 185 b

darüberstehender Königlicher Crone geschnitten" (goblet on which had been carved a large grenadier and the initials of the King of Poland, AR, with surmounting crown) by the *kgl. Hof-Glasschneider* (court glass engraver).[10] However many influences converged in the making of the Wolf Augustus Rex goblet, the result is unusual. Under any circumstances, this is a masterpiece of glass, and there are few others from the eighteenth century that can be ranged beside it.

101

Fig. 187

Fig. 188

There is also another impressive goblet from the Dresden glasshouse in this collection, decorated with a continuous stag hunt (cat. no. 143, fig. 184a and b). It is not only the form of this glass, with its vertical emphasis in the extended, teared, baluster stem and faceted knop and base of bowl, but also the engraving, which indicates that this glass belongs to a large group, all decorated by the same Dresden metic. Characteristic of this master are the riders on horses, their chests with marked vertical grooves, the short-necked, snub-nosed hounds and the stags with tiny heads and slender antlers. Most are decorated with landscapes, in the background overgrown ruins of stone castles, while in the foreground bushy trees spring up, sometimes between rocky outcrops, or at the edge of woodland glades, or stretches of water. A close-ly-related example is in the Collections of the Veste Coburg, and in the Kestner Museum, Hano-ver[11] (figs. 185a and b, Coburg; 186, Hanover). Sa-bine Baumgärtner also rightly attributes the fol-lowing goblets to the same artist: the goblet deco-rated with an animal fight and the Orpheus goblet

in the Museum für Kunsthandwerk in Dresden, and a goblet with stag hunt in the Thuringian Museum at Eisenach. Her measured opinion even goes so far as to identify Johann Christoph Kiess-ling, established as the best-known contemporary Dresden engraver, although not without reserva-tions, owing to lack of proof. The work of the en-graver of the Wolf goblet shows him as an able and lively master, whose lack of anatomical draw-ing ability in no way detracted from his pleasure in his art. He has considerable rhythmic and com-positional abilities, resulting in an attractive ten-sion between matt and polished engraved areas, and an harmonious overall impression.

In connection with the products of the Dresden glasshouse, two small teapots in ruby glass and mounted in silver-gilt must be mentioned (cat. nos. 144 and 145, fig. 187). On the one hand they are noteworthy for their tiny proportions, and the thickness of their sides with resultant depth of colour, and on the other for their depressed globu-lar form with everted foot and neck, leaving room

102

for embellishment with silver-gilt mounts. While the elegant "S" shaped spout was applied at the furnace, the foot, handle, and cover were left to the silversmith. Two comparable pieces in the Germanisches Nationalmuseum, Nuremberg, and the Green Vaults in Dresden, are engraved with the arms of Saxony-Poland and the AR monogram,[12] (fig. 188). The mounts on the Nuremberg teapot bear a Dresden mark, so that a connection with the Saxon court is obvious.

It is possible that these pieces are products of the glasshouse set up on the orders of Augustus the Strong as early as 1700, and Sabine Baumgärtner has already suggested this provenance for the whole group.[13] We learn through Johann Melchior Steinbrück, the first inspector of the porcelain manufactory, that Johann Friedrich Böttger, the brilliant discoverer of European porcelain at Augustus's court, also discovered the secrets of ruby-glass manufacture in 1713, possibly with the help of Johann Kunckel, with whom he was known to be in contact.[14] Steinbrück's 1717 and 1718 reports only mention what is obviously ruby overlay, *inwendig oder außerhalb roth* (red inside or outside), confirmed by surviving examples.[15] Possibly, pieces were made in pure ruby glass alongside the overlaid examples, which would have caught Steinbrück's eye where the engraving or cutting had revealed the colorless-glass core. Nowhere does he mention pure ruby-glass products, from either Dresden, Potsdam, Bohemian, or South German centers, as he might have felt these were not worth mentioning.

Gisela Haase has put forward the hypothosis that teapots decorated with the arms and monogram of Augustus the Strong, as well as comparable parallels, could not have originated in Dresden, as the color of the glass is obviously darker and more intense than Böttger ruby-overlay glasses.[16] This is difficult to understand, as pure thick colored glass is in itself always darker in tone than overlaid glass. The small amount of gold in the Dresden ruby-overlay glass would correspondingly agree with Haase's stress on the lighter weight, as opposed to the massive gold-ruby glasses of the Potsdam and other glass centres.[17] As the colour of the Wolf and Nuremberg teapots (fig. 188) moves from a dark red to purple-violet tone, S. Baumgärtner's hypothesis, that the teapots with Saxon arms and monogram are overlaid, cannot be taken absolutely for granted. Certainly the similarities within this group point to a common origin.

Among the ranks of the more common Saxon glasses, originating from outside the artistic metropolis of Dresden, there is a goblet and cover with applied molded portrait in relief of Duke Viktor Friedrich von Anhalt-Bernburg. This is possibly the only surviving glass with a portrait of this prince (cat. no. 148, fig. 189). The facial details are less succint than those of the applied portrait of Augustus the Strong,[18] which we have already discussed, and this may be due to their origins in a medallic prototype. There are various possibilities, for instance the one- sixth of a thaler piece of 1758[19] (fig. 190), which carries the Duke's profile. As these coins all date from the late 1750s vary hardly at all from one another, they help to pinpoint the date of this goblet to around 1760.

A further Saxon covered goblet is probably attributable to the Glücksburg glasshouse on the grounds of the arcade flutes on the baluster stem,

Fig. 189          Fig. 190

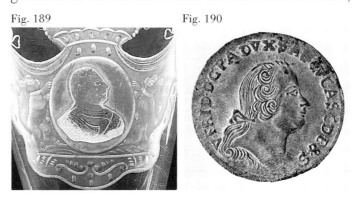

Fig. 191                    Fig. 192 (under)   193 (over) ↑                    Fig. 194

base of bowl, and finial. It was commissioned, as the coat-of-arms confirms, for Andreas Ludwig Leitgeb (1683–1751) (cat. no. 150, fig. 191). Over two different periods Leitgeb was successively town clerk (1729–32 and 1741–1744) and mayor of Vienna (1732–1736 and 1745–1748). The inscriptions relate to these periods of municipal office. There is a man holding a tankard (a reference to the Leitgeb coat-of-arms) standing between two houses bearing the dates of his terms of office. The figure on the coat-of-arms is probably a pun on the family surname, i.e. *Leutgeb* (inn-keeper) and *leit* meaning "must" in Central High German dialect, literally a fruit wine.

The townscape which appears on the cover was possibly based on a simplified version of a medallion or a coin (fig. 192). Schematic views of church towers and bastions of Vienna were common on various medals, for instance on the one struck to celebrate the relief of Vienna in 1683,[20] (fig. 193). While the townscape of Vienna obviously refers to Leitgeb's municipal career, it is not certain whether the country house depicted among vineyards is a reference to mayor Leitgeb's property at Dornbach.[21] The 1737 chronosticon as well as the inscription suggest the possibility that there is a veiled allusion to Leitgeb's successor as mayor, Johann Adam von Zahlheim, who inherited a brewery and vineyard in *Braittenbrunn am Hungarischen See* from his father, and was therefore in a sense also a "publican." Perhaps the donor of this goblet wished to clarify his relationship to Leitgeb and also explain the nature of the gift. It is interesting that there is an identical goblet in the Landesmuseum Joanneum in Graz (fig. 194).

Thuringia

Among the half dozen or so documented, signed works by the Weimar court glass engraver Andreas Friedrich Sang, the glass in the Wolf Collection dated 1729 is one of richest and most elaborate (cat. no. 151, fig. 195, without cover). It is a

104

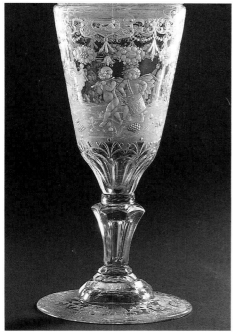

Fig. 195               Fig. 197               Fig. 196

covered goblet decorated with music-making and carousing children flanked by medallion borders on the foot, rim, and cover, enclosing tiny allegories of the Four Seasons, Virtues, and Elements.

The spacious and lively portrayal of the procession of children, down to the delicate miniature glasses they are holding, is similar in detail to the Sang goblet in Cologne, dated 1725,[22] (fig. 196). It fills the main decorative area and is contained by the fine-detailed foliate borders with delicate cartouches. Until now only the cover in the form of a flask, inscribed with full signature and date on the base, has been published.[23] While it was still in the Anhalt ducal collection, the two parts were probably separated by mistake, and they were only reunited again in the Neuburg collection. The monogram "AL" on the goblet refers to the former owner, probably Prince August Ludwig von Anhalt-Köthen who reigned between 1728 and 1755. Perhaps it was commissioned to celebrate the completion of his first year's rule as it is also inscribed with a "Vivat."

There is evidence as early as the 1725 Cologne glass that Andreas Friedrich Sang must have been in close contact with engravers from Potsdam and Berlin at an impressionable period of his stylistic development. The Wolf goblet also indicates this, as it can be no coincidence that there is a goblet attributed to Gottfried Spiller still in the Weimar collections[24] (fig. 197) which is engraved with the same pair of music-making children, but reversed (fig. 195). Identical subjects, apart from their basis in the same printed source, are mostly handled so differently by engravers that the same source is often recognised only with difficulty. However, as soon as stylistic similarities are seen in the same motifs, it is usually based on definite workshop connections. Thus the Wolf goblet throws light on Sang's artistic development, an area which had previously been obscure.

Finally there is another goblet in this collection, which is very similar in the arrangement of decorative elements. As well as the type of wide scroll borders on the foot, the rim of the bowl, and the cover, it is also punctuated by small cartouches (cat. no. 152,

Fig. 198 a                    Fig. 198 b                    Fig. 199 ↑

fig. 198 a and b, details). The richness and fantasy of ornament, in particular the winged herm caryatids with chubby faces quartering the lower zone, as well as the small hunting scenes in the interstices and in the border cartouches, indicate that this can only be the hand of Andreas Friedrich Sang. The lack of signature is probably to do with the strange repair at the base of bowl, which was almost certainly contemporary, and a solution undoubtedly proposed by Sang himself. Over the caryatids he has skilfully inserted a fillet to form a parapet, above which only the head and shoulders of Bacchus and Diana appear. As we have already seen on the signed pieces by this master, Bacchus holds a delicate, miniature-glass tankard and goblet in his hands (figs. 195 and 196). The elegant intertwined calligraphic ornament, and the *Laub- und Bandlwerk* scrolls, or the motif of Bacchus astride a barrel (a popular motif with Sang),[25] can be compared on the second signed Sang glass in Cologne (fig. 199). The prototype for the winged, herm caryatids may have come from a decorative element by Jean Bérain I[26] (fig. 200) which ap-

Fig. 200

pears in several of his ornament engravings. Sang's diverse talents enabled him to expand and reinterpret motifs with great brilliance, culled from the riches of contempory engravings, in con-

106

trast to engravers in other regions, for instance Bohemia and Silesia, who tended to repeat their ornamental vocabulary, once learned, without variation.

Notes to Chapter on Engraved Glasses from Central Germany.

1  Hans von Schlieben, "Deutsche Glaskunst im 18. Jahrhundert. Die Gläser der königlich-polnischen kürfürstlich-sächsischen Glashütte Dresden," in: *Keramische Rundschau und Kunstkeramik 45*, 1937, no. 16, pp. 178–179; Holzhausen 1954, p. 116; Baumgärtner 1977, p. 61.

2  Schmidt 1914 B. G., p. 76.

3  Schmidt 1917, p. 38. Both spellings are used in contemporary records, Gundelach and Gondelach. Since Franz-Adrian Dreier's monograph the latter spelling has become standard (see *Zeitschrift des Deutschen Vereins für Kunstwissenschaft*, XXIV, parts 1–4, pp. 101–140).

4  Pazaurek 1927, p. 40.

5  Ibid., fig. 25.

6  Oral communication in September 1984.

7  Watzdorf 1962, pp. 96 onwards, figs. 100 and 105a.

8  Stengel 1948, p. 23.

9  Schmidt 1914 B. G., pl. 6, no. 3, pl. 15, no. 2.

10  Stengel 1948, p. 22. It is not known who the "Kgl. Hof-Glasschneider" at the Prussian court was at this time, as, according to Eckhart Berckenhagen (1956, p. 19) Gottfried Spiller was already dead in 1728.

11  Baumgärtner 1977, pp. 64–66, fig. 58; Mosel 1957, no. 120, pl. 38.

12  The mounts on the Nuremberg glass illustrated here (Inv. No. Gl 231) are stamped with the marks of Schwerino Bergkstädt, master in 1749 (see Baumgärtner 1977, p. 83, fig. 120; a further parallel example appeared recently on the art market: Sotheby's, London, 10 February 1986, lot. no. 178, col. pl.; for the Dresden piece see Fetzer 1977, no. 3, col. pl.)

13  Baumgärtner 1977, p. 83; a ruby-glass teapot in the Kunstmuseum, Düsseldorf, also decorated with the Saxon-Polish arms, and published by Holzhausen ("Ein Teekännchen aus Böttger-Rubinglas," in: *Dresdner Anzeiger*, 18 April 1935, no. 108) is neither in complete ruby glass, nor overlaid, but stained. It therefore does not belong to this group.

14  See Holzhausen 1934, p. 17 ; Baumgärtner 1977, pp. 82 onwards; Haase, 1982, pp. 219–226.

15  See Holzhausen 1934, fig. 24; Haase 1975, no. 176–178, ill.; Baumgärtner 1977, pp. 82 onwards, figs. 119, 120; Haase 1982, col pl. after p. 220.

16  Haase 1982, p. 226, note 14.

17  Ibid., p. 224.

18  See cat. no. 130, and see above, p. 94.

19  In this connection see: Gisela Förschner, *Deutsche Münzen, Mittelalter bis Neuzeit, der münzprägenden Stände von Aachen bis Augsburg*, vol. I, Melsungen 1984, no. 313, ill.

20  Exhibition catalog: *Die Türken vor Wien*, Historisches Museum der Stadt Wien im Künstlerhaus, Vienna 1983, cat. no. 13/81 – 13/87.

21  Felix Czeike, *Wien und seine Bürgermeister*, Vienna 1974, pp. 234–235.

22  Signed on the barrel engraved on the bowl "Sang," dated "1725" on the baluster stem (Cologne 1963, no. 350, as well as 1973, no. 417, ill.).

23  See the references mentioned below cat. no. 151.

24  Hörning (1979), no. 93, ill.; although the attribution to Gottfried Spiller is not completely convincing, the Potsdam provenance of the goblet is hardly in doubt.

25  Signed on the lower rim of the bowl "A. F. Sang," without date. The stem, due to a past break, has been reduced in height (Cologne 1963, no. 351, as well as 1973, no. 418, ill.).

26  The graphic source illustrated is from the print collection in the Kunstgewerbemuseum, Cologne.

# Diamond Engraving and Stippling in the Netherlands

## Diamond Engraving

The technique of decorating a glass in lines or dots with the point of a diamond was practiced in the Netherlands with a high degree of competence. The following section has the most representative selection of glass from one particular area and includes some of the most interesting examples of glass in the whole collection.

Fig. 202

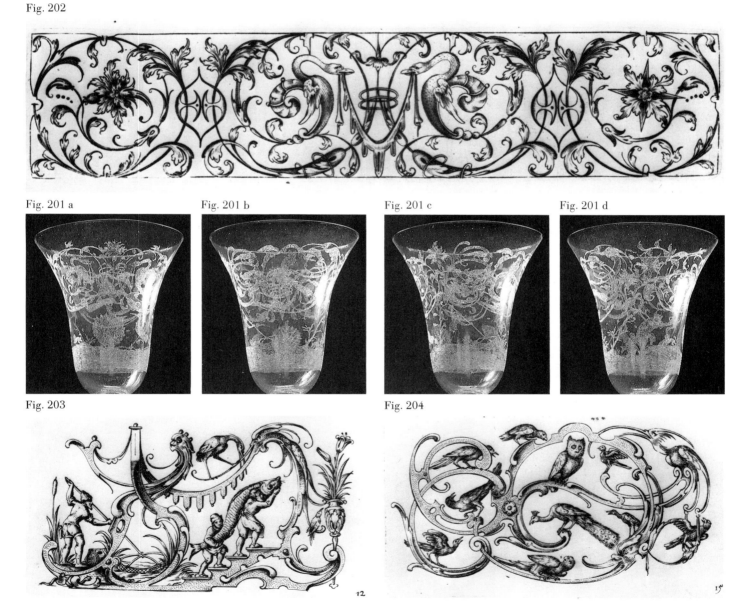

Fig. 201 a        Fig. 201 b        Fig. 201 c        Fig. 201 d

Fig. 203        Fig. 204

One of the earliest glasses in this group is a very thinly blown goblet with a bowl of exaggerated, bell shape whose possible origin is something of a puzzle (cat. no. 158, fig. 201a–d, details). Convincing parallels are found neither in the unusually thin glass nor in the imbalanced proportions, whereby the delicate stem seems almost too fragile to support the elegantly-curved bowl. A certain weakness of design, as in the disproportionately large bowl in relation to the other elements, can be observed in glass of Spanish origin.[1] In the forefront were the Catalonians, who, instructed by Italians, had quickly reached a high level of dexterity and were capable of blowing glass of the finest thinness. Perhaps this is an example of an imported glass, which was then decorated in the Netherlands.[2] The engraver has adhered to a prescribed late seventeenth-century decorative arrangement with small, narrative elements in a continuous landscape, surmounted by a richly-embellished border; on later examples it is often replaced by calligraphy.[3] It is worth mentioning that he has also used German ornamental prototypes; the flower scrolls and swan grotesques (fig. 201a) are taken from a print from a folio of friezes by the Nuremberg engraver Theodor Bang,[4] (fig. 202). On the other hand, the ribbonwork scrolls inhabited by birds (fig. 201b) and the fishing scene (fig. 201c and d), derive from two pages from a series of eighteen decorative panels for gun decoration by Johann Schmischek, published in 1620–1622 in Munich[5] (figs. 203 and 204). The engraver has insured the careful integration of the two decorative zones. In this selection of decorative motifs it is again noticeable how the glass decorator has selected various motifs, at the same time stripping them of their original symbolic meaning, as in the case of the peacock and stork, and used them in a purely decorative sense.

This combination of genre motif and ornamentation is found again on a flute in this collection (cat. no. 159, fig. 205). Here three angels with

Fig. 205                                    Fig. 206

harp, shawm, and viol, as well as a putto with kite, and a bird, appear at irregular intervals among the foliate and floral scrolls which meander over the entire surface of the bowl. On technical and stylistic grounds, Robert Schmidt described this glass as "unsigned, but definitely the work of Willem Mooleyser".[6] Another flute with angels in similar robes and other figures among scrollwork, in the Musée du Verre in Liège, is certainly by the same hand[7] (fig. 206), and a flute with the same subject was formerly in the Ruhmann Collection in Vienna.[8] The drawing on all three glasses is more hurried than is the case on examples of earlier signed works by Mooleyser. On the other hand, there are a number of distinct differences within his documented *œuvre*, above all, a certain deterioration of quality in his later works, so that an attribution to Mooleyser cannot be entirely dismissed.

The decoration on the pair of blue-tinted flasks (cat. nos. 160a and b) is naturally also loosely connected with Mooleyser, where the bands of fruit-

110

Fig. 207                                   Fig. 208                                   Fig. 209

ing vine punctuated by large and small animals in various combinations are motifs typical of his ornamental vocabulary. As such a large number of flasks, including examples of more flattened form, have survived with similar engraving.[9] They were probably the output of a large group of diletantes who adopted Mooleyser's style.

A goblet and cover, of a form particularly associated with the Netherlands in the second half of the seventeenth century, also belongs to Mooleyser's generation (cat. no. 161, fig. 207). On one side there is an equestrian portrait of a military commander with marshall's baton in early seventeenth-century costume, flanked by small, cavalry skirmishes within vine meander frames. The possibility that the portrait is Prince Maurice I of Nassau is negated by the appearance of the *Reichsadler* with the arms of Austria on its breast. Earlier graphic sources would have served for the equestrian figure, such as the *Ritterliche Reutterkunst* published in 1584 by Jost Amman[10] (fig. 208). Only with the conscious intention of en-

graving an historical rather than contemporary figure, very unusual on glass, would the glass engraver have used this outdated reference. The identity of the portrait has not as yet been discovered. The engraver uses an unusually dense *scraffiato* technique, in which few elements of horse and rider are left clear, and an attribution to a known master is unlikely. The same hand is found on a very similar goblet with a large equestrian figure and small battle scenes in vine-leaf frames, in the Gemeentemuseum at the Hague[11] (fig. 209). Perhaps a whole series of commemorative glasses with historical figures was executed for a particular occasion.

Three further glasses in this collection originate within Willem Mooleyser's close circle or were possibly engraved by Mooleyser himself. One of them is of the same form as the equestrian portrait glass and, thanks to the presence of arms and inscription, can be dated fairly accurately (cat. no. 162). The arms are those of William of Orange, who married Mary, daughter of James II of Eng-

111

Fig. 210

Fig. 211

land, and ascended the English throne with his wife as William III in 1689. As the inscription on the reverse refers to "William en Maria" it can be assumed that the glass was decorated to commemorate their coronation. Although it coincides in date with Mooleyser's career, stylistically it does not. The next glass came from the Marianne Pelliot Collection in Paris, as did the William III glass (cat. no. 163, fig. 110. detail). This type of glass, with its tall conical bowl, was also popular during this period. On one side, enclosed within a fence, is the crowned lion of Holland with brandished sword and seven arrows for the seven United Provinces. Standing on the reverse is the female figure symbolic of Freedom, with palm and freedom's cap on a staff. These subjects are found in almost identical form on glasses in London[12] and in Hamburg[13] (fig. 212), and obviously they are all three by the same hand. Thirty years ago Robert Charleston attributed the Wolf glass to Willem Mooleyser,[14] which is confirmed by a comparison with the signed and dated goblet of 1697 with similar allegorical theme in the Rijksmu-

seum in Amsterdam.[15] The looser, more strongly-contrasted technique of the early work has, in this example, developed into a more harmonious style, using a *scraffiato* technique to create a flat dense effect, as can be seen on the Amsterdam goblet. A variant formerly in the Biemann Collection,[16] with a seated allegorical figure of Freedom, and a further example with only the heraldic lion, is in the Kunstmuseum, Düsseldorf,[17] and it appears to be by a hand working in Mooleyser's style.

A tall-stemmed goblet engraved with the arms of Holland is excellently engraved, and it is of almost higher quality with regard to modeled effects than the Mooleyser goblet (cat. no. 164). The sprays of fruit and flowers on either side are also drawn with such a fine eye for botanical detail that the artist must have been an extremely talented amateur working in the Mooleyser tradition. The inscription "Hollandia" speaks also for the Dutch love of calligraphy on glass, of which there are two fine examples in the Wolf Collection. A globular flask with the inscription "Drink

112

Fig. 212

calligraphy himself is evident, not least from the latest addition to the body of his work.

We know nothing, other than his name, about the engraver of the next glass, who was a latecomer to the art of diamond engraving in the mid-eighteenth century (cat. no. 169, fig. 213a and b, details). The diamond-inscribed signature "K. Coster" can be deciphered on the stem of this Newcastle light-baluster glass. The small bell-shaped bowl is engraved with a farmer's wife asleep in a chair, and on the other side, the standing figure of a farmer. Both figures are based on engravings by Bernard Picart (1673–1733), one of a "Boerinne van Boiksloot by Amsterdam" (a farmer's wife from Boiksloot near Amsterdam), and a "Schevelingse Boer" (a farmer from Scheveling)[20] (fig. 214 and 215). Marianne Pelliot, the former owner of this glass, discovered another glass engraved with the same farmer's wife (fig. 216) in a Paris exhibition of 1936,[21] in this case combined with a Dutch milkmaid after Picard (fig. 217), which is now in the Musée du Verre in Liège.[22] Here the technique also consists of thickly-scratched areas, creating an almost "white" effect, contrasting with other "dark" areas only bounded by a single line. In her discussion of the Wolf glass, Mme. Pelliot also referred to the goblet signed "C. Koster," formerly in the Snouck Hurgronje Collection, the Hague, with the portrait, arms, and monogram of William IV of Orange,[23] which she attributed to the same engraver on stylistic grounds. Insofar as can be judged from the illustration in the auction catalogue, the same contrast in technique between *scraffiato* areas and looser linear effects are to be found on this glass. In this case Koster ( Coster) used a goblet of English type of the late seventeenth or early eighteenth century. The date of the engraving can be established with some accuracy, as William IV's short reign only lasted from 1747 to 1751.

wyn met maat, Na Paulus raad" (Drink wine sparingly, as advised by Paul) (cat. no. 167) is reminiscent of many similar flasks which have survived from the hand of Willem van Heemskerk or the calligraphy instructor Bastiaan Boers. Being unsigned it is not possible to recall the engraver from the mists of anonymity, for, while the script is finely done, it does not attain the tense curves of Heemskerk's work. Happily this is not the case with a signed and dated (20 June 1699) roemer (cat. no. 168, fig. 212), which is a previously unrecorded addition to the small corpus of glasses decorated by Bastiaan Boers, recently compiled by P. Ritsema van Eck.[18] As a schoolmaster and writing instructor in a French school in Warmond near Leiden from 1678, the decoration of glasses seems to have been very much a hobby, as only seven pieces by his hand have survived. Among them is another roemer dated 1697 in the Boymans-van Beuningen Museum in Rotterdam[19] of slightly differing proportions, but of a similar overall character as the Wolf glass. That Boers as a writing master was capable of particularly delicate

I am grateful to Pieter C. Ritsema van Eck for

Fig. 213 a

Fig. 213 b

Fig. 216

Payſane de Buikſloot, près d'Amſtredam.
Boerinne van Buiksloot by Amſterdam.
B. Picart fec.

Fig. 214

Deſſine d'apres nature par B. Picart.
Paiſan de Schevelingen pres de la Haye.
Schevelingse Boer.

Fig. 215

Laitiere Holandoise
Hollantſche Melckverkoopſter

Fig. 217

bringing my attention to a further signed glass by Coster, which was in a London private collection in 1982, and was engraved with the arms of the Dutch family of De Swart.[24] In this case Coster used a contemporary glass of Newcastle type with trapped air beads in the knopped stem. Despite the different subject and the rather out-dated style of engraving (which is however common to all four glasses and may reflect Koster's age when he engraved them), these glasses are all by the same hand. As Coster ( Koster) is such a common name in the Netherlands, and only the initial "K" (C) is given, one must hope that a chance discovery will shed further light on his identity.

114

Fig. 218

Fig. 219

## Stipple Engraving

One of the highlights of the Wolf Collection is without doubt the group of fifteen stipple-engraved glasses, all of which are of the highest quality. In almost all cases the decoration is applied on English lead glasses, the brilliant material showing off the delicate motifs to advantage. Although there is no example by Franz Greenwood, who, as is generally known, first introduced the technique of stipple engraving in the Netherlands in the eighteenth century, there are two glasses by Greenwood's closest pupil, the talented painter, drawer, and etcher Aert Schouman (1710–1792). The first glass is of Newcastle type which was common between 1730 and 1770. The conical bowl is decorated with an unframed half-length portrait of Prince William V of Orange and Nassau (1748–1806) as a youth (cat. no. 170, fig. 218). The portrait is based on a pastel by Jean Etienne Liotard[25] (fig. 219) from which a drawing was made by Aert Schouman in 1757. This in its turn was engraved by J. Houbraken and printed by Is. Tirion in 1759. The way in which the artist has discarded the heavy frame and concentrated on capturing the freshness and clarity of the childlike expression suggests that Aert Schouman not only drew the prototype for the printed source, but he executed the portrait on this glass as well. It is possible that the portrait on the glass was effected before the drawing, in which small details appear stylized to facilitate the process of reproduction. This portrait is stippled in a technique very close to that of Frans Greenwood,[26] although it fits in with other signed pieces by Schouman. Particularly noticeable is the way in which the strongly-lit face contrasts with the softer modeling of the more shaded details of costume, a decorative formula which appears in very similar fashion on the dated and signed allegory *Pictura* in the Gemeentemuseum, the Hague.[27] This portrait on the glass can therefore be dated to between the execution of the drawing and the print, that is between 1757 and 1759. On the other hand one cannot link the Wolf glass with an-

Fig. 220                    Fig. 221                    Fig. 222

other which Aert Schouman executed in 1766 on the occasion of the nomination of the eighteen-year old prince as patron of the Hague Guild of Painters, called *Pictura,* decorated with his portrait, and donated to this *Schilders-Confrerye*.[28] Later, in his capacity as president *(Hoofdman)* of this body (1777–1792) he executed yet another portrait of William V on glass, this time on a roemer, to celebrate the foundation of the Free Drawing Academy in the the Hague on the 13 March 1787.

The second stippled portrait by Schouman dates from twenty years after the one of the youthful prince (cat. no. 171, fig. 220, detail). According to the inscription it is of "JOANNES VAN SPAAN PREDIKANT IN S'HAAGE" (Joannes van Spaan, cleric at the Hague) which is quite clearly taken from an engraving by J. Houbraken dated 1776. This in turn was based on a drawing (now lost) done "ad viv(am)" by Aert Schoumann[29] (fig. 221). The interdependence of engraving on glass and print can be seen, not just in the similarity of the portrait itself, the identical inscriptions, but also in details such as the two unfastened buttons on the soutane, justifying the assumption that not only the sketch for Houbraken's print, but also

the diamond-stippled portrait are from the hand of Schouman. Perhaps he knew Pastor Spaan personally, as they were both living at the Hague for about twenty-five years. This portrait, using the stippled technique, invites comparison with a portrait of Joost Van den Vondel on a glass in the Gemeentemuseum signed by Schouman and dated 1774[30] (fig. 222, detail). In contrast to the portrait of William V, there is direct, frontal light playing over Spaan's face and chest, so that shading is mainly limited to contours and essential facial lines. Obviously the face of the fifty-year old pastor is rounder and less wrinkled than that of the aged poet Van den Vondel. The fairly regular density of stippling in the "light" areas merges more softly into the "dark" areas than was the case in Schouman's style twenty to thirty years earlier, so that all sharp contrasts are now toned down in a balanced handling of the modeling.

A similar stylistic development is also noticeable in the work of David Wolff, if one follows it from the Leiden *Justitia* glass of 1775 to his work of the late 1780s and 1790s.

Before moving on to David Wolff, mention must be made of a group of glasses by a highly talented

Fig. 236                                    Fig. 237                                    Fig. 238

less tiny dots. Even the braids and curls of her hair appear as if beneath a delicate veil. From an English mezzotint of 1775[47] (fig. 235) the rather sharp and angular features of the princess can be seen to have undergone a beneficial aesthetic transformation. Earlier, Robert Schmidt described this portrait glass, at that time still in the Friedrich Neuburg Collection, as a "sichere Arbeit Wolffs" (definite work by Wolff) of around 1780.[48] By contrast the portrait of the mayor of Amsterdam, Egbert de Vry Temminck (1700–1785) is in no way idealized (cat. no. 184, fig. 236, detail). Again in three-quarter profile, this time to the left, his massive head, with official full-bottomed wig within oval frame, is sternly composed. The large, intelligent eyes under expressive eyebrows dominate the face, while the lines round

the mouth speak of energy and willpower. The glass engraver has followed reasonably faithfully the 1780 etching by Reinier Vinkeles after a drawing by Jacob Buys, in its turn based on a portrait by Jan Wandelaar of 1758 (fig. 237). Temminck, who counted as one of the most important political personalities in Amsterdam in the eighteenth century was, between 1749 and 1784 alone, twenty-three times mayor of the city.
Another glass with his portrait is in the Kunstmuseum, Düsseldorf[49] (fig. 238, detail). Here he is definitely younger by at least a decade, suggesting that it was based on the Buys version or after Wandelaar. The overall impression makes the attribution to Wolff highly likely as it agrees in technique and composition with a whole series of his portraits of famous Dutch statesmen.[50]

Notes to Chapter on Diamond Engraving and Stippling in the Netherlands.

[1]    Alice Wilson Frothingham, *Spanish Glass*, London 1963, for example pls. 8, 18, 28, 39B.

[2]    A somewhat later glass, of similar proportions was published by R. J. Charleston as "perhaps French" ("French Glass of the 17th and 18th Centuries," in: *Glass Notes*, edited A. Churchill, no. 12, December 1952, p. 19, fig. 23a). Concerning the Wolf glass, R. J.

Charleston has also suggested a French provenance by letter 29 August 1985).

[3]    In this connection see cat. no. 165, and the other examples from this group listed there.

[4]    Carsten-Peter Warncke, *Die ornamentale Groteske in Deutschland 1500–1650*, vol. II, Berlin, 1979. fig. 802.

[5]    Ibid., fig. 1212 and 1215; figs. 202–204 illustrated are from the Kunstbibliothek, Staatliche Museen Preußischer Kulturbesitz, Berlin.

6 Ms 1931, pp. 93–94, no. 84.

7 *Trois Millénaires 1958*, no. 589, ill.; a further flute with three amorini between similar scrollwork in the museum in Liège, definitely belongs to the same group (Ibid., no. 588, ill.; Philippe 1982, fig. 113).

8 I. Schlosser, "Some Diamond Engraved Glasses from the Ruhmann Collection," in: *Burlington Magazine*, 70, 1937, pp. 246–251, pl. II C; idem 1956, fig. 160, as well as 1965, fig. 153. The glass was on the Amsterdam art market in 1984/5.

9 See comparable example mentioned in notes to cat. no. 160 a.

10 See also above, p. 31, figs. 38, and 41. The example illustrated is in the Kunstbibliothek, Staatliche Museen Preußischer Kulturbesitz, Berlin.

11 Jansen 1962, no. 120, ill. A possiblity here is one of the greatest and most successful Imperial commanders Albrecht von Wallenstein (1583–1634), Duke of Friedland. Whether this goblet was produced to celebrate the centenary of his birth, as well as his feats of arms, must remain conjectural.

12 Schmidt 1927, p. 36, pl. 64 A.

13 Buddensieg 1958, p. 234, ill.

14 Charleston 1956, p. 42.

15 Three sides illustrated in: Klesse/Saldern 1978, pp. 20–21, figs. 21, 22, 30.

16 Ibid., pp. 20–21, figs. 26, 27, and no. 80, ill.; Lucerne 1981, no. 711, ill.; Sotheby's, Biemann, no. 159, ill.

17 Heinemeyer 1966, no. 406, ill.; Klesse/Saldern 1978, pp. 20–21, fig. 29.

18 See Pieter C. Ritsema van Eck, "Bastiaan Boers en Matthieu Petit Schrijfmeesters, Schoonschrijvers en glasgraveurs," in: *Bull. van het Rijksmuseum Amsterdam*, 30, 1982, no. 2, pp. 51–62.

19 Van Gelder 1955, pl. XXIV, no. 5; Ritsema van Eck 1982, fig. 8.

20 The pages illustrated are in the print collection of the Albertina, Vienna.

21 Pelliot 1936, p. 85, note 4.

22 *Trois Millénaires 1958*, no. 586, ill.; Philippe 1982, fig. 144.

23 Published by Schmidt 1911, p. 821; Hudig 1926, p. 10; auction cat. Hurgronje 1931, lot no. 614, ill.

24 Information by letter of 15 September 1983.

25 Having been in London, Liotard remained in Holland for a long period, during which he painted the Prince of Orange's portrait, before returning to Paris in 1757.

26 On these grounds, Marianne Pelliot, the former owner of this glass, attributed the engraving to Frans Greenwood in her publication of 1929. Only after she had discovered the afore-mentioned engraving, after a drawing by Aert Schouman, did she reattribute the hand to that of Schoumann (in a letter to Alfred Wolf, about 1935).

27 Buckley 1931, pl. 13; Jansen 1962, no. 216, ill.

28 Buckley 1931, pp. 16, 20; see also A. Bredius, "De Boeken der Haagsche Schilders-Confrerye," in: *Archief voor Nederlandsche Kunstgeschiedenis IV*, 1881–1882, p. 195.

29 The engraving by Houbraken is reproduced by courtesy of the Stichting Iconographisch Bureau, the Hague. It is not possible to accept a relationship between Johannes van Spaan and the glass engraver Izaak Spaan based on an isolated example of an amateur's work. A glass engraved by him, formerly in the Krug Collection, Baden-Baden, was inscribed with an inscription to Count Bentinck and dated 1787 (Klesse 1965, no. 320, ill.).

30 See Jansen 1962, no. 217, ill.; according to B. Jansen this glass was presented by Aert Schoumann to the Society of Poets called *Kunstliefde spaart geen vlijt*. Schoumann's stippled portrait was taken from the portrait by Philipp de Koninck of 1674, and given to this society by J. Hudde Dedel in 1774.

31 Smit 1982, particularly pp. 2623-2624; Idem., "The Bradford Collection of Dutch Engraved Glass," in: *Glass Engraver 31*, 1983, pp. 22–28; Idem, auction cat. "The Bradford Collection of 18th Century Dutch Engraved Glass," Christie's, London, 4 June 1985, particularly pp. 38–39, lot nos. 21–28, ill.

32 Schmidt 1914, p. 17: this obviously "finer and more delicate" group was already known to Schmidt; however he still incorrectly ascribed the glass to D. Wolff. See also Buckley 1935, particularly pp. 24–26.

33 E. Pelinck, Stedelijk Museum "De Lakenhal," Leiden, Catalogus, 1951, no. 143, fig. 26; Tait 1968, pp. 102–103, fig. 2; Smit 1982, p. 2623, fig. 4.

34 At this point I must correct my former attribution of stippled glasses in the Biemann Collection (Klesse/Saldern 1978), where nos. 83 and 84 are certainly not by David Wolff, but rather by his *Doppelgänger* or "alias."

35 For subject see two very similar glasses: auction cat. Sotheby's, London, July 1983, lot. no. 73, ill., as well as Christie's, London, 4 June 1985, lot. no. 26, ill.

36 See Buckley 1935, pl. 22.

37 Ibid., pls. 21 and 22.

38 Ibid., p. 26.

39 D. H. de Castro, "Een en ander over Glasgravure," in: *Oud Holland I*, 1883, p. 285.

40 Smit 1982, p. 2624.

41 Buckley 1935, pl. 14.

42 Jansen 1962, no. 220, ill.

43 Smit sees this as the work of David Wolff (1982, p. 2623).

44 Buckley 1935, pl. 5 and 6.

45 Van Gelder 1955, pl. XXXII, no. 4; Tait 1968, p. 108, fig. 18.

46 A. J. van der Aa, *Aardrijkskundig Woordenboek der Nederlanden*, vol. VII, Gorinchem 1846, pp. 155–156. We are grateful to Mr. Frides Laméris, Amsterdam, for pointing out this reference (in a letter to Mr. Ernesto Wolf of 7 February 1985).

47 The original is in the Bildarchiv of the Österreichische Nationalbibliothek, Vienna (Inv. no. Pg 138 132/3)

48 Schmidt Ms. 1931, p. 98, no. 91.

49 Heinemeyer 1966, no. 415, ill.; Helmut Ricke, *Glas, ausgewählte Werke*, Kunstmuseum Düsseldorf V, Dusseldorf 1976, V-19, ill.

50 Tait 1968, p. 107, fig. 11–13.

# Wheel-Engraved Glass in the Netherlands

In the Netherlands wheel engraving tended to be overshadowed by the outstanding achievements in stippled engraving. However, there are a number of notable glasses in the Wolf Collection decorated in this technique.

matt ground resembling the upper part of a gourd. A companion piece, unfortunately without cover, but definitely by the same hand, was formerly in the Krug Collection, Baden-Baden[2] (fig. 240). Here the decoration consisted of fruiting

Fig. 239                    Fig. 240                    Fig. 241

A fine goblet and cover in this collection belongs to a group of early engraved glasses, recently so commendably compiled by Ritsema van Eck[1] (cat. no. 185, fig. 239). The goblet dating from the second half of the seventeenth-century of a classic type with cylindrical bowl was frequently preferred by glass engravers (see cat. nos 162 and 163). The large, flat surface area is particularly suitable for continuously engraved motifs, as seen here in the profusion of entwined gourd trails with large, delicately veined leaves and fruits. The low, domed cover is decorated in a wholly original manner with polished, engraved striations on a

vine embellished with small insects, caterpillars, crickets and dragonflies, somewhat reminiscent of the *Vanitas* theme in Dutch still life painting. The fine details of the leaf structure and their curling edges is so typically Dutch that, in this group at least, the influence of the Nuremberg school on early Netherlands engravers has been cast off completely.[3] Two goblets of this type are in Amsterdam, one decorated with the arms of the Province of Holland, and the other with the arms of the United Provinces. Both are decorated with a luxuriant vine, orange, and oak-leaf band[4] (fig. 241), and are probably from the same workshop,

Fig. 242                          Fig. 243                          Fig. 244

if not by the same master. As one of these glasses was possibly made on the occasion of William III's elevation to the English throne in 1689, it gives a clue as to the date of this group.

As opposed to this north Netherlands example, the engraving on a goblet from the south Netherlands is of a completely German character (cat. no. 186, fig. 242). In this instance a German engraver probably used a Netherlands glass, as only a German client would have been interested in the Imperial eagle and the arms of the seven Electors. Moreover the style of engraving is typical of the Nuremberg school. The glass with hollow, quatralobe knops in the stem and pinched, moulded ribs ("nipt-diamond-waies") round the base of the bowl and on the cover, with its ring finial, is one of a distinct group. Robert Charleston has convincingly attributed them, despite undeniable similarities with Ravenscroft's lead-glass examples, to a south Netherlands rather than an English glasshouse.[5] He points out that the Bonhommes family, already established glassmakers

in Liège in 1680, were producing *verres à l'Angleterre* (glass in the English manner). Although the sources are not more specific, Charleston argues that its must have been a particular type of "English lead-glass." Since almost all the glasses in this group are crizzled and date from the last ten or fifteen years of the seventeenth-century, this would definitely suggest a non-English origin, added to which, most are decorated with subjects relevant to the Netherlands, the Wolf goblet being an exception.

With the next wheel-engraved examples we make a jump to the mid-eighteenth-century. The best-known, and, judging by his surviving work, most prolific Dutch engraver at this time was Jacob Sang, from Thuringia,[6] and there are two examples of his signed works in the Wolf Collection. The first is dated 1762, the bowl decorated with the principally matt-engraved figure of the god Mercury in "antique" costume with winged helmet, sandals, and messenger's staff (*kerykeion*) in his right hand (cat. no. 188, fig. 243). The money-

124

Fig. 245             Fig. 246             Fig. 247

bag in his left hand, as well as the packages and barrel at his feet, are symbolic of his role as patron deity of trade and travel, two of the mainstays of the economic wealth of the Netherlands at that time. This is reinforced by the inscription "De algemeene Welvaerd" (the Common Weal). Five years earlier, in 1757, Sang engraved a very similar allegorical scene with Mercury and an identical inscription on a glass published by H. E. van Gelder.[7] As far as can be judged from van Gelder's description, the figure of Mercury is almost identical, but with reversed attributes, while the base is supported by scrolls, on which a cockerel is perched. The engraving on the Wolf *welvaerd* glass is executed with the delicacy and accuracy typical of Jacob Sang's work. Certainly there are fewer scenes with figures within his *œuvre*, which is why they always appear a little dry and stiff. On the other hand, his engraving of ships is of exceptional quality. They are depicted down to the smallest detail, and they form a subject which he returned to again and again in his thirty-year span as an engraver. The second glass in this collection is engraved with a large two-masted sailing vessel below the inscription "T' WELVAREN VANT' SCHIP DE VIGILANTIE" (cat. no. 189, fig. 244). Sang depicts the complicated web of tackle and rigging right to the top of the masts with great knowledge and affection, and he achieves a delicacy of line with the engraver's tool

which is generally only possible with the point of a diamond.

A further glass in this collection is of exceptionally fine-detailed quality, decorated as it is with a continuous stag hunt surmounted by a cartouche inscribed "LF" or "LT" and coronet (cat. no. 190, fig. 245, detail). The identical monogram, composed of small floral motifs, is found on a Thuringian goblet in the manner of G. E. Kunckel in the Sichel Collection, San Francisco.[8] This type of floral initial is a traditional Thuringian motif. This applies to the hunting scene as well, which is obviously related to similar Saxon-Thuringian examples.[9] The hand of this engraver appears on a whole series of Dutch glasses, of which one example in the Heine Collection, Karlsruhe, as well as another in the former Krug Collection, will serve as a comparison,[10] (figs. 246 and 247). The particularly small figures of humans and animals and the many different types of trees are typical but have lost none of their vigor and detail. The polished figures against a matt landscape background are very close to those on a glass inscribed "Liefhebry" formerly in the Biemann Collection, Zurich, which I then tentatively attributed to Jacob Sang's brother Simon Jacob Sang.[11] Clearly his style would seem to have been more original and spirited than that of his brother, judging from the few signed works that have survived. However,

125

Fig. 248 b

Fig. 248 a

Fig. 251

Fig. 250

Fig. 249

Fig. 252

there is also evidence that, besides the Sang brothers, there were other German glass engravers active in the Netherlands in the mid-eighteenth-century; for example, Johann Christoph Orban (Urban), son of the Gotha court glass engraver Johann Martin Orban. In 1756, the latter is recorded as applying to Grand Duke Ernst August II of Weimar for the post of court glass engraver on behalf of his son, justifying it on the grounds that he "einige Jahre zu Amsterdam und anderen Seestädten in dieser Kunst unterrichtet ... habe" (had spent some years teaching this art in Amsterdam and other maritime cities). Although Johann Christoph Orban did not obtain this post, he reappears in 1762 as an engraver at the Gehlberg (Sachsen-Gotha) glasshouse.[12] He certainly could have been responsible for the decoration of Netherlandish glasses with continuous hunting scenes, for, as we know from his father, he was active in Amsterdam and possibly other Dutch centers during the period when these glasses were executed.

It is perhaps easier to determine an attribution for the impressive goblet and cover with the portrait medallions of William V of Orange and his wife Princess Friederike Sophie Wilhelmine (cat. no. 193, fig. 248a and b, details). The portrait of the *Stadtholder* is based on a print by J. Houbraken after a drawing by Aert Schouman, in its turn based on a painting by the court artist Tethart Philipp Christian Haag[13] (fig. 249). An engraving after a painting by Daniel Chodowiecki of 1767 was definately used for the portrait of the Princess[14] (fig. 250). This can be seen in the particular treatment of her decolleté, with flowers and lace, and the flowers in her hair flowing onto her shoulders, although the engraver has added the choker fastened with ribbons at the back. These matt, engraved portraits, punctuated with polished details particularly noticeable in the eyes and in their dress, are stylistically reminiscent of portraits signed by Christiaen Schröder or Christoffel Grisnich (Gotlieb) Schröder on glass and mirrors. Details concerning these engravers, who migrated from Germany or Austria to the Netherlands, were first compiled by H. E. Van Gelder.[15] In comparison with the portraits of William IV and his wife in the Gemeentemuseum, the Hague, dated 1757[16] the likenesses on the Wolf goblet seem less strongly modeled or differentiated. They seem two dimensional with coarse details, and with greater emphasis on decorative and polished effects. In this they are closer to Schröder's work of later date, for instance the portraits of Frederick the Great of Prussia (1763) and the Empress Maria Theresa (1769) (fig. 251) in the British Museum. Also the dates of those portrayed would suggest rather that it is a product from the workshop of the younger Schröder. By chance a goblet by the same hand with an identical portrait of William V alone, appeared in the German art trade[17] (fig. 252). Whether the glass itself was imported from Saxony or the product of a Dutch glasshouse is a question which remains unresolved. Certainly there was a highpoint in the exchange of fine glass and artistic influence between the Netherlands and Germany in the second and third quarters of the eighteenth-century. This exchange was not as obviously intensive and fruitful either before or after this date.

Notes to Chapter on Wheel-Engraved Glass in the Netherlands.

[1]    Pieter C. Ritsema van Eck, "Early Wheel Engraving in the Netherlands," in: JGS 26, 1984, pp. 86–101.

[2]    Klesse 1965, no. 324, ill.; Sotheby's, Krug IV, lot. no. 667, ill.

[3]    Similar veining on the leaves of foliate decoration combining large vegetable motifs is only encountered in the work of Paulus Eder, among members of the Nuremberg school of engravers (see Meyer-Heisig 1963, WT 173, 174, 178).

[4]    Ritsema van Eck, 1984, figs. 27–29.

[5]    Charleston 1957, pp. 234–237, figs. 7 and 8.

[6]    For the Sang family of glass engravers see: Schmidt 1922, p. 363; G. E. Pazaurek, "Die Glasschneiderfamilie Sang," in: *Der Kunstwanderer 1930*, pp. 434 onwards; L. F. Fuchs, "Jacob Sang, ein holländischer Glasschneider deutscher Nation," in: *Weltkunst XXIV*, 15 August 1954, pp. 3 onwards; Van Gelder 1958, I, pp. 3 onwards; Janda 1962, pp. 80 onwards, 88 onwards.

[7]    Thirty years ago it was in the collection of Jhr. Mr. v. Kinschot, Leiden (Van Gelder 1958, I, p. 15, no. 6, fig. 23; Janda 1962, p. 130, note 221).

[8]    Sichel 1969, no. 162, ill.

[9]    See the examples mentioned below cat. no. 190.

[10]    Baumgärtner 1971, no. 41, ill.

[11]    Klesse/Saldern 1978, p. 27, fig. 48, no. 92, ill.

[12]    Pazaurek 1933, p. 330; Kühnert, *Urkundenbuch*, 1934, pp. 198, 296/63; Van Gelder 1958 III, p. 154, and 1958 IV, pp. 217–218; Janda 1962, pp. 56, 123, note 129.

[13]    The original is in the Bildarchiv of the Österreichisches Nationalbibliothek, Vienna (Inv. no. 2083).

[14]    The original engraving is in the print collection of the Rijksmuseum, Amsterdam.

[15]    Van Gelder 1958 III, pp. 148–154, ill.

[16]    Jansen 1962, no. 201, ill.

[17]    At Karl Brunnarius, Obershagen (Uetze).

# Zwischengold Glasses

The group of *Zwischengold* glasses in the Wolf Collection is particularly well-represented, both in quantity and quality.

Fig. 253

Fig. 258 a

Fig. 258 b

We begin with a group of glasses only partially decorated in *Zwischengold* technique in the form of inset medallions, while the remaining surface is decorated in wheel engraving (cat. nos. 194–197). One goblet in particular is distinguished both by its rarity and charming decoration (cat. no. 194, fig. 253). Within its three inset medallions the *Zwischengold* technique is reduced to a small frame while the actual motif is painted in strong transparent red, yellow, brown, blue, and green enamels. The motifs were selected from the German edition of the emblem book by Daniel de La Feuille, first published in Amsterdam in 1691, which was published under the German title *Emblematische Gemüths-Vergnügung bey Betrachtung ... der curieusesten und ergötzlichsten Sinn-Bildern ... .*[1] Each picture is inscribed with an aphorism which does not appear on the glass. The disarmed and blindfolded Cupid is inscribed "Augen schöner Jungfrauen seynd meine Pfeil" (the eyes of young maidens are my arrows)[2] (figs. 254a and 255) and the Cupid forging a heart on an anvil is inscribed "Nur für euch allein" (for you alone) (figs. 254b and 256) in the original, and an enraged Mars being pacified by Cupid, "Bezwinget den Zorn" (Rage mollified) (figs. 254c and 257). The painting on the glass is fresh and lively, and conveys these sentiments to the user without the aid of inscriptions. They appear harmoniously inserted into their wheel-engraved cartouches which are flanked by elegant symmetrical scrolls. Among a few comparable pieces in various museums,[3] there are four small glasses with flared bowls, as well as two beakers with comparable medallions preserved in Schloss Favorite,[4] near

Fig. 254 a

Fig. 254 b

Fig. 254 c

Fig. 255

Fig. 256

Fig. 257

Rastatt. These are further related to examples mentioned in the notes to cat. no. 98 which all belonged to larger sets in the same household (figs. 258a and b). The Margravine Franziska Sibylla Augusta of Baden-Baden furnished her summer residence, the *Favorite* (built in 1710–1711), from her Bohemian homeland up until about 1720. The five hundred glasses preserved in sets of six or twelve in Schloss Favorite are described in an *Inventarium* of 1762 as: "Alle diße vorgemelde Glässer bestehn aus dem feinesten Böhmischen Glas, alle fein und künstlich geschliffen" (all the aforementioned glasses are of the finest Bohemian glass, all beautifully and artistically cut).[5]

Even if the inventory entry was unreliable, these glasses are of such good quality that they could only have been produced by the best contempory glassmakers, situated at that time in North Bohemia. We know that the Duke of Reichstadt took a personal interest in the production of good glass in his Juliusthal glasshouse in Reichstadt, North Bohemia, in the 1680s, where ruby glass was also made[6] (see cat. no. 94). There is possibly a direct connection here with the ruby-glass threads enclosed in the stems of these glasses. The engraved cartouches flanked by delicate, foliate scrolls, reminiscent of Saxon decoration, also indicate, in the final analysis, their Bohemian origin. They correspond both in quality and stylistically to decoration known to have been carried out by Bo-

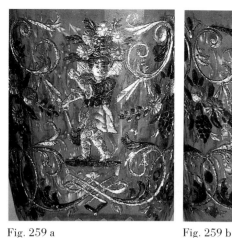

Fig. 259 a        Fig. 259 b        Fig. 259 c        Fig. 259 d

hemian engravers in Dresden in the early eighteenth century. They are found on Böttger stoneware and gold-ruby glasses produced by Johann Friedrich Böttger in the Dresden glasshouse of Augustus the Strong.[7] Later it was absorbed into the vocabulary of Saxon decoration, but in the process it soon lost its momentum and profusion.

In the Wolf Collection there are a surprising number of examples from another very rare group of glasses which have engraved and painted *Zwischengold* decoration (cat. nos. 200–205). The exterior of the inner wall is engraved and then gilded and painted, in places with red and green glazes, before the outer sleeve was fitted over it. Foliate decoration predominates, and figures are the exception. Two further goblets are particularly rare. They are decorated with children portrayed as allegories of the four seasons. Both are taken from the same printed source: Spring with a basket of flowers on his shoulder, Summer with a wheatsheaf, Autumn with a basket of fruit, and Winter with a bundle of faggots (cat. no. 202, fig. 259a–d, details). The figures are flanked by scrolls and pendant floral sprays. For the engraved source for these little allegorical scenes, the glass engraver has used the title page from Johann Ulrich Krauss's 1687 Augsburg German/French edition of engravings by André Félibien published in

Paris in 1665 mentioned earlier, and based in their turn on designs for Gobelins tapestries by Charles Lebrun for Louis XIV entitled *Les Quatre Elémens*[8] (fig. 117). What the muscular little figures in the original print have lost in realism, they have gained through the bright colours combined with the gilding. Relatively simple engraving is justified in this case as any delicate engraving would have disappeared under the gilding. There is another noticeable difference on the glass compared to the engraved originals. While Krauss's children are scantily clad with bare extremities, the glass engraver has added modest clothing with long-sleeved shirts and knee-length shifts. Whether this was simply a matter of creating a larger decorative area for coloring, or whether it was for reasons of decorum (which would strengthen the long-held opinion that *Zwischengold* glasses were produced in monasteries) is difficult to decide. With reference to this, finds have been made at the Cistercian foundation of Hohenfurth on the Moldau,[9] which indicate that monasteries as centers of *Zwischengold* production must be seriously taken into consideration. In addition to these unusual figures, the decorative vocabulary usually consists of a narrow range of decorative motifs, flowers, baskets of fruit with birds, pendant floral sprays, calligraphic motifs, and symmetrically arranged scrolls (see cat. no. 201).

Fig. 260

These glasses can only have been produced within a very short time span, somewhere between 1720 and 1725. In addition, the "handwriting" of these glasses, which becomes apparent when comparing the four goblets and two beakers in the Wolf Collection, is repeated in so many comparable details, that they must have originated in the same workshop. The origins of these glasses are also accurately pinpointed, as the type of glass is of the classic Bohemian form of the first quarter of the eighteenth century.

Of the remaining twenty *Zwischengold* glasses in the Wolf Collection decorated in the conventional manner with imbricated gold and silver foil sealed between two walls of glass, the Father Pacificus beaker and cover is the most important (cat. no. 206, fig. 260, detail). The unusual subject on this beaker is a church interior with a Fransiscan monk preaching from a pulpit of baroque form, while beneath it is a ribbon inscribed "P. PACIFICVS KLIEGEL." This has long excited interest as being the possible reference to the decorator of the glass, or at least providing a clue as to the region where *Zwischengold* glasses were produced. Gustav E. Pazaurek, who saw this glass in Cologne in 1894 was the first to publish it, interpreting the name as an artist's signature, thereby strengthening his theory that these glasses were produced in Bohemian monastic workshops.[10]

Thirty years or so later Robert Schmidt agreed with him as to the origins of this group, but not with regard to the name: "Thanks to information supplied by Father Nicolaus von Lutterotti, the name Pacificus has been found to belong to a member of the Franciscan order. I do not believe that the name Kliegel refers to the decorater of this glass, but is rather the surname of the preacher, Father Pacificus. One can however certainly presume that the beaker originated close to his monastery."[11] As Schmidt's comments remained unpublished, and the glass, changing owners, disappeared for nearly ninety years, Jarmila Brožová and Olga Drahotová supported Pazaurek's contention that the name referred to the artist.[12] J. Brožová's archival discovery of Father Pacificus's dates of birth and death, and the various foundations he was successively attached to, did not lead to any more accurate information as to where this glass was made.[13] In his capacity as priest he was obviously successful and well known, as the scene on the glass suggests; however, there is not the least hint in the archival records that he was an artist as well. The fact that, in the course of his pastoral duties, he would have paid regular visits to all the main North Bohemian glass-making centers, makes it possible to con-

132

clude that the *Zwischengold* beakers in Chicago,[14] Frankfurt a. M."[15] and Prague all with views of the Haindorf monastery,[16] were possibly executed by the same anonymous hand as the Kliegel beaker. This opinion has also been supported by J. Brožová and O. Drahotová after the whereabouts of the Kliegel beaker was discovered in 1982.[17] It can only be said with certainty that this glass must have originated in North Bohemia, within an area bounded by the extent of Father Pacificus' reputation as a successful preacher.

All efforts to lift the veil of anonymity over the origins and authors of these *Zwischengold* glasses, have so far remained unsuccessful. Also, any attempts to distinguish one master from another on stylistic traits, as for example R. Schmidt[18] and J. Brožová[19] have tried, have not produced satisfactory results, as in the final analysis, there is no definite proof. Even inscriptions, portraits, or coats-of-arms do not help in these circumstances, as we have seen with the Kliegel beaker. Neither do the two goblets in the Wolf Collection decorated with Prussian motifs (cat. no. 207 and 208), one with the portrait of the King of Prussia, the other with an inscription concerning Brandenburg, provide any further clues. The Bohemian type of goblet, which is used here and on almost all examples with *Zwischengold* decoration, only indicates their origins in the broadest geographical sense.

As well as these particular types of *Zwischengold* decoration mentioned so far, the Wolf Collection also includes some fine examples of courtly and peasant subjects, including a beaker and goblet with scenes of gallants in a park, musicians, and a table of card players (cat. nos. 209 and 210), and an interesting conical flask decorated with peasant dancers (cat. no. 213). Hunting scenes were the most popular motifs on all types of glass. Of these, stag hunts predominate, and hare and bear hunts also frequently occur (cat. no. 212). On the

Fig. 261

other hand, those with ibex hunts which appear in a number of variations are somewhat rarer (cat. no. 211). They are perhaps connected with an etching by Matthäus Merian.[20] Among these various masters, all of whose work is consistently of high quality, and lively and elegant draughtsmanship, there is one who is easily recognizable. His style is almost a caricature in his hilarious depiction of clumsy riders with ridiculously exaggerated hats, their weapons emitting huge clouds of smoke (cat. no. 212, fig. 261). Robert Schmidt had already noted that this artist[21] deviates from the normal pleasing standards in his ill-proportioned figures. He was in fact a skilled draughtsman, who was no less adept with the needle than his rivals. On other glasses where the gold and silver leaf is embellished with colored glazes, the majority are of hunting scenes (cat. no. 216). Duelling scenes are also popular within this group, and these take place mostly on horseback with swords or pistols (cat. no. 215). There is a particularly unusual example of a beaker whose sides are decorated entirely with silver foil and

133

flanked by gilt lappet borders (cat. no. 217). In order to give the beaker a uniformly silver appearance, the joining of the two glass walls takes place on the rim, as it does on the early beakers with painted, marbled decoration. On the outer side of the inner wall the painter has added scattered sprigs and sprays of tulips, roses, pinks, lilies, and narcissi in colored glazes, which are particularly effective against the plain silver background. The only other example recorded of a comparable type was in the Lanna Collection, now in the Kunstgewerbemuseum in Prague, and one other formerly in the Mühsam Collection in Berlin.[22]

Johann Joseph Mildner of Gutenbrunn in Lower Austria, the last practioner of the technique of *Zwischengold*, seldom used this completely double-walled technique, but instead he embellished the sides of his beakers with inset *Zwischengold* medallions. Occasionally, these were decorated with portraits done in gouache on vellum, as in the example in the Wolf Collection painted with the well-known Fürnberg portrait (cat. no. 218).

A most unusual beaker bearing the arms of the Wirth family is a rich exception to this, in that the whole body is decorated in sandwiched gold foil[23] (cat. no. 219). Mildner has achieved an effect almost akin to that of a goldsmith in the delicate contrast between gold and silver foil which shines through on both the outside and inside walls of the beaker. At the rim there is an imbricated band of silver beads, from which hang laurel festoons above the inset armorial medallion. The arms and scrolled mantling stand out strongly against the red lacquer ground. The basal medallion with full signature and the date 1795 is treated in the same manner. In these rare examples, Mildner's artistry can be appreciated in its most developed form.

From J. Brožová's researches we now know that this artist was born in 1765 into a family of glass decorators and cutters in Kaltenberg, near Rochlitz, not far from the Neuwelt glasshouse in the Bohemian Riesengebirge.[24] J. Brožová suggests that *Zwischengold* glasses were being produced on the nearby estate of Harrachsdorf at Stakenbach-Branna. It is possible therefore that Mildner absorbed his skills through his mother's milk, so to speak. It would certainly explain his natural predisposition towards this type of decoration on glass.

Another beaker in this collection demonstrates even more convincingly that he enjoyed exercising the full range of his talents (cat. no. 220). This is only revealed on closer inspection. At first glance, one is aware of the delicate, diamond-engraved web of ribbon-tied garlands of forget-me-nots decorating the colorless-glass sides between the central *Zwischengold* medallion and the upper and lower rims with silver stars. It is only when one views the base of the interior, and observes the portrait silhouettes of a youth and two young girls, that the "friendship" inscription, on the inside of the monogramed medallion and the inside of the upper rim, becomes clear. Unfortunately, there is only Mildner's own short signature and the date 1797 on a gold star on the base, and he gives no indication as to the identity of the sitters. It is interesting that this particularly rich example of Mildner's art was unknown to Pazaurek, when he compiled a list of Mildner's work sixty years ago, as it was perhaps not yet in the Neuburg Collection.[25] Mildner's work brings us to the turn of the eighteenth century, which marks the conclusion of the natural development of the art of European glass, and so presents us with an appropriate culmination to this survey of the Wolf Collection.

Notes to Chapter on *Zwischengold* Glasses.

[1] Henkel/Schöne 1976, p. LXVI, no. 338. See also cat. no. 78.

[2] For these illustrations the fifth edition of 1703 in the Kunst-bibliothek of the Staatlichen Museen Preußischer Kulturbesitz, Berlin, was used. As opposed to statements in Henkel/Schöne (1976) the fifth edition in Berlin is dated 1703. The sequence of illustrations is as follows: p. 8, no. 3; p. 50, no. 9, and p. 9, no. 8.

[3] See the parallel examples listed under cat. no. 194.

[4] They are the goblets Inv. no. G 310, G 989, G 990 and G 4385, as well as the beakers Inv. no. G 984 and G 985. Schloss Favorite is maintained as part of the Badisches Landesmuseum in Karlsruhe, who kindly supplied the photograph for fig. 258 (Inv. no. G 989 and G 985).

[5] Rudolph Sillib, *Schloß Favorite und die Eremitagen der Mark-gräfin Franziska Sibylla Augusta von Baden-Baden*, Heidelberg 1914, p. 96; Dietrich Rentsch, *Kunstschätze in Badischen Schlössern* (Bildhefte des Badischen Landesmuseums Karlsruhe), Karlsruhe 1972, p. XII.

[6] Drahotová 1973, pp. 8–11.

[7] Among others Holzhausen 1934/37, p. 18; Drahotová 1967, pp. 196–199; the most recent Haase 1982 B, p. 224.

[8] Henkel/Schöne 1976, p. LXI, nos. 299 and 300.

[9] Rückert 1982, II, p. 246.

[10] Pazaurek 1898, pp. 53 onwards; idem 1902, p. 24.

[11] Schmidt Ms 1931, pp. 328–329.

[12] Drahotová 1982, p. 29.

[13] Brožová 1973, pp. 60–84, 167–168; see the notes to cat. no. 206.

[14] Schmidt 1914, no. 307.

[15] Ohm 1973, no. 444, ill.

[16] Brožová 1973, ill. p. 83.

[17] Informed orally in August 1984.

[18] Schmidt 1914, pp. 60–61.

[19] Brožová 1981, pp. 15–19.

[20] See Wüthrich 1966, I, no. 410, fig. 191.

[21] Schmidt 1914, p. 59.

[22] Idem 1926, no. 257.

[23] It has not been possible to substantiate whether these arms are related to the Vienna medallist Johann Nepomuk Wirth, who was possibly known to Mildner.

[24] Brožová 1980, pp. 133–140, 224–225.

[25] Pazaurek 1923, pp. 321–344.

# Bibliography (titles abbreviated in catalog section)

Barrington Haynes 1959
E. Barrington Haynes, Glass through the Ages, Baltimore, Penguin Books, 1959 (2nd edition)

Bauer 1975
Sophie Charlotte Bauer, Ein neues Glas aus der Umgebung des Koula-Bechers, in: Festschrift für Peter Wilhelm Meister zum 65. Geburtstag, Editor A. Ohm und H. Reber, Hamburg 1975, pp. 150–156

Baumgärtner 1971
Sabine Baumgärtner, Edles altes Glas, Die Sammlung Heinrich Heine, Karlsruhe. Exhibition cat. Badisches Landesmuseum Karlsruhe, Karlsruhe 1971

Baumgärtner 1977
Sabine Baumgärtner, Sächsisches Glas – Die Glashütten und ihre Erzeugnisse, Wiesbaden 1977

Baumgärtner 1977 R
Sabine Baumgärtner, Glas – Antike, Mittelalter, Neuere Zeit, Katalog der Glassammlung. Museum der Stadt Regensburg, Brauser Collection, Karlsruhe 1977

Baumgärtner 1981
Sabine Baumgärtner, Porträtgläser, Munich 1981

Baumgärtner 1984
Sabine Baumgärtner, Zwei südböhmische Gläser: ein spanisches Geschäft, in: Weltkunst 54, Nr. 15, 1. August 1984, pp. 2012–2017

Berlin 1965
Günter Schade (Editor), Ars vitraria – 3000 Jahre Glas, Exhibition cat., Staatliche Museen zu Berlin, Kunstgewerbemuseum, Schloß Köpenick, Berlin 1965

Berlin-Köpenick 1981
Angelika Wesenberg, Venezianisches Glas 16. bis 18. Jahrhundert aus Museen der Deutschen Demokratischen Republik, Exhibition cat., Staatliche Museen zu Berlin, Kunstgewerbemuseum, Schloß Köpenick, Berlin 1981

Berliner 1924
Rudolf Berliner, Eine Münchner Glashütte im letzten Viertel des 17. Jahrhunderts, in: Münchner Jahrbuch für bildende Kunst, N. F. I, 1924, pp. 109–125.

Bernt 1933
Walter Bernt, Religiöse Darstellungen auf alten Hohlgläsern, in: Die christliche Kunst XXX, 1933, Nr. 2, pp. 40–53

Bernt 1950
Walter Bernt, Altes Glas, Munich (1950)

Berryer 1957
Anne-Marie Berryer, La verrerie ancienne aux Musées Royaux d'Art et d'Histoire, Brussels 1957

Billeter 1969
Erika Billeter, Glas, Sammlungskatalog 4 des Kunstgewerbemuseums der Stadt Zürich, Zurich 1969

Boesen 1960
Gudmund Boesen, Venetianske Glas på Rosenborg, Copenhagen 1960

Bon 1981–1983
Caterina Bon, Le verre en Italie, Napoli, Museo Nazionale di San Martino, in: Bulletin de l'Association Internationale pour l'Histoire du Verre, Nr. 9, Liège 1981–1983, pp. 170–176

137

Bosch 1984
Helmut Bosch, Die Nürnberger Hausmaler, Munich 1984

Bremen 1964
Walther Bremen, Die alten Glasgemälde und Hohlgläser der Sammlung Bremen in Krefeld (Beihefte der Bonner Jahrbücher Vol. 13), Cologne/Graz 1964

Brožová 1973
Jarmila Brožová, České dvojstěnné sklo a jeho autoři (Böhmische Doppelwandgläser und ihre Autoren), in: Acta UPM (Kunstgewerbemuseum Prag) VIII, C. Comentationes 1, Prague 1973, pp. 60–84, 167–168

Brožová 1980
Jarmila Brožová, zur Herkunft Johann Josef Mildners, eines Glasschleifers und -malers im niederösterreichischen Gutenbrunn, in: Acta UPM (Kunstgewerbemuseum Prag) XV, C. Comentationes 2, Prague 1980, pp. 133–142, 224–225

Brožová 1981
Jarmila Brožová, Jagdmotive auf böhmischem Doppelwandglas, in: Tschechoslowakische Glasrevue 36, 1981, pp. 15–19

Bucher 1888
Bruno Bucher, Die Glassammlung des K. K. Österreichischen Museums, Vienna, 1888

Buckley 1931
Wilfred Buckley, Aert Schouman and the Glasses That He Engraved, London 1931

Buckley 1935
Wilfred Buckley, D. Wolff and the Glasses That He Engraved. With a supplementary note on a Glass engraved by Frans Greenwood, London 1935

Buckley 1939
Wilfred Buckley, The Art of Glass. Illustrated from the Wilfred Buckley Collection in the Victoria and Albert Museum, London, London/New York 1939

Buddensieg 1959
Tilman Buddensieg, Erwerbungen 1950–1957, Europäische Abteilung – Glas, in: Jahrbuch der Hamburger Kunstsammlungen 3, 1958, pp. 231–240

Cambridge 1978
Michael Jaffé (Editor), Glass at the Fitzwilliam Museum, Cambridge 1978

Chambon 1955
Raymond Chambon, L'Histoire de la Verrerie en Belgique du II$^{me}$ Siècle à nos Jours, Brussels 1955

Charleston 1953
Robert J. Charleston, A Painter of Opaque-White Glass, in: Glass Notes, Editor: A. Churchill, Nr. 13, London Dec. 1953, pp. 13–20

Charleston 1954
Robert J. Charleston, English 18$^{th}$ Century Opaque White Glass. in: Antiques, Dec. 1954, pp. 488 onwards.

Charleston 1956
Robert J. Charleston, At Zürich Four Thousand Years of Glass, in: The Connoisseur CXXXVIII, Nr. 555, August 1956, pp. 42–43

Charleston 1957
Robert J. Charleston, Dutch Decoration of English Glass, in: Transactions of the Society of Glass Technology XLI, 1957, pp. 229–243

Charleston 1965
Robert J. Charleston, The Import of Venetian Glass into the Near East: 15$^{th}$–16$^{th}$ Century, in: Annales du 3$^e$ Congrès des Journées Internationales du Verre, Liège 1965, pp. 158–168

Charleston 1969
Robert J. Charleston und G. With, Skrinet med det rare i (bes. The Glasses), in : Årbok 1968–69, Kunstindustrimuseet i Oslo, Oslo 1969, pp. 94–114, esp. 102–114

Charleston 1975
Robert J. Charleston, Types of Glass Imported into the Near East and some Fresh Examples: 15th–16th Century, in: Festschrift für Peter Wilhelm Meister zum 65. Geburtstag, Editor: A. Ohm und H. Reber, Hamburg 1975, pp. 245–251

Charleston 1977
Robert J. Charleston und Michael Archer, Glass and Stained Glass – The James A. De Rothschild Collection at Waddesdon Manor, London/Fribourg 1977

Charleston 1980
Robert J. Charleston, Masterpieces of Glass, A World History from The Corning Museum of Glass, New York 1980

Charleston 1984
Robert J. Charleston, English Glass and the Glass used in England, circa 400–1940 (English Decorative Arts, I, Editor: Hugh Wakefield), London 1984

Chrzanowska 1963
Anna Chrzanowska, Odbitki dekoracji skiel Christiana Gottfrieda Schneidera, in: Roczniki Sztuki Slaskiej II, (Warsaw) 1963, pp. 128 ff.

Clarke 1974
Timothy H. Clarke, Lattimo – A Group of Venetian Glass Enamelled on an Opaque–White Ground, in: JGS XVI, 1974, pp. 22–56

Coburg 1969
Heino Maedebach et al., Neuerwerbungen 1960–1968, Ausstellungskatalog Kunstsammlungen der Veste Coburg, Coburg 1969

Collection Spitzer 1891
Edouard Garnier (Chap. Glass) in: La Collection Spitzer, Bd. III, Paris 1891

Cologne 1963 bzw. 1973
Glas, Kataloge des Kunstgewerbemuseums Köln, Vol. 1, 1st ed. edited by Brigitte Klesse, Cologne 1963, 2nd ed. edited by Brigitte Klesse and Gisela Reineking von Bock, Cologne 1973

Cologne 1980
Ein rheinischer Silberschatz – Schmuck und Gerät aus Privatbesitz. Ausstellungskatalog, Kunstgewerbemuseum Köln, edited by H.-J. Heuser, R. Joppien, B. Klesse, C. W. Schümann, Cologne 1980

Corning 1965
Glass from The Corning Museum of Glass: A Guide to the Collections. The Corning Museum of Glass, Corning, N. Y., 1965 (2nd ed.)

Czihak 1891
E. Czihak, Schlesische Gläser. Nebst einem beschreibenden Katalog der Gläsersammlung des Museums schlesischer Altertümer zu Breslau, Breslau 1891

Dexel 1962
Walter Dexel, Das Hausgerät Mitteleuropas, Braunschweig/Berlin 1962

Drahotová 1965
Olga Drahotová, Der Kreis um den Meister des sog. Koula-Bechers, in: Tschechoslowakische Glasrevue 20, 1965, Nr. 11, pp. 340–343

Drahotová 1967
Olga Drahotová, Bohemian Glass Decor in the Style of Jean Berain, in: Annales du 4e Congrès des Journées Internationales du Verre (Ravenna-Venice 1967), Liège 1967, pp. 193–199

Drahotová 1972
Olga Drahotová, Medaillen und Münzen als Vorlage für geschnittenes Barockglas im Prager Kunstgewerbemuseum, in: Tschechoslowakische Glasrevue 27, Nr. 7, 1972, pp. 216–221

Drahotová 1973
Olga Drahotová, Das böhmische Rubinglas an der Wende des 17. und 18. Jahrhunderts, in: Tschechoslowakische Glasrevue 28, 1973, Nr. 4, pp. 8–11

Drahotová 1980
Olga Drahotová, Die Schürer und Preussler als Hersteller von Kobaltgläsern. Zur Geschichte der Kobaltglaserzeugung und der Wechselbeziehungen böhmischer und sächsischer emailbemalter Renaissancegläser, in: Acta UPM (Kunstgewerbemuseum Prag) XV, C. Comentationes 2, Prague 1980, pp. 72–96, 219–222

Drahotová 1981
Olga Drahotová, Comments on Caspar Lehmann, Central European Glass and Hard Stone Engraving, in: JGS 23, 1981, pp. 34–45

Drahotová 1982
Olga Drahotová und Gabriel Urbánek, Europäisches Glas, Prague/Hanau 1982

Dreier 1965
Franz-Adrian Dreier, Stichvorlagen und Zeichnungen zu Gläsern Christian Gottfried Schneiders, in: JGS VII, 1965, pp. 66–78

Dreier 1969
Franz-Adrian Dreier, Glaskunst in Hessen und Kassel, Kassel 1969

Dreier 1981
Franz-Adrian Dreier, Glasveredelung in Venedig, in: 3000 Jahre Glaskunst, Ausstellungskatalog Kunstmuseum Luzern, Lucerne 1981, pp. 144–152

Egg 1962
Erich Egg, Die Glashütten zu Hall und Innsbruck im 16. Jahrhundert (Tiroler Wirtschaftsstudien 15), Innsbruck 1962

Fetzer 1977
Wolfgang Fetzer, Johann Kunckel – Leben und Werk eines großen deutschen Glasmachers des 17. Jahrhunderts, s. l. 1977

Fuchs 1928/29
Ludwig F. Fuchs, Johann Kunckels Erfindung des Goldrubins, in: Kunstwanderer 1928/29, pp. 153–158

Fuchs 1938
Ludwig F. Fuchs, Die frühen süddeutschen Wappenhumpen, in: Münchner Jahrbuch für bildende Kunst, N. F. XII, Nr. 3, 1938, pp. 219–232

Fuchs 1954
Ludwig F. Fuchs, Jacob Sang, ein holländischer Glasschneider deutscher Nation, in: Weltkunst XXIV, 1954, No. 16, pp. 3–5

Gasparetto 1958
Astone Gasparetto, Il vetro di Murano dalle orgini ad oggi, Venice 1958

Gasparetto 1979
Astone Gasparetto, Matrici e aspetti della vetraria Veneziana e Veneta Medievale, in: JGS XXI, 1979, pp. 76–97

Van Gelder 1955
H. E. van Gelder, Glas en Ceramiek, Utrecht 1955

Van Gelder 1958
H. E. van Gelder, Achttiende-eeuwse glas-snijders in Holland, I–IV, in: Oud Holland 73, 1958, pp. 1–17, 148–155, 211–219

Gelder/Jansen 1969
H. E. van Gelder und Beatrice Jansen, Glas in nederlandse musea, Bussum 1969

Haase 1975
Gisela Haase, Sächsisches Glas vom 17. bis zum Anfang des 19. Jahrhunderts. Ausstellungskatalog, Staatliche Kunstsammlungen Dresden, Museum für Kunsthandwerk, Schloß Pillnitz, Dresden 1975

Haase 1982
Gisela Haase, Johann Friedrich Böttger und die Glashütte zu Dresden, in: Johann Friedrich Böttger zum 300. Geburtstag – Meissen Frühzeit und Gegenwart, Staatliche Kunstsammlungen Dresden und VEB Staatliche Porzellan-Manufaktur Meissen, Dresden 1982, pp. 219–226

Haase 1983
Gisela Haase, Stichvorlagen für Emblemdarstellungen auf sächsischen Gläsern des 18. Jahrhunderts, in: JGS XXV, 1983, pp. 35–49

Haase 1984
Gisela Haase, Glas um 1700 bis um 1800 aus dem Museum für Kunsthandwerk, Exhibition cat., Schloß Pillnitz, Staatliche Kunstsammlungen Dresden, Dresden 1984

Hackenbroch 1956
Yvonne Hackenbroch, Meissen and other Continental Porcelain, Irvine Untermyer Collection, New York 1956

Hamburg 1961
Sechs Sammler stellen aus, Exhibition cat., Museum für Kunst und Gewerbe, Hamburg 1961

Hampe 1919
Theodor Hampe, Das altnürnberger Kunstglas und seine Meister, Nuremberg 1919

Heine 1912
Axel Heine, Johan Kunchel (sic!) von Löwenstern, in: Tidsskrift for Industri 13, (Kopenhagen) 1912, pp. 127–159

Heinemeyer 1966
Elfriede Heinemeyer, Glas, Kataloge des Kunstmuseums Düsseldorf, Vol. 1, Düsseldorf 1966

Hejdova 1981
Dagmar Hejdova, The Glasshouse at Rejdice in Northeastern Bohemia Late sixteenth – Early Seventeenth Centuries, in: JGS XXIII, 1981, pp. 18–33

Henkel/Schöne 1967 und 1976
Arthur Henkel und Albrecht Schöne, Emblemata, Handbuch zur Sinnbildkunst des 16. und 17. Jahrhunderts, Stuttgart 1967, Supplement to 1st ed. 1976

Hetteš 1960
Karel Hetteš, Venezianisches Glas aus tschechoslowakischen Sammlungen, Prague 1960

Hetteš 1963
Karel Hetteš, Venetian Trends in Bohemian Glassmaking in the Sixteenth and Seventeenth Centuries, in: JGS V, 1963, pp. 38–53

Hörning (1979)
Jutta Hörning, Gläser vom 16. bis 19. Jahrhundert. Aus dem Bestand der Kunstsammlungen zu Weimar, Weimar s. d. (1979)

Holzhausen 1954
Walter Holzhausen, Sächsische Gläser des Barock, in: Zeitschrift für Kunstwissenschaft VIII, H. 1/2, 1954, pp. 95–124

Honey 1946
William B. Honey, Glass, Victoria and Albert Museum, London 1946

Isings 1966
Clasina Isings, Schönes altes Glas, Hanover 1966

Janda 1962
Annegret Janda, Der Thüringer Glasschnitt im 17. und 18. Jahrhundert, phil. diss., Universität Leipzig, Leipzig 1962 (Manuscript in the Universitätsbibliothek Cologne)

Jansen 1962
Beatrice Jansen, Catalogus van Noord- en Zuidnederlands Glas, Gemeentemuseum, the Hague 1962

Jantzen 1960
Johannes Jantzen, Deutsches Glas aus fünf Jahrhunderten, Düsseldorf 1960

Jiřík 1934
František X. Jiřík, České Sklo, Prague 1934

JGS 1959 onwards
Journal of Glass Studies, The Corning Museum of Glass, Corning N. Y. 1959 onwards.

Kämpfer 1966
Fritz Kämpfer und Klaus G. Beyer, Glas aus vier Jahrtausenden, Dresden 1966

Klar 1961
Martin Klar, Ein Trinkspiel Augusts des Starken, in: Forschungen und Berichte der Staatlichen Museen zu Berlin (East) 3/4, 1961, pp. 52–59

Klesse 1965
Brigitte Klesse, Glassammlung Helfried Krug Vol. I, Munich 1965

Klesse 1972
Brigitte Klesse, Allegorische und mythologische Kupferstichvorlagen im Glasschnitt des Barocks, in: JGS XIV, 1972, pp. 117–140

Klesse 1973
Brigitte Klesse, Glassammlung Helfried Krug, (Vol. II), Bonn 1973

Klesse 1976
Brigitte Klesse, Eine Gruppe von Nürnberger Goldrubingläsern, in: Festschrift für Waldemar Haberey zum 75. Geburtstag, Editor: Th. E. Haevernick und A. von Saldern, Mainz 1976, pp. 65–70

Klesse/Mayr 1977
Brigitte Klesse und Hans Mayr, Verborgene Schätze aus sieben Jahrhunderten – ausgewählte Werke aus dem Kunstgewerbemuseum der Stadt Köln, Cologne 1977

Klesse/Saldern 1978
Brigitte Klesse und Axel von Saldern, 500 Jahre Glaskunst – Sammlung Biemann, Zurich/Rastatt 1978

Kühnert 1934 and/or 1973
Herbert Kühnert, Urkundenbuch zur Thüringer Glashüttengeschichte, Jena 1934 (reprinted Wiesbaden 1973)

Lipp 1974
Franz Carl Lipp, Bemalte Gläser, Munich 1974

London 1968
D. B. Harden, K. S. Painter, R. H. Pinder-Wilson, Hugh Tait, Masterpieces of Glass, Exhibition cat., The British Museum, London 1968

Lorenzetti 1953
Giulio Lorenzetti, Murano e l'arte del vetro soffiato, Guida del Museo Vetrario di Murano, Venice 1953

Lucerne 1981
3000 Jahre Glaskunst von der Antike bis zum Jugendstil, Exhibition cat., Kunstmuseum Luzern, Lucerne 1981

Mallè 1971
Luigi Mallè, Museo Civico di Torino – Vetri, vetrate, giade, cristalli di rocca e pietre dure, Turin 1971

Mareš 1893
František Mareš, České Sklo, Prague 1893

Mariacher 1960
Giovanni Mariacher, Il vetro soffiato da Roma antica a Venezia, Milan 1960

Mariacher 1963
Giovanni Mariacher, Vetri Italiani del Rinascimento, Milan 1963

Mariacher/Causa 1974
Giovanni Mariacher und Marina Causa, Kostbarkeiten der Glaskunst, Munich 1974

Mariacher/Roffia 1983
Giovanni Mariacher und Elisabetta Roffia, Vetri, in: Museo Poldi Pezzoli, Ceramiche, vetri, mobili e arredi, Milan 1983, pp. 165–307

Messner 1965/1966
Gisela Messner, Geschnittenes Glas aus Böhmen und Schlesien im Museum für Kunsthandwerk Dresden, in: Jahrbuch der Staatlichen Kunstsammlungen Dresden, 1965/1966, pp. 141–151

## 2  FOOTED BOWL
## WITH STYLIZED DECORATION

Venice, late 15th – early 16th century

Height: 7.2 cm; diameter: 26.3 cm;
thickness of glass: about 2 mm

Colorless and blue glass with enamel and gilt decoration. Large unpolished pontil mark. Gilding completely rubbed in places.

Low spreading foot with blue-trailed rim. Shallow bowl with lightly-everted rim embellished with applied blue trail. Underside of bowl decorated with mold-blown, pinched ribs (variation of "nipt-diamond-waies") emphasized with gilt. The oval spaces between the ribs are decorated with circular enameled disks in alternate dark-blue or brick-red, each within a circle of white dots. On the central circular depression is a gilt rectangle with red dots at the corners. It encloses a gilt ring embellished with blue dots. The gilding has been almost entirely rubbed. The center is decorated with a white enamel and gilt florette centered by red-and-white and blue dots.

Comparable examples: a very similar bowl in the collection of Erwin Baumgartner, Basel.
Compare with further variants, the decoration of which matches that on the beaker, cat. no. 1 of the Wolf Collection, one in the Victoria and Albert Museum (Perrot 1958, no. 6, ill.), the British Museum (Tait 1979, no. 2, ill.), and the Fitzwilliam Museum (Cambridge 1978, no. 141, ill.).

## 7 ENAMELED AND GILT TAZZA WITH LAMB OF GOD

Venice, first third 16th century

Height: 7.3 cm; diameter: 27 cm;
thickness of glass: about 2.5–3 mm

Colorless glass with enamel and gilt decoration. Large, unpolished pontil mark. Gilding rubbed in places.

Provenance: Spitzer Collection, Paris.

Shallow, circular bowl with everted, folded rim (originally gilt) and gilt molded wrythen gadroons on the underside, bowl supported on short spreading foot with folded rim (remains of gilding). Central medallion painted in colors with the Lamb of God, standing on a greensward, water in the foreground, its head with nimbus, and holding a flag (Labarum), the sky embellished with "golden rain," all within a gilt scale border with red and blue enamel dots superimposed, and flanked by white enamel dot borders, rim decorated on the exterior with broad gilt scale border embellished with diagonally-arranged red, green, and blue dots, and flanked by blue-white dot borders.

For comparison of subject see a tazza in the Museo Civico, Bologna (Venice 1982, no. 123, ill.).

Among the many examples of gadrooned tazzas with figural representation, it is only necessary to quote those most typically Venetian, for instance those decorated with the Winged Lion of St. Mark in the Fitzwilliam Museum, Cambridge (Cambridge 1978, no. 143, ill.); the British Museum, London (Tait 1979, no. 6, ill.); in the Musée Curtius, Liège, (*Trois Millénaires* 1958, no. 257, ill.; Philippe 1982, col. pl. p. 75, no. 84).

Lit.: Edouard Garnier: *La Collection Spitzer*, vol. III, Paris, 1891, p. 92, no. 17, col. pl. VIII.

## 8  INSCRIBED GILT BOWL

Venice, early 16th century

Height: 5 cm: diameter: 24.1 cm;
thickness of glass: about 2 mm

Colorless glass with gilt decoration. Unpolished pontil mark. Gilding considerably rubbed.

Of circular form with central depression and everted, folded rim, supported on applied foot ring. Underside of bowl decorated with mold-blown, radial gadroons. Rim with broad, gilt band decorated with imbricated inscription in Roman capitals: "AVE · REGINA · CE-LI · LETARE · ALELVIA," flanked by geometric borders.

Comparable examples, probably from the same workshop with differing inscriptions, are in the British Museum, London (London 1968, no. 193, ill.; Tait 1979, no. 28, ill.; Venice 1982, no. 88, ill.), and the Victoria and Albert Museum (Honey 1946, pl. 32C).
Also the following variants (with gilt border but inscription replaced by colored enamel dots) in the Kunstmuseum, Düsseldorf (Heinemeyer 1966, no. 216, ill.); Victoria and Albert Museum, London (Perrot 1958, no. 37, ill.); Metropolitan Museum, New York, Robert Lehmann Collection (Perrot 1958, no. 30, ill.); Kunstgewerbemuseum, Prague (Hetteš 1960, pp. 34, 35, pl. 4 and 9; Prague 1973, no. 10, fig. 7; Venice 1982, no. 84, ill.); and the Museo Civico, Turin (Mallè 1971, pp. 35–36, fig. 8).

## 9    ENAMELED AND GILT BOWL
WITH CLASSICAL PROFILE

Venice, late 15th – early 16th century

Height: 5.5 cm; diameter: 13.4 cm;
thickness of glass: about 2–2.5 cm

Dark amethyst-tinted glass with enamel and gilt decoration. Unpolished pontil mark. Enamel decoration slightly worn. Gilding considerably rubbed.

Provenance: formerly Freiherr von Rothschild Collection.

Bowl with flared sides and slightly everted rim supported by an applied basal ring. Base of the interior painted with a bust profile to dexter of a young man dressed in classical style with ribbon-tied laurel wreath in his hair, tunic and sash, against a background of "golden rain," all within circular rows of enameled dots in green, white and violet. Exterior decorated with a broad, gilt imbricated frieze of Islamic palmettes infilled with white dots, and pairs of opposed sea-horses whose entwined tails end in stylized flowers, all flanked by gilt-line borders with superimposed white-enamel dots.

For the form, compare with examples in blue glass (with a variety of decorative motifs) in: the British Museum, London (decorated with IHS monogram and exterior gilt scale border: Tait 1979, no. 18, ill.); Museo Poldi Pezzoli, Milan (painted with St. Anthony of Padua or St. Francis, exterior with gilt scale border: Mariacher 1960, col. pl. 32; idem 1963, pl. 46 A, B; Mariacher/Roffia 1983, no. 38, fig. 38; see above, p. 17, fig. 12); Museo Nazionale di San Martino, Naples, exterior with gilt scale border (Marina Causa Picone, *Vetri a San Martino*, Naples 1967, pp. 28–30, fig. 3; C. Bon, 1981–83, p. 172, fig. 1b); Museo Civico, Turin, exterior with enamel dot rosettes (Mallè 1971, pp. 28–29, col. pl. 3).
Compare also the variants in milk glass in the Kunsthistorisches Museum, Vienna (decorated with a female bust to dexter, exterior with gilt scale border: Clarke 1974, pp. 50–51, no. C4, ill.; Venice 1982, no. 100, ill.); private collection (profile bust of a youth to sinister with scale border: Clarke 1974, p. 51, no. C5, ill.).

Lit.: Auction catalog of collection V of pewter, arms, and English private glass collection, Fischer, Lucerne, 30–31 August 1937, lot no. 484, ill. pl. 37.

## 10   FOOTED BOWL

Venice, about 1500–1510

Height 12.6 cm; diameter: 14.6 cm;
thickness of glass: about 1.5–2 mm

Dark amethyst-tinted glass with enameled and gilt
decoration. Unpolished pontil mark.

Conical bowl with gadrooned base heightened in gilt,
the rim embellished with broad band of imbricated
scales with sky-blue enamel dots, flanked by white
and green dot borders, and gilt lappet frieze. High
trumpet foot with folded rim and gilt vertical ribs.

Lit.: São Paulo 1957, no. 33, ill.

## 11  FOOTED BOWL
## WITH GILT SCALE DECORATION

Venice, about 1500

Height: 17.3 cm; diameter: 27.5 cm;
thickness of glass: about 2–2.5 cm

Colorless glass with enameled and gilt decoration.
Large unpolished pontil mark. Gilding rubbed.

Bowl with everted and folded rim. Sides decorated
with six rows of gilt scales, the scales outlined in white
and centered with red, blue, and green dots, flanked
by rows of blue and white dot borders.

Compare with almost identical parallels in: the Victoria and Albert Museum, London (Savage 1965,
fig. 29); the Museo Poldi Pezzoli, Milan (Mariacher/
Roffia 1983, no. 43, pl. 43); the Museo Vetrario,
Murano (Lorenzetti 1953, pl. XLIX; Schack 1976,
fig. 109), as well as colorless and amethyst-tinted
variants in: the Metropolitan Museum, New York,
Robert Lehmann Collection (Buckley 1939, no. 122,
123, fig. 20–21; Perrot 1958, no. 40, ill.).
Plain bowls are not as common as the gadrooned examples.

## 12   FILIGREE TAZZA

Venice, second half 16th century

Height: 7.1 cm; diameter: 26.7 cm;
thickness of glass: about 2–2.5 mm

Colorless glass with trailed filigree decoration. Unpolished pontil mark.

Spreading conical foot with folded rim, the upper part with filigree ribs supporting the wide shallow bowl with upturned rim. From the center of the underside radiate pairs of nipped ("nipt-diamond-waies") filigree ribs.

For the decorative motif of pinched filigree radials used with the tazza form (additionally found with two concentric milk-glass trails) see examples in: the British Museum, London (Tait 1979, no. 86, ill.); the Metropolitan Museum of Art, New York, Robert Lehmann Collection, (Perrot 1958, no. 64, ill.); private collection (Venice 1982, no. 161, ill.); and the Museo Poldi Pezzoli, Milan (Mariacher/Roffia 1983, no. 112, pl. 111).
A coarser variant could be of Spanish (Catalonian) origin (compare José Gudiol Ricart, *Los vidrios catalanes*, *Monumenta Cataloniae*, vol. III, Barcelona 1941, pl. 85 B.

## 13   TALL SILVER-GILT MOUNTED
## FILIGREE DRINKING VESSEL

Venice, second half 16<sup>th</sup> century

Height: 40.8 cm; diameter: 10.9 cm (foot),
4.8 cm (mouth);
thickness of glass: about 2.5 mm

Filigree glass. Unpolished pontil mark.


Silver-gilt mount marked "N" for Nuremberg,
1550–1650 (R³ 3758); master's mark "HR", perhaps
Hannß Resth (Resch), master 1563, died 1593 (R³
3955).

Spreading conical foot with folded rim bound with a
silver-gilt foot ring with upper lappet border, below a
flattened knop between clear-glass collars supporting
the extended, rounded, elegantly-tapering bowl, the
whole with vertical arrangement of white, twisted filigree threads.

No other example of this form has so far been recorded.

## 14  KUTTROLF

Venice, late 16<sup>th</sup> – early 17<sup>th</sup> century

Height: 29.7 cm;
thickness of glass: about 2 mm

Filigree glass. Unpolished pontil mark.


High spreading foot with folded rim below a flattened knop flanked by clear collars (merese), supporting the body with globular base and tapering curved neck ending in an auricular spout, the whole in *vetro a retorti*.

Comparable examples (without knop) in: the collections of the Veste Coburg (Inv. no. HA 502); Kestner Museum, Hanover (Mosel 1979, no. 20, ill.); formerly in Cologne, Thewalt Collection (Auction cat. Thewalt, lot no. 493, ill.); private collection (Weiss 1966, ill. p. 111); formerly Biemann Collection, Zurich (Klesse/ Saldern 1978, no. 55, ill.: Lucerne 1981, no. 668, ill.).

Lit. : São Paulo 1957, no. 29, ill.

## 17   NET-GLASS TAZZA

Venice, mid-16th century

Height: 7.9 cm: diameter 18.1 cm;
thickness of glass: about 2–3 mm

"Net"glass, (*vetro a reticello*). Unpolished pontil mark.


Shallow, wide-bottomed bowl with lightly up-turned rim, supported on baluster stem with basal plinth and conical foot, all in swirling, white, overlapping threads (*vetro a reticello*). Foot rim with applied colorless-glass band.


There is no known direct parallel with upturned sides and everted rim.
Other comparable examples (but with various stem and foot combinations) in: Auction catalog, Galerie Fischer, Lucerne, 30–31 August 1937, lot 527, pl. 35; Cologne 1963, no. 173, and 1973, no. 262, ill. (Cologne, Kunstgewerbemuseum); Kunstmuseum, Düsseldorf (Heinemeyer 1966, no. 247, ill.); The Toledo Museum of Art, Toledo, Ohio (Toledo 1969, ill. p. 49); Museum für Kunsthandwerk, Frankfurt a. M. (Ohm 1973, no. 158, ill.); British Museum, London (Tait 1979, no. 113, ill.); Green Vaults, Dresden (Berlin-Köpenick 1981, no. 14, ill.); and the Bayerisches Nationalmuseum, Munich (Rückert 1982, I, no. 94, ill.).

## 18  SILVER-MOUNTED STIRRUP CUP WITH DRAGON WHISTLE

Venice or *façon de Venise*, late 16<sup>th</sup> – early 17<sup>th</sup> century

Height: 19.6 cm; diameter across mouth: 10.1 cm; thickness of glass: about 1 mm

Filigree glass with unmarked silver mount.

Trumpet-shaped bowl in *vetro a retorti* with vertical arrangement of crossed-over threads. Base mounted in silver with a coronal knop with two gargoyles flanked by opposed columns on which stand outward-facing satyrs, holding up an arched strap on which is a seated lion supporting a shield (St. Mark?). In transverse position, between the pillars, is a dragon with gaping mouth, scaly crocodile-like body and coiled tail, and bat-like wings. The hollow body has a back aperture for use as a whistle, activating a wheel above it.

This type of stirrup cup often doubles as a kind of joke glass, the whistle having various connotations, as is the case on many *façon de Venise* examples; mostly of Lowland origin.
(Compare also cat. no. 19). Examples of beakers sur-mounted by watermills, and entirely of silver, were produced by Nuremberg goldsmiths in the last quarter of the sixteenth century (Klar 1961, p. 59, fig. 10).
For examples with whistles where the dragon sits on top of a round bell, see those in The Corning Museum of Glass, Corning (Perrot 1958, no. 77, ill: silver mount dated 1673; filigree conical bowl perhaps ear-lier than the mount); and the Museum für Kunst und Gewerbe, Hamburg (JGS II, 1960, p. 142, no. 20; Newman 1977, ill. p. 302: clear glass ribbed trumpet bowl, formerly Spitzer Collection, Paris).
Compare also with a dragon pipe on a stirrup cup in the form of a female figure in filigree glass, formerly in Zurich, Biemann Collection (Klesse/Saldern 1978, no. 58, col. pl.; Lucerne 1981, no. 669, ill.; Venice 1982, no. 217, ill.; Sotheby's, Biemann, London, lot 53, ill.).
Compare the form and type of patterned filigree with a Netherlands-mounted table bell in the Victoria and Albert Museum, London (Chambon 1955, pl. XV, no. 51; Weiss 1966, ill. p. 113; Newman 1977, ill.

p. 306; (Collections of the Veste Coburg); in the Staat-liche Galerie Moritzburg, Halle (Berlin-Köpenick 1981, no. 20, ill.); and Spiegl 1983, p. 52, fig. 11.

## 19 SILVER-MOUNTED STIRRUP CUP WITH WINDMILL WHISTLE

Netherlands, *façon de Venise*, late 16th century

Height: 17 cm; diameter (at mouth): 7.9 cm; thickness of glass: about 2.5–3 mm

"Net"glass with unmarked silver mount, in the form of a windmill and dial (hands missing).

Upturned bell-shaped bowl in *vetro a reticello*, the criss-crossing white threads separated by small bubbles of air. Silver mount with cylindrical base decorated with chased foliate band, supporting on four volutes a windmill with pitched roof and engraved tiles, sails, balance boom, and ladder on which stands a small, male figure; on the gable a spike originally intended for a pointer.

For this type of stirrup cup see also cat. no. 18 and notes. Examples of beakers surmounted by windmills and entirely of silver, were produced in the Netherlands from the middle of the sixteenth century (Klar 1961, pp. 52 onwards, ill.).
For glasses with windmills see variants in: the Rijksmuseum, Amsterdam, Nathusius Collection (Chambon 1955, p. 314, pl. XII, no. 42); Kunstgewerbemuseum, Schloss Köpenick, Berlin (*Ars Vitraria* 1965, p. 166, fig. 64); The Corning Museum of Glass, Strauss Collection (Strauss 1955, no. 152); Gemeentemuseum, the Hague (Jansen 1962, no. 199, ill.); Victoria and Albert Museum, London, Buckley Collection (Schmidt 1927, pp. 32–33, pl. 54; Chambon 1955, p. 314, pl. XI); Neumeister Auction catalog, Munich, 10 February 1982, lot 16, pl. 38; and one formerly in the Spitzer Collection, Paris (Spitzer Catalog, vol. III, 1891, p. 96, no. 35, ill.; ibid. vol VIII, pl. L, no. 2003).
For the function of the windmill whistle see Chambon 1955, p. 314; "*Le Catalogue Colinet*, 1555, (Beauwelz glasshouse) montre ce type de coupe apode, destinée à recevoir une montre en métal. Après avoir vidé son verre, le buveur devait donner la preuve de la puissance des ses poumons en faisant tourner les ailes mobiles du moulin, qui inscrivaient sur un petit cadran ad hoc la force de souffle, plus ou moins grande, déployée par le buveur." (The *Catalogue Colinet*, 1555

(Beauweltz glasshouse) illustrates this type of glass, without foot, made to be mounted in metal. Having emptied his glass, the drinker had to give proof of the strength of his lungs by making the sails of the windmill turn, registering the strength of his breath on a little dial).
Jerome Strauss comments on his own windmill beaker: "When ... blowing through the tube, the vanes and the index arrow turn. Reputedly, the number at which the arrow stopped indicated the number of times the glass was to be emptied."
H. Seling illustrates a windmill beaker in the Kassel Museum in his monograph *Kunst der Augsburger Goldschmiede*. (II, fig. 166). It has a silver-gilt mount by Georg Christoph Erhard of 1595–1600, the windmill being very similar to the Wolf example. In describing the windmill, Seling comments, "Bei diesen Trinkspielen mußte der Zecher durch ein Röhrchen blasen und damit die Windmühle in Bewegung setzen; sodann hatte er den Becher schnell auszutrinken, solange sich die Flügel der Windmühle drehten." (I, p. 85), (In the case of these amusing glasses, the imbiber has to blow through a little pipe, therefore setting the windmill in motion; he then had to drain the contents of the beaker as long as the sails kept moving.)
The earliest dated piece amongst the above-mentioned examples is the stirrup cup in the Rijksmuseum, Amsterdam, formerly in the Nathusius Collection, whose silver mount bears the date 1585, against which the bowl, diamond decorated with the arms of Prince Maurice of Orange and the town Berg-op-Zoom, bears the date 1595.

## 20 GOBLET ON SCREW MOUNT

Venice or *façon de Venise*, 17th century
Mount probably Netherlands, 17th century

Height: 23.8 cm with mount; 13 cm without mount;
diameter bowl: 9.4 cm;
thickness of glass: about 1.5 mm

Filigree glass with partly-gilt bronze mount (gilding partly rubbed). Foot replaced.

Funnel bowl and stem with three hollow knops in *vetro a retorti*, separated by a colorless-glass merese.
The mount consists of a leaping stag, supported by four dolphin rising from a lobed pierced and foliate base. Between its forelegs it holds up a chased and turned vase-shaped section from which rise three griffin terminals.

For glass form compare Spiegl 1983, p. 56, no 21.
The metal mount, predominantly in silver-gilt, was developed in the Netherlands as a particularly fine support for glasses of the *Römer type* (in this connection see Anna-Elisabeth Liederwald, *Niederländische Glasformen des 17 Jahrhunderts*, Ph. D. Thesis, University of Freiburg i. Br. 1964, pp. 59–61). The researches of A. E. Liederwald, including a thorough search through contemporary illustrated sources, have shown that this type of mount was intended for the roemer only, as opposed to other glass forms for which fantastic inventions were created from the sixteenth to the nineteenth century. It would seem, therefore, that the glass and mount must have been married at a later date.

## 21  FILIGREE WING-STEMMED GOBLET

South Netherlands, *façon de Venise*,
second half 17th century

Height: 32 cm; diameter of bowl: 13.2 cm;
thickness of glass: about 2.5 cm

Colorless glass and opaque-white tapes. Unpolished
pontil mark.

Provenance: Marianne Pelliot Collection, Paris.

Rounded conical bowl in colorless glass with honeycomb pattern ("nipt-diamond-waies") marvered
opaque-white tapes, supported on an elaborate stem
comprising two gadrooned hollow knops separated by
collars, and with applied opposed scrolls with multi-
spiral opaque-twist cores and dorsal applied clear pin-
cered trails. Wide conical foot with folded rim.

This goblet belongs to a group of wing-stemmed goblets *à la façon de Venise* which probably originated in
the Netherlands; the bowl, as in the Wolf example,
with reticulated threads, or pinched ribs (compare
Schmidt 1922, pp. 117–118, fig. 71). A similar example, the bowl diamond-decorated in the manner of
Willem van Heemskerk, and dating from the second
half of the seventeenth century, is in the British Museum, London (see London 1968, no. 240, ill.).
The reticulated opaque, white, decoration on the Wolf
glass is obviously very rare. A very similar glass with
slightly-differing stem formation, and so far untraced,
was used by the firm of Salviati & Co. in Murano, as a
prototype to create a late nineteenth-century imitation (Klesse/Saldern 1978, no. 198, ill.; Sotheby's,
Biemann, lot. no. 234, ill.).
The opaque-white decoration is also comparable with
that on a tazza in the Victoria and Albert Museum,
London, Buckley Collection, (Schmidt 1927, pl. 14A).

Lit.: Zurich 1956, no. 26, ill.; Charleston 1956, p. 42; São Paulo
1957, no. 36, ill.; Klesse/Saldern 1978, p. 242, no. 198 (the doubts
expressed in this publication as to the seventeenth century origin
of this glass have since been withdrawn).

## 22   ICE-GLASS BUCKET

Venice, first half 17th century

Height: 21.5 cm (with handle raised), 13.5 cm (with lowered handle);
diameter: 14.5 cm;
thickness of glass: about 3–5 mm

Ice glass and pale-blue glass. Unpolished pontil mark. Base with large crack.

Depressed, globular body with everted rim in ice glass, supported on a plain, everted foot ring. Rim with applied, pale-blue translucent trail and opposed, clear-glass lugs through which pass the ends of the bowed, incised twist handle.

For type see cat. no. 34.

Also parallels in the Museo Poldi Pezzoli, Milan (Mariacher/Raffia 1983, no. 153, pl. 150); Städtisches Reiss-Museum, Mannheim (Franz Swoboda, *Kunst- und Kunsthandwerk, Neuerwerbungen 1964–1973*, Bildhefte des Städtischen Reiss-Museums no. 1, Mannheim 1974, pl. 27); Museo Vetrario, Murano (Gasparetto 1958, fig. 75; Mariacher 1963, col. pl. op. p. 28; Mariacher/Causa 1974, col. pl. 62; Venice 1982, no. 183, ill., in addition with four lion-mask prunts); Kunstgewerbemuseum, Prague (Prague 1973, no. 74, fig. 23; Drahotová 1982, fig. 13).

## 26  GOBLET WITH BLUE BOWL

Probably Netherlands, *façon de Venise*, second half 16th century up to beginning 17th century

Height: 22.2 cm; diameter at rim: 10 cm; thickness of glass: about 1 mm

Gray-tinted and strong blue glass. Small unpolished pontil mark.

Conical foot with folded rim. Clear, hollow, tapering stem with two molded lion masks flanked by rosettes and swags, gadroons above and below, all flanked by collars. Deep blue, funnel bowl with rounded base.

Comparable goblets with varied colored bowls have been recorded in: London art market (with emerald-green bowl: A. Churchill, "English XVIIth Century Glass", in *Glass Notes*, 6 Dec. 1946, pp. 26–28, fig. X, "English, seventeenth century"; Barrington Haynes 1959, pl. 53b described as "Antwerp or London, 17th century."); British Museum, London (with blue bowl and replaced silver foot: Tait 1979, no. 186, ill.); Collection Baar, Liège (colorless glass with cover: Chambon 1955, p. 311, pl. VII, 24; described as "South Netherlands, second half 16th century"). This type of goblet was probably the prototype for a group of armorial glasses probably decorated in Nuremberg with cold painting or diamond engraving at the beginning of the seventeenth century (compare for example Hetteš 1960, pl. 30; Tait 1979, no. 45 and 46, ill.).
Compare also with examples of more extended form: in the Kunstgewerbemuseum, Prague (with amethyst-tinted bowl: Hetteš 1960, p. 40, pl. 36; Drahotová 1982, col. pl. 45, where a blue-bowled example with vertically-ribbed stem is mentioned); and in the Österreichisches Museum für angewandte Kunst, Vienna (with colorless bowl: Egg 1962, fig. 54).

## 27   A PAIR OF CARAFES

Possibly Tuscany or Umbria, *façon de Venise*, about 1560–90

Height: 23.2 cm (with warrior), 23.7 cm (with baptism);
thickness of glass: about 2–3mm

Deep-blue glass with cold-painted and gilt decoration and wash enamel. Unpolished pontil marks. Large parts of gilding and painting rubbed. Foot of carafe with baptism rejoined with small areas of damage; where handle applied to body also partly damaged.

Provenance: Max Goldschmidt Collection (base of carafe with baptism scene bears printed label inscribed "COLLECTION MAX GOLDSCHMIDT").

Each with folded, conical foot decorated with gilt bands flanking wrythen gilt, gray, white and dark-red leaves. Basal node with upper gilt band. Shouldered, ovoid body divided by gilt bands into three vertical panels and shoulder zone, and decorated on the front panel in cold painting and gilt; with an erect warrior with sword and shield, in "antique" style, above him, within an oval cartouche the letters "AA"; and with the Baptism of Christ beneath the radiating nimbus of the Holy Dove, on the shoulder a heart pierced with crossed arrows and the letters "s" and "s," respectively, these panels flanked by further panels of symmetrical dragon and bird grotesques. Slender, cylindrical neck with central, gilt ring and everted rim with pinched spout. Applied, loop handle ending at the base joint in a wax-modeled, painted, and gilt putto mask within gilt sunburst.

There are no known parallels for either form or decoration.

The engraved sources for the vignettes were taken from the illustrations by Bernard Salomon for the Bible printed by Jean de Tournes in 1558 (see above p. 18, figs. 15 and 16).
The carafe bearing the letters "AA" (for Aqua?) shows the divinely-appointed leader of the Israelites, Gideon, as though standing before his tiny army, appropriate

to the preceeding text illustration, who triumphed over the enemy Midianites with trumpets and torches set in empty jugs (Judges 7, 16–23).

The other carafe with letters "ss" (for *Spiritus Sanctus?*) shows the Baptism of Christ by St. John, quite faithfully copied from the Salomon original (Matthew 3, 13–17).

The shape of the body is slightly reminiscent of the sprinkler vases with three, vertical tubes, which were produced in blue, green, and colorless glass at Hall in Tyrol (compare Mariacher 1960, pl. 53; Egg 1962, fig. 47; Tait 1979, no. 228, col. pl. 10).

When discussing the origin of these carafes, particular attention must be paid to the sophisticated grotesques. Whether knowledge of the Bernard Salomon Bible illustrations would have been disseminated as rapidly throughout Germany, as is evidenced by contemporary maiolica painting in Italy and France, there is nothing there to compare with these fantastic grotesques. The only stylistic analogies are on maiolica products of the workshops of Fontana and Patanazzi in Urbino, where grotesques of this type are typical of the third quarter of the sixteenth century (see p. 19, fig. 18). It would therefore seem that these carafes are most likely products of a mid-Italian *à la façon de Venise* glasshouse, (Tuscany or Umbria).

The function of these vessels is also obscure. Thanks to Eva Neuroth, Cologne, this problem has been researched (report 13 January 1986). These vessels neither satisfy the liturgical regulations as utensils for the Mass (for which colorless glass marked with the letters "A" and "V" or their symbols of fish and grapes is stipulated) or as Christening ewers (where a ewer and basin is normal). Whether it is possible that two complementary carafes were commissioned for two domestic or private christenings and then remained unused due to the incompatible decoration, must remain hypothetical.

## 28   PFINZING ARMORIAL COVERED GOBLET

Glass (with diamond-point decoration): Innsbruck or Hall in Tyrol, about 1590–1600
Cold painting, possibly Nuremberg, about 1600

Height: 28.9 cm (with cover), 21.2 cm (without cover); diameter at rim: 10.7 cm;
thickness of glass: about 1.5–2 mm

Smoky, gray-tinted glass with cold painting, gilding, and diamond-point engraving. Unpolished pontil mark. Small crack on cover; paint and gilding rubbed. Deep slightly-flared bowl with flattened base supported on a hollow, inverted-baluster stem flanked by collars, flattened, conical foot with folded rim. Bowl decorated in cold-painted enamels and lacquer with the arms of the Nuremberg family of Pfinzing, surmounted by two helmets bearing crests and flanked by foliate mantling, all on a red-gold ground within an oval cartouche embellished with fruit. Rim decorated with gold-brown, foliate band with pendant tassels and fruit festoons. Cover with everted rim and diamond-engraved dot border round the rim and engraved, radial, foliate motifs round the finial.

For the armorials of the Pfinzing family see the family genealogical manuscript, Nuremberg, about 1680, with further entries up to 1791 (Nuremberg, Germanisches Nationalmuseum Library Hs 4836a) and the *Stammbuch* of Jakob Scheurl (1577–1623), particularly the handwritten entries 1592–1601 (ibid., Hs 128793, fol. 103), kindly made accessible by Ursula Mende.

The coat-of-arms on this glass corresponds to the 1594 rendering of the arms of one "Carolus Pfinzing" in the above-mentioned book of Jacob Scheurl (see above, p. 21, fig. 20). At the same time the crests were transposed in the copying, a harmless error which occurred on engraved and cut glasses as well, right into the eighteenth century.

Karl (Carl) Pfinzing von Henfenfeld, Gründlach, Reutless and Letten (1578–1629: Nuremberg, Germanisches Nationalmuseum Library, Hs 4836a, fol. 50r) – son of Hans Pfinzing (1546–1582: ibid., fol. 37r) and nephew of Martin Pfinzing (1490–1552: ibid., fol. 30r–30v) was assessor and *Schöpf (Schöffe)* to the Land and Farm Court of Nuremberg (see Joh. Gottfried Bie-

dermann, *Geschlechtsregister des hochadeligen Patriziats in Nürnberg*, Nuremberg 1740, vol. 6, pl. 409). Compare also with very similar glasses with the Pfinzing arms in the Germanisches Nationalmuseum, Nuremberg, which came from Schloss Henfenfeld near Nuremberg (E. Meyer-Heisig 1953, pp. 85–86, ill. 1; see also above, p. 20, fig. 22). Among this group of Pfinzing glasses in the Germanisches Nationalmuseum is one of tall, cylindrical form, which, in addition to the arms, bears the monogram KP over the medallion and the partly rubbed date (16)01. This probably refers to the above-mentioned Karl Pfinzing who in 1599 married Clara Holzschuherin of Neuenberg, and who are both depicted on the reverse in front of their marriage bed (see above, p. 20, fig. 21). This glass could have been commissioned on the occasion of the birth of the first of their five children, Clara Magdalena on 15 August 1601 (Biedermann, vol. 6, pl. 409), and who thus bore the same monogram as her father.

Compare the form of the goblet with other diamond-engraved examples from the Court Glasshouse, Innsbruck, in: the Victoria and Albert Museum, London, as well as in the Kunsthistorisches Museum, Vienna (Egg 1962, pp. 61 and 62, fig. 37 and 38). Stylistically, the cold-painted decoration is close to that of Innsbruck (Egg 1962, pp. 45 onwards). In view of the close trade connections between Nuremberg and the glassmaking centers of the Tyrol (see Hampe 1919, pp. 13–15), it would not be surprising if the undecorated glasses came from there. As to whether they were also decorated there, or, as Meyer-Heisig has suggested (op. cit. 1953) by Nuremberg *Hausmalers*, the latter would seem more likely.

## 29 COVERED HUMPEN INSCRIBED WITH THE NAMES SUNDTMAN AND FRISSE

Possibly South Bohemian, early 17th century
Date 1664 added later

Height: 43 cm (including cover), 33.8 cm (without cover);
thickness of glass: about 2–3 mm

Smoky-gray, tinted glass with diamond-point engraving, cold-painting, and gilding. Cover possibly not original. Unpolished pontil mark. Body cracked. Four hasps broken off. Five rings missing. Finial knop on cover rejoined. Painting rubbed in places.

Cylindrical body on high cylindrical foot with everted, folded rim and kicked-in base. Sides decorated with three pairs of vertically-arranged rings held by hasps. Also two, gilt, applied, cherub-mask prunts with gilt, outspread wings and connecting shoulder pieces, arranged one above the other. Flanking the lower cherub mask are two angels in red and blue robes, holding up a coat-of-arms, no longer decipherable, above them the date "Anno 16/64" and the names "Fridrich/ Sundtmann" and "Mattheus/Frisse."
The reverse engraved in diamond point with three rows of various inscriptions, viz: "Wer daß glass zu (!) bricht / der gebe geldt, daß / Man ein anders / bestelt," and "Mein Handwerck weiß / Brauch ich mit fleiß / Kan mich Ernehren / Mitt gott unnd Ehren," as well as "Eß darf sich niemandt Rühmen / daß glück stehet auff bluhmen / Eß kombt ein windt In einer nacht / Undt schläckt die blumen / aller ab." All flanked by decorative borders, the lower diamond-engraved with rope and lappet design, the rim with gilt and lacquered lozenge border flanked by diamond-engraved lappet borders. Cover with everted rim and two flattened knops and button finial, cold painted with three stylized foliate circlets.

The rare decoration of partly gilt, partly applied cherub masks can be seen on a small *façon de Venise* goblet of the late sixteenth century in the Westböhmisches Museum in Pilsen, and which formed part of an exhibition there in 1984 titled *České sklo ze sbírek západočeského Muzea v Plzni*. It is described there as an

archeological find at Dominikanska 2 (see above, p. 22, fig. 25; unfortunately not illustrated in the exhibition catalogue). The cherub masks with their large gilt wings flank a rendering of the brazon serpent, of the type found on early *Reichsadlerhumpen*. The chemical decomposition which has affected the whole glass makes it impossible to gauge the original color scheme, except for the gilding. This glass belongs to a group of Bohemian glasses in *façon de Venise* style published by K. Hetteš (JGS 5, 1963, pp. 39–53) and D. Hejdová (JGS 23, 1981, pp. 18–33), fragments of which have been found during excavations of sixteenth and seventeenth century Bohemian glasshouse sites. As Olga Drahotová rightly assumes (orally 1 July 1987) the Wolf *Humpen* originates from the beginning of the 17th century, the diamond-inscribed date being a later addition.

Tyrol, Court Glasshouse, Innsbruck, second half 16th century

Height: 15.8 cm; diameter: 17.5 cm;
thickness of glass: about 1 mm

Light, smoky-tinted glass. Opaque-white trails. Diamond-point engraved and gilt decoration. Unpolished pontil mark. Gilding rubbed.

Small, conical foot with engraved, foliate collar. Stem with central, hollow, mold-blown knop with lion masks, rosettes, and swags flanked by gadroons and short baluster-and-collar sections. Shallow, concave bowl, the interior embellished with opaque-white, twisted, applied trailing around the central field engraved with stiff-leaf border. Remainder divided into twelve rectangular panels of alternate, engraved acanthus-leaf scrolls and gilt decoration, now almost completely worn away, all bordered by rope and stiff-leaf bands.

Compare with parallels (with slightly varying decoration) in: the Collections of the Veste Coburg, Coburg (Egg 1962, fig. 48; Weiss 1966, ill. p. 122; Coburg 1969, no. 80, ill.); The Corning Museum of Glass, Corning, Jerome Strauss Collection (Perrot 1958, no. 93, ill.); at one time in London art market (A. Churchill, "Two Diamond Point Glasses" in: *Glass Notes* 11, Dec. 1951, pp. 14–17, fig. 16, 17; Barrington Haynes 1959, pl. 38a and b).
The engraved decoration is comparable with that on a bowl in the British Museum, London (Tait 1979, no. 229, ill.).

## 37  COVERED DIAMOND-ENGRAVED BOWL

Tyrol, Court Glasshouse, Innsbruck (?),
about 1570–90

Height: 15 cm; diameter: 17 cm;
thickness of glass: about 2 mm

Straw-tinted glass with diamond-point engraved decoration. Unpolished pontil mark. Small chip on rim.

Ovoid bowl supported on applied foot ring. Low cover
with everted rim and hollow knop finial. Both cover
and sides of bowl engraved with matching decoration
in the form of broad bands of continuous foliate scrolls
and smaller foliate borders, as well as dot borders.
For shape, see a Venetian example with slightly higher
foot (decorated with border of grotesques) in the Museo Cristiano, Brescia (W. Buckley, *Diamond Engraved Glasses of the 16th Century*, London 1929,
pp. 17, 18, pl. 19–21).
See also a comparable variant with applied side
handles in the Museo Civico, Brescia (Venice 1982,
no. 173, ill., also no. 171 and 172, but without cover).
A bowl of lower profile is in the Metropolitan Museum
of Art, New York, Robert Lehmann Collection (Perrot
1958, no. 91, ill.). The diamond-point engraving on
these examples is altogether of a different type: that is,
in typical Venetian style with asymmetrical play of
scrolling foliage inhabited by large and small animals.
For this type of decoration see cat. no. 32.
This type of two-tiered, firmly-symmetrical decoration of stylized foliage would seem to be without parallel so far. A distant influence is to be found in the ornamental diamond-engraved friezes on the hurricane
lamps executed for Cardinal Christoph von Madrutz,
Bishop of Trent and Brixen, now in the Bayerisches
Nationalmuseum (Rückert 1982, I, no. 135, ill.).
Rückert suggests that the Innsbruck glasshouse is a
more likely origin than a Venetian one, and this would
apply to the Wolf covered bowl with its glass of straw
tint as well. The accuracy and elegance of execution
suggests Italian training, which could only really apply to artisans from the Court Glasshouse in Innsbruck (see also above, p. 29, figs. 35 and 36).

Bohemia, dated 1607

Height: 43.9 cm; diameter: 10.3 cm;
thickness of glass: about 3.5 mm

Smoky glass with diamond-point engraving. Large
unpolished pontil mark. Base cracked.


Tall cylindrical body with kicked-in base supported
by a high, cylindrical foot with everted, folded rim.
Body divided by three bands of stylized decoration into two equestrian friezes: in the upper one the Holy
Roman Emperor inscribed "Röm:(isch) Kay:(serli-
che) May:(estät)" in his capacity as King of Bohemia
as well, flanked by the three ecclesiastical electors
with respective inscriptions "Mentz," "Cöllnn" and
"Tryer;" the lower one with the Imperial Eagle bearing the arms of Austria on its breast, flanked by the
three temporal electors with respective inscriptions
"Pfaltz," "Sachssen" and "Brandenburgk," all upon a
base with lily of the valley sprays. The band beneath
the rim is embellished with the inscription "TRINCK ·
MIT · FREVDEN" within rope borders flanked by
stiff-leaf and chain borders: the central band inscribed
"HALT · DICH · BESCHEIDEN," and the lower band
with pendant stiff-leaf border.
Foot bears a later cursive inscription in diamond
point: "Anno 1639/den 2 8bris" (= Octobris).

The *Ritterliche Reutterkunst* with illustrations by Jost
Amman, published in 1584 in Frankfurt a. M., would
have acted here for the engraver as a rough prototype
for the portrayal of the Emperor and Electors. (See
above, p. 31, figs. 38 and 41).
Within the rare group of only four other known *Humpen* with diamond-engraved equestrian electors, the
Wolf *Humpen* is stylistically closest to the covered
*Humpen* in the Kestner Museum, Hanover (Mosel
1979, no. 271, ill.: see above, p. 30, fig. 39). The close-
ness in style of the drawing, the arrangement of the
figures, the inscriptions and recurrent "toast," together with the lily of the valley sprays and similar ornamental borders, would make an attribution to the
same, possibly Bohemian workshop, a possibility. A
related *Humpen*, but with more schematic and less
lively decoration, formerly from Burg Buchlau, is in

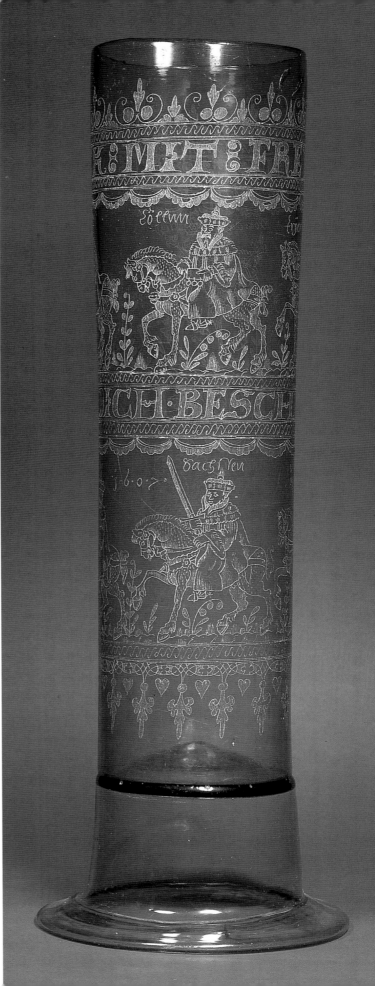

the Kunstgewerbemuseum in Prague (Vávra 1954, fig. 133).

As opposed to these Bohemian examples, the piece in the Kunsthistorisches Museum in Vienna differs markedly, both iconographically and stylistically. Whether the form (the cylindrical body is raised in goblet fashion on a high, conical foot with shoulder knop) justifies a Hall attribution and date around 1610–15, as is suggested by H. Klapsia ("Ein diamant-gerissener Kurfürstenpokal aus der Haller Glashütte" in: *Pantheon* 32, 1944, pp. 125–128, ill.) is difficult to prove. The quality of the decoration indicates its origins in one of the most skilled glass-making centers of the time, probably also in this case in Bohemia.

Lit.: São Paulo 1957, no. 35, ill.

Röm: Kay: May:

Cöelln

Pfaltz    j · 6 · 07

Brandenburgk

## 39  HUMPEN WITH ALLEGORICAL VIRTUES

Bohemia, dated 1607

Height: 25.5 cm; diameter at rim: 11 cm;
thickness of glass: about 3.5 mm

Pale, green-tinted glass with diamond-point engraving, enameling and gilt decoration. Unpolished pontil mark. Gilding completely rubbed. Number "1" painted in sealing-wax red on underside of base.


Cylindrical body slightly tapering towards the rim, with kicked-in base and applied foot ring decorated with white enamel dot border. Sides divided into a central frieze by lower and upper flanking borders, and engraved with two elaborately-draped female figures, identified as allegories of the Virtues by the inscription above them, "PRVDENTIA" and "CHARI-TAS" respectively, standing on either side of the date "1607." The reverse with seven-part inscription in Roman capitals: "HEB MICH AVF VND / SETZ MICH NIDER / TRINCK MIECH AVS / VND FVEL MICH / WIDER · VND GIEB / MICH EINEM GVTTEN/BIERBRVDER WIDER," the continuation in normal script: "Wolan Ihr Lieben brüder all / Trinckt nur und schreit nit allßu schal / Wer mich in seinen händen hatt / Sehe das er Ja nicht werd ßu / spott." Figures and inscription separated by tall, flowering plants. Rim embellished with gilt band (rubbed away), engraved rope, enameled lily of the valley, and dot borders. Lower zone with encircling inscription in Roman capitals: "DEVM TIMERE SVPER OMNIA," flanked by rope borders and pendant scrolls.


While the exact engraved source for the allegorical figures has not yet been identified, there is definitely a connection with the engravings of Virgil Solis or Jost Amman.

As opposed to the many known examples of *Stangen* glasses and *Humpen* decorated with the Virtues in diamond point, combined with cold-painted decoration (compare among others with Czihak 1891, pp. 101–102; Schmidt 1922, pp. 223–224; Klesse/Saldern 1978, no. 284) which are either attributed to Silesian glasshouses, the Wilhelmsberg Glasshouse in South Bohemia (Mareš 1893, p. 169; Schmidt 1922,

p. 224) or the Court Glasshouse at Innsbruck (Rückert 1982, I, pp. 79–80, no. 145–146), on the Wolf example, the diamond engraving is combined with high-fired enamel decoration. The band of lily of the valley florettes, already mentioned, is a clear indication of a North Bohemian provenance, as this motif (combined with rows of dots and gold band) is found there on very early, enameled *Humpen* of the late sixteenth century (compare with: Saldern 1965, figs. 111, 115, 130, 213). These motifs remained popular for a long time and can still be found on a *Humpen* in the Kunstgewerbemuseum, Prague, with a view of the Zeilberg Glasshouse, which Christian Preissler dedicated to Caspar Steiner of Volpersdorf in 1680 (ibid., fig. 234). Perhaps the Wolf *Humpen* can be seen as a "key" piece in defining the possible Bohemian origin of glasses in this group.

Lit.: Bernt 1950, p. 51, fig. 26 and 27 (described as "Silesian, about 1600"); (see above, p. 31, fig. 42).

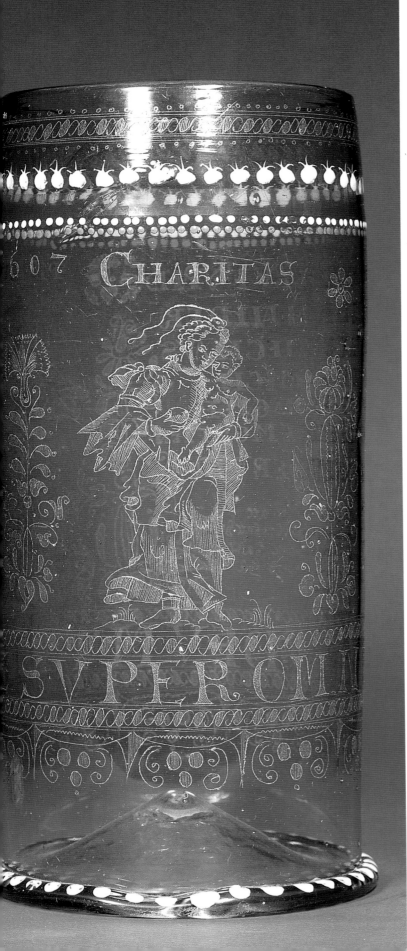

607 CHARITAS

PRVDENTIA 16

SVPEROM

NTIMERE

## 40  DIAMOND-ENGRAVED WING-STEMMED GOBLET

Glass: Netherlands or Germany, *façon de Venise*, 17th century.
Engraving: Germany, dated 1666, in the manner of Peter Wolff

Height: 28.4 cm; diameter of bowl: 9.6 cm; thickness of glass: about 1–1.3 mm

Colorless to straw-tinted glass, as well as opaque-white and blue glass. Diamond-point engraving. Unpolished pontil mark.

Funnel bowl and wide, conical foot separated by an elaborate stem of coiled glass enclosing blue and white spiral threads and terminating under the bowl in outward-facing clear-glass birds' heads, the outer sides edged in clear-glass, crimped trails. Bowl decorated in diamond-point on one side with the double-headed Imperial Eagle grasping orb and sword in its claws and surmounted by the Imperial Crown. The reverse inscribed in Roman capitals: "LEOPOLDVS. D. G. ROMAN. / IMPERATOR SEMPER / AVGVSTVS. VIVAT. / ANNO 1.6.6.6." The base with band of spirals.

In 1666 the Emperor Leopold I celebrated his marriage. It took place in Vienna and was to Margaretha Theresia, daughter of Philip IV of Spain, at that time only fifteen years old. He was kept informed of the physical appearance of his bride through a series of portraits of the Infanta by Velázquez, which were sent from Madrid to the court at Vienna. The festivities lasted the entire winter and attracted the well-born from all over Europe, as well as a large group of peripatetic artists.

Stylistically the engraving is comparable with that of contemporary Netherlands engravers, and there are certain similarities, tentatively suggested here, with the work of Peter Wolff (compare with Schmidt 1911, p. 823, fig. 8; JGS I, 1959, p. 111, no. 29, ill.; Saldern 1968, no. 110, ill.; Cologne 1963, no. 227, ill. pl. 2, as well as 1973, no. 318, ill. pl. 4). This hypothesis applies only to the "naturalistic" interpretation of the heraldic motifs. and a statement concerning engraver or locale can only be approached with caution (see also above, p. 32, fig. 43).

BER," followed by "4 GRAVEN," these being "CLE-VE," "SAPHOY," "SCHWARTZBVR," "ZILLI," followed by "4 RITTER," these being "ANDELAW," "WEISSENBACH," "FRAWBER," "STRVNDECK," followed by "4 DORFFER," these being "BAM-BE(RG)," "VLM," "HAGENAW," "SLETSTAT," followed by "4 BIRG," these being "MAGDABVRG," "LVTZELBVRG," "ROTTENBVRG," "ALDEN-BVRG." The whole inscribed above in white Roman capitals "DAS HAILIGE ROMISCH REICH MIT SAMPT SEINEN GLIEDERN / 1572." At the wingtips, the blue flames symbolizing the Order of the Golden Fleece with red-gold flying sparks. Rim embellished with gilt scale border set with green dots and flanked by rows of blue-white dots.

The *Reichsadler* motif is based on a woodcut by Hans Burgkmair of 1510, also published by the monogramist "H" in 1511, as well as among others a version by Nickel Nerlich around 1570 (Schmidt 1922, pp. 167–168, fig. 90; Saldern 1965, figs. 43–45) which could also have served as a source.

Apart from the closely-related *Reichsadlerhumpen* dated 1571 in the British Museum (London 1968, no. 219, ill.), the Wolf *Humpen* is one of the earliest in this genre.
See other examples also dated 1572 in: the British Museum (Nesbitt 1871, p. 139; Stengel 1916, p. 324); the Focke Museum, Bremen (formerly Gewerbemuseum: Stengel 1916, p. 327, fig. 6 and 7); the art market (with Adam's skull at the base of the cross, noted as "Bohemian 1572": Auction 17, Jürgen Fischer, Heilbronn, 10 October 1981, lot no. 30, col. pl. on cover) as well as a flask with the same date in the Los Angeles County Museum (Saldern 1965, fig. 51).
Sabine Baumgärtner includes the 1571 London *Humpen* with a group of three variants dating from the 1570s, all bearing the monogram "GP," arguing convincingly that they are all products of the Saxon Glasshouse Marienberg lying in the Erzgebirge (1977, pp. 39–40). She suggests that rather than the painter's mark, the initials "GP" stand for Georg Preussler, the director of the Marienberg Glasshouse. In this respect even the three "GP" *Humpen* display small stylistic differences from each other.

On many points there is a high degree of similarity between these *Humpen* and the Wolf example above. Although they they do not bear the motif of the Brazen Serpent on the reverse, it is significant that on all of them the broad tailfeathers are arranged on either side almost like fins, right down to the last layer. The brown, as opposed to the more frequent black tones of the eagle, would not seem to indicate anything particular in this instance. (For further information see above, p. 37, figs. 47–49).

Bohemia, dated 1582

Height: 35.9 cm; diameter at rim: 14.3 cm;
thickness of glass: about 3.5–4 mm

Colorless to smoky-tinted glass with enameled and
gilt decoration. Unpolished pontil mark. Foot ring replaced with pewter mount (probably later).

Cylindrical, slightly-tapering body with kicked-in
base, mounted on a pewter foot ring. Painted in colored enamels with the double-headed Imperial Eagle
of the Holy Roman Empire, on its breast the crucified
Christ, painted in flesh tones, white loin cloth and yellow halo, nailed to a green cross with white ribbon inscribed "INRI." The outspread wings are set with fif-
ty-six coats-of-arms (*Quaterniones*) arranged in rows
representing the extent and unity of the Empire,
painted in white, black, rust brown, yellow, green, and
blue, with corresponding inscriptions in Roman capitals. To dexter are the ecclesiastical electorates
"TRIER," "COLN," "MENTZ," and the (temporal)
Podesta of Rome "POTESTAT · ZV · ROM.," to sinister, the temporal electorates "BEHEM," "PFALTZ,"
"SACHSEN," "BRANDENBVRG." On the six long
wing feathers are four coats-of-arms arranged one over
the other with the respective inscriptions (from the
center outwards): on the right "4 · SEILL," these being "BRANSCHWEIG," "BAIRN," "SCHWABEN,"
"LVTRING," followed by "4 MARGGRAVEN," these
being "MERCHERN," "BRADEN·BVRG," "MEICH-
SEN," "BADEN," followed by "4 BVRGGRAVEN,"
these being "MAIDBVRG," "NVRNBVRG," "RE-
MECK," "STRAMBERG," followed by "4 SEMVER-
FREIEN," these being "LVNDBVRG," "WESTER-
BVRG," "THVSSIS," "ALWALTEN," followed by
"4 STETT," these being "AVGSBVRG," "METZ,"
"ACH," "LVBECK," followed by "4 BAVRN," these
being "COLN," "REGENSPVRG," "COSENITZ,"
"SALTZBVRG"; on the left: "4 VICARI," these being
"BRABAND," "N SACHSEN," "WESTERREICH,"
"SCHLESSI," followed by "4 LANDTGRAVEN,"
these being "DVRMG," "EDELSASS," "HESSEN,"
"LEVCHTENBVRG," followed by "4 GRAVEN,"
these being "CLEVE," "SAPHOY," "SCHWARTZ-

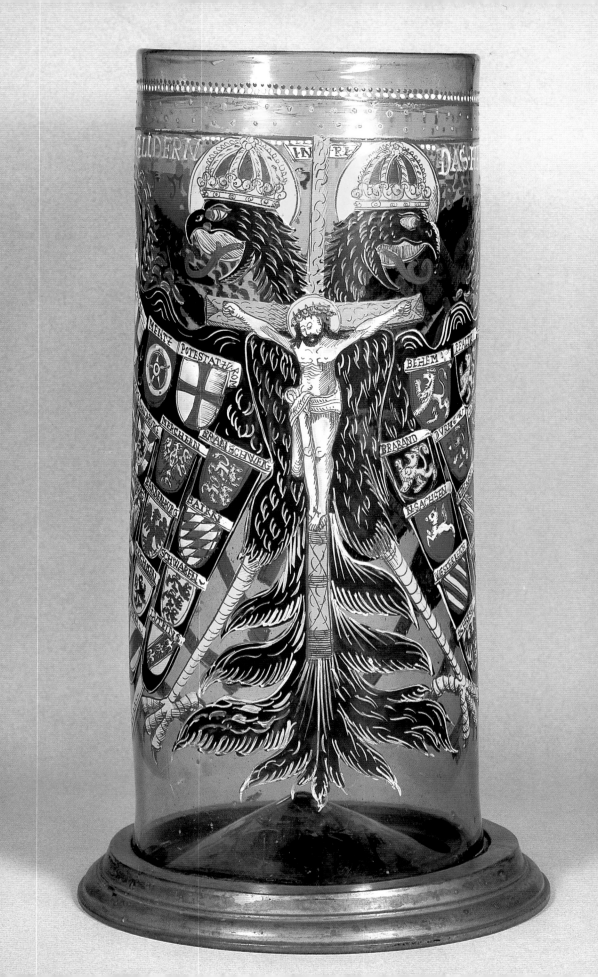

BVRG," "ZILLI," followed by "4 RITTER," these being "ANDELAW," "WEISENBACH," "FRAAN-BERG," "STRVNTECK," followed by "4 DORFER," these being "BAMBERG," "VLM," "HAGENAW," "SCHETSTAT," followed by "4 BIRG," these being "MAGDABVRG," "LVTZELBVRG," "ROTTEN-BVRG," and "ALTENBVRG." Below the rim the inscription in white Roman capitals: "DAS · HEILIG · ROMISCH · REICH · MIT · SAMPT · SEINEN · GLIDERN / 1582." The upper wing tips painted with streaming yellow and red sparks symbolizing the Golden Fleece. The reverse painted with the Brazen Serpent, symbol of the cruxified Christ, in blue on a red-brown cross. Rim embellished with gilt scale border with green enamel dots and flanked by rows of white dots.

For a discussion of the inscription, engraved sources, and earlier parallels compare with cat. no. 42.
This *Humpen* differs from those dating from the 1570s discussed at the end of cat. no. 42 in the confident, but mechanical, brushwork and the bright yellow of the Eagle's claws, and is likely to be of Bohemian rather than Saxon origin (see above, p. 37).
Compare other examples close in date in: The Corning Museum of Glass, Corning, Beinecke Collection (dated 1585, as well as an undated one: Saldern 1965, pp. 260–263, cat. no. 11 and 12, ill.); Staatliche Galerie, Moritzburg (dated 1585; H. Raum and R. Gründig, *Glas aus zwei Jahrtausenden, Bestände der Galerie von 700 v. d. Zt. bis 1975*, Halle, 1977, no. 7, ill. p. 30); Metropolitan Museum of Art, New York (formerly Mühsam Collection, dated 1587: Schmidt 1926, no. 72, col. pl. 9).

## 44 ELECTORS' HUMPEN

Bohemia, dated 1606

Height: 43.8 cm (with cover), 30.8 cm (without cover); diameter at rim: 12.7 cm;
thickness of glass: about 3–3.5 mm (*Humpen*); about 1.5 mm (cover)

Colorless glass (cover) to smoky-tinted glass (*Humpen*) with enameled and gilt decoration. Unpolished pontil mark. Gilding partly rubbed. Cover probably not original.

Provenance: Collection of the Dukes of Anhalt-Dessau (according to Alfred Wolf papers).

Tall, cylindrical body with kicked-in base and applied foot ring. Decorated in bright enamels with the central figure of the Holy Roman Emperor enthroned in state below a baldequin, and holding sceptre and sword, at his feet the Imperial Insignia, and flanked by the date "16/06." On either side the seven Electors robed in ermine; on his right the three ecclesiastical electors inscribed "Trier," "Cöllen," and "Mentz," on his right the four temporal electors holding their official insignia as Chancellor, Steward, Marshall and Treasurer, and inscribed above: "Behem" (with crown rather than electoral cap), "Pfaltz," "Sachssen" and "Brandenburg." Below, three white cursive inscriptions: in the center "All so in all iren ornadt / sitzt Kaisserliche magstadt / sampt dem sieben churfürsten gut / wie denn ein ieder sitzen thutt / Ihn churfürstlicher Kleidung fein / mit anZeigung des amptes sein"; on the left: "Der ertzbischoff zu mentz bekandt / ist cantzler in den deutschen landt / So ist der ertzbishof zu cölen gleich / auch cantzler in gantz frankenreich / Dar nach der ertzbischof zu Trier / ist cantzler in welscher refier"; on the right: "Der Könnig ihn behem der ist / der reichs ertzschenck zu aller frist / Her nach der Pfaltzgraf bey den rein / des Heiligen reichs truchsas thut sein/ Dar nach der Hertzog zu sachssen geborn / Ist des reichs marschalch aus erKornn / Der marggraf von brandenburg gutt / des reichs ertzKammer sein thut." Rim embellished with a band of gilt scales with superimposed blue enamel dots, bordered by rows of white dots. Double-ogee cover with a band of enameled, foliate decoration flanked in two zones by gilt-line borders and large spiral borders in white, yellow, blue, green and rust, surmounted by rosettes and small leaves. Knopped finial.

A woodcut by Hans Vogel published in Augsburg in the first half of the sixteenth century served here as the source for the iconography and text (Schmidt 1922, fig. 91; Schade 1968, fig. 4; Saldern 1965, fig. 59).
It is unusual here that the iconography lacks a title; the majority of electors' *Humpen* bear the inscription after the original Vogel print: "Anzaigung der Kayserlichen Mayestat / sampt den siben Churfürste Inn irer Klaidung Ampt und sitz ec" (also included in Vogel's woodcut).
There are similar untitled electors' *Humpen* in: the Museum für Kunsthandwerk, Frankfurt a. M. (Ohm 1973, no. 303, ill., with similar arrangement of date numbers on either side of the throne "15/96"); the Bayerische Landesgewerbeanstalt, Nuremberg (Saldern 1965, fig. 58, here the date "1597" is found beneath the middle verse).
For further examples of this genre, on which the date does not, as on nineteenth-century examples, appear on the front of the baldequin (Spiegl 1980, fig. 274; Saldern 1965, pp. 286–287, cat. no. 31, ill.), see: the Otto Dettmers Collection, Bremen (Saldern 1968, no. 148, ill.); The Corning Museum of Glass, Corning, Beinecke Collection (Saldern 1965, pp. 288–289, cat. no. 32 with col. ill.) and the Biemann Collection, Zurich (Klesse/Saldern 1978, no. 278, with col. pl.; Lucerne 1981, no. 785, ill.).

## 45 GOBLET WITH FOX HUNT

Bohemia, Erzgebirge, dated 1598

Height: 16.4 cm; diameter at rim: 8.3 cm;
thickness of glass: about 2.5 mm

Cobalt-blue tinted glass with enameled and gilt decoration. Unpolished pontil mark; gilding almost completely rubbed.
Glass rings missing.

Provenance: Friedrich Neuburg Collection, Dresden/Leitmeritz.

Flared bowl with rounded base, supported on two, flattened knops and high, conical foot with everted, folded rim. Flared section of bowl painted in colors with an animal frieze comprising two hounds in pursuit of a fox, and the date "1598" interspersed, flanked by a gilt band within rows of white dots and white lines and vesica band with pendant dots. At this point are three applied hasps interrupting a milled, yellow line border and three decoratively coiled yellow bands alternating with dot florettes.

The printed source for the fox hunt could have been either "Windspiel" or "Fuchs" from Jost Amman's *Thier-Büchlein* published in Franfurt a. M. in 1592 (see above, p. 38., fig. 53), as well as similar hunting scenes by Virgil Solis (Saldern 1965, fig. 315; O'Dell-Franke 1977, pl. 76, 78, 169).
Comparable examples with hunting scenes are in: the Kunstgewerbemuseum, Prague (colorless glass with deer hunt, dated 1594: Hetteš 1963, pp. 49–50, fig. 25; Drahotová 1982, p. 76, col. pl. 47) and the Biemann Collection, Zurich (blue glass with hounds coursing a hare: as yet unpublished; see above p. 38, fig. 52).
For a comparison of form with various enameled scenes see others in: the Hermitage, Leningrad (blue glass with Turk's head, 1592: Saldern 1965, fig. 309) and the Boymans-van Beuningen Museum, Rotterdam (blue glass with male bust, 1592: Saldern 1965, fig. 310).
In connection with the hunting scene see also cat. no. 46 and 47 and the parallels mentioned in the footnote.

For the pinpointing of the production of cobalt-blue glass to the Erzgebirge, see Olga Drahotová 1980, pp. 72–96 and pp. 219–222.

Lit.: Schmidt Ms 1931, p. 42, no. 40 (as "Bohemian").

## 46    TANKARD WITH HARE COURSING

Bohemia, Erzgebirge, dated 1605

Height: 21.8 cm (with cover), 17.7 cm (without cover);
diameter at rim: 5.4 cm;
thickness of glass: about 3 mm

Blue glass with enameled and gilt decoration. Unpolished pontil mark. Pewter cover probably later. Broken at the lower atachment of the handle; gilding almost completely rubbed.

Globular body with high, slightly-tapering neck and everted foot. On a continuous green and brown base line with regular trifoliate motifs, a blue and a white hound coursing a pink-tinted hare below the date "1605" flanked by yellow dot rosettes. Reverse with stylized foliate motifs and lily of the valley sprays, a tree beneath the handle. Shoulder with applied trail embellished with light-blue dash border. Neck with broad band of yellow-outlined scales infilled with slanting rows of white, green, dark-blue, and rust-red dots, all flanked by yellow line borders. Rim embellished with further applied, blue-dashed trail and gilt line (rubbed) flanked by white-dot borders. Applied loop handle with pewter hinged joint to the domed pewter cover with turned finial.

For a discussion of the printed source see cat. no. 45, and also above, p. 38, fig. 53.
For a large group of cobalt-blue tankards of the late sixteenth, early seventeenth century which are mostly attributed to the Schürer and Preussler glasshouses in the Bohemian Erzgebirge see Saldern 1965, pp. 165 onwards; Klesse/Saldern 1978, pp. 288–289; Drahotová 1980, pp. 72–96, 219–222.
Further examples and variants are to be found in: the Musées Royaux d'Art et d'Histoire, Brussels (dated 1601: Berryer 1957, pp. 36–37, fig. XVII; *Trois Millénaires* 1958, no. 389, ill.; Isings 1966, fig. 69); the Moritzburg Museum, Halle (with stag hunt, dated 1597: O. H. Werner, *Schönes Glas in der Moritzburg zu Halle*, Halle 1957, no. 60, fig. 15); Bayerische Landesgewerbeanstalt, Nuremberg (dat. 1597: Elisabeth Bornfleth, *Landesgewerbeanstalt Bayern in Nürnberg, Gewerbemuseum, Ausgewählte Werke*, Nuremberg

1979 no. 81, ill.); one formerly in the Biemann Collection, Zurich (dated 1608: Klesse/Saldern 1978, no. 267 B with col. pl.; Lucerne 1981, fig. 778b; Sotheby's Biemann, lot no. 24, with col. ill.), as well as in: the Metropolitan Museum of Art, New York (formerly Mühsam Collection, with fox hunt inscribed around the neck "LAVF HIN": Schmidt 1926, no. 85, ill.); The Corning Museum of Glass, Corning, Beinecke Collection (with hare coursing, the neck with frieze of oval panels, dated 1610: Saldern 1965, pp. 248–249, cat. no. 4 with col. ill.); British Museum, London (with hare coursing, neck dated 1618: Saldern 1965, fig. 296); James A. de Rothschild Collection, Waddesdon Manor (with fox hunt, dated 1605: Charleston 1977, no. 40 with col. pl.).
For the hunting motif compare also with cobalt-blue glasses in: the Kunstmuseum, Düsseldorf (beaker with hare coursing, dated 1601: Heinemeyer 1966, no. 167, ill.; Drahotová 1980, fig. 89); British Museum, London (beaker with stag hunt, dated 1599: Saldern 1965, fig. 296; London 1968, no. 218, ill.); Los Angeles County Museum, Los Angeles, Hans Cohn Collection (beaker with stag hunt, dated 1599: Axel von Saldern, *Glass 500 B.C. to A.D. 1900, The Hans Cohn Collection, Los Angeles, California*, Mainz 1980, no. 215, col. pl. 27).

## 47   TANKARD WITH STAG HUNT

Bohemia, about 1590–1600

Height: 16.6 cm; diameter at rim: 5.1 cm;
thickness of glass: about 3 mm

Pale, yellowish-brown, tinted glass with gilt and enamel decoration. Unpolished pontil mark. Gilding almost completely rubbed; enamel chipped in one area.

Globular body with cylindrical tapering neck and doubled, everted foot. On a green-painted basal ring a continuous hunting frieze of a rust-red stag with yellow antlers pursued by three hounds painted in flesh-pink, white and black, interspersed with lily of the valley sprays and a tree under the handle. Neck with two applied trails, the upper painted in yellow, the lower in rust-red, flanking the inscription in Roman capitals "LAVF HIN." Rim embellished with gilt band with superimposed blue dots flanked by rows of white dots.

On the question of the printed source see cat. no. 45, and see above, p. 38, fig. 54.
This tankard belongs to a distinct group from the last quarter of the sixteenth century, which in form and decoration are closely related to the blue-tinted examples, and which all probably came from the same Bohemian glassmaking center (compare with cat. no. 46). The attempt by Hugh Tait to ascribe an example from this group to a Netherlandish glasshouse (in: JGS IX, 1967, pp. 110–112) as well as an Hungarian origin put forward by J. Kortona (in: *Annales de 6e Congrès de l'Association Internationale pour l'Histoire de Verre*, Cologne 1973, Liège 1974, pp. 169–176) has already been doubted by A. von Saldern (1978, p. 314).
From dated examples, it would appear that the production of colorless-glass tankards began some twenty years earlier than that of the blue ones.

Compare parallel examples with differing hunting scenes in: The Corning Museum of Glass, Corning, Beinecke Collection (undated: Saldern 1965, p. 253, cat. no. 7, ill.).

See also the similar hunting scene and same inscription on a blue tankard in the Art Institute, Chicago (formerly Mühsam Collection: Schmidt 1926, no. 85, ill.).

Compare also with further colorless glass examples with modified decoration in: the Art Institute, Chicago (formerly Mühsam Collection, with portrait medallion, dated 1597: Schmidt 1926, no. 83, pl. 12); The Corning Museum of Glass, Corning, Beinecke Collection (with Lion of St. Mark, dated 1590: Saldern 1965, pp. 256–257, cat. no. 9, with col. ill.); Kunstmuseum, Düsseldorf (with betrothed couple, dated 1577: Jantzen 1960, no. 43, pl. 19; Heinemeyer 1966, no. 155, ill.); the Landesmuseum Joanneum, Graz (with the fox's punishment, dated 1590: Saldern 1965, fig. 163); the Hermitage, Leningrad (with foliate motifs, dated 1594: Saldern 1965, fig. 300); the Metropolitan Museum of Art, New York (formerly Mühsam Collection, with inscription, dated 1576: Schmidt 1926, no. 81, pl. 12); Kunstgewerbemuseum, Prague (with plant motifs, dated 1600: Saldern 1965, fig. 301; Drahotová 1982, col. pl. 47); and the Biemann Collection, Zurich (with Crucifixion, dated 1573, and one with inscription dated 1593: Klesse/Saldern 1978, no. 266 and 268 with col. ill.).
For the hunting motif compare with those mentioned under cat. nos. 45 and 46, and a barrel-shaped glass dated 1588 with stag hunt and arms of *Anna von Freidenbergk geborne von Druppach* in the Kestner Museum, Hanover (Mosel 1957, no. 72, ill; 1979, no. 80 with cover ill.). Robert Schmidt (1922, p. 176) suggests an origin in the Bayerische Wald for this glass, in view of the geographical origins of the two families (Friedenberg from Bavaria, Trupbach from Upper Franconia), a suggestion which he himself poses without great conviction.

## 48 ARMORIAL STANGENGLAS OF LORENZO BILLER AND BARBARA ZEILNERIN

Southern Germany or Hall in Tyrol, about 1560–1580

Height: 29.2 cm; diameter at rim: 7.8 cm; thickness of glass: about 2.5 mm

Smoky-gray glass with enamel and gilt decoration. Unpolished pontil mark.

Tall, cylindrical body with slightly convex sides on a high conical foot with spreading, folded rim, and gilt band at the join. Body enameled with opposed coats-of-arms. On one side the arms of the Augsburg family of Biller (on a black shield three peaks or, below three vertically arranged stars or, crest with three peaks or, surmounted by a star or between black horns, black and gold mantling) surmounted by the name in capitals "LORENZO BILLER." The reverse with the arms of the Augsburg family of Zeilner (gules: a camel argent; crest: a demi-camel between horns, with red and silver mantling) with name above in capitals "BARBARA ZEILNERIN." Rim embellished with white dots flanking a border of gilt scales superimposed with blue dots.

The Augsburg origin of the arms has been identified thanks to Irene Stahl, Nuremberg (by letter, 24 March 1984) with reference to Johann Siebmacher's *Genealogical Tables* (for Biller see: *Bürgerliche Wappen*, vol. V, 5, pl. 6; for Zeilner see: *Abgestorbener Bayerischer Adel*, VI, 1, III, pl. 103). Here Siebmacher comments on the unusual heraldic animal of the Zeilner family: "... of Augsburg stock, questionably descended from one Dietegen Zeyllner, a porter who according to family tradition delivered a camel from King Stephen of Hungary to the Emperor Henry II, for which he received a grant of arms (27 Feb. 1015). Johann Zeilner received a grant of arms in Augsburg from the Emperor Charles V (Regensburg 14 May 1546)." As opposed to members of the renowned Augsburg family of goldsmiths with the recorded name of Lorenz Biller in the seventeenth and eighteenth centuries, no information has been uncovered concerning the owner of this *Stangen*: Helmut Rischert from the Augsburg City Archives was unable to find any trace of an alliance between Lorenz Biller and Barbara Zeilner in the official marriage records (by letter 18 April 1984).

This glass belongs to a large group of armorial *Humpen*, which Robert Schmidt originally dated between 1550 and 1605 as being of Venetian manufacture for the German market (*Die venezianischen Emailgläser des XV. und XVI. Jahrhunderts* in: Jahrbuch d. Kgl. Preuss. Kunstsammlungen 32, 1911, pp. 284–286). If Robert Schmidt later felt that only the glass was Venetian and the decoration executed in Southern Germany (1926, p. 24, no. 71, pl. 8; 1927, pl. 27b), Ludwig Fuchs places the origins of this group firmly in the area of Southern Germany ("Die frühen süddeutschen Wappenhumpen" in: *Münchner Jahrbuch d. bild. Kunst* N. F. XII, 1937/38, pp. 219–232). This attribution is reinforced by A. von Saldern (1965, pp. 40 onwards, figs. 16, 18, 20, 22, 25–28; Klesse/Saldern, 1978, p. 287, no. 262 and 263, with reference to all important parallels), who, based on the origins of the armorial families depicted, suggests glass-making centers practising *façon de Venise* techniques in the Tyrol, Bavaria or Bohemia. More recently Rainer Rückert has suggested a possible Hall in Tyrol provenance, based on the example inscribed "Michiel Merz" in the Bayerisches Nationalmuseum (1982, I, no. 155, pl. 40, col. pl. VII).

The Italian form of the christian name "Lorenzo" (for Lorenz Biller) is also found on the *Humpen* of "Michiel" (for Michael Merz) as well as the London *Stangen* of "Roccho" (for Rochus) Grasl (Honey 1946, p. 61, pl. 248). Perhaps it is only a reminder of a contemporary Italian sojourn, which the missing marriage reference in the contempory marriage records would clarify (see also above, p. 39, fig. 55).

LORENZO BILLER
ZEILNERIN

BARBARA ZEILNERIN
NZO BILLER

## 49 ANHALT AND MANSFELD ARMORIAL HUMPEN

Saxony, Erzgebirge, dated 1591

Height: 23.5 cm; diameter at rim: 9 cm; thickness of glass: about 3–4 mm

Yellow-greenish tinted glass strongly striated, with enamel and gilt decoration. Unpolished pontil mark. Gilding mostly rubbed. Enamel chipped on the Mansfeld crest.

Provenance: Friedrich Neuburg Collection, Dresden/Leitmeritz; before that the collection of the Dukes of Anhalt-Dessau at Schloss Dessau.

Cylindrical body, with kick to base, slightly narrowing towards the rim, supported on an applied foot ring decorated with three rows of dots in white, blue, and green, originally on a gilt band. Sides painted in colors with the opposed arms of Anhalt and Mansfeld: the central upper field of the Anhalt arms overpainted to hide an original incorrect quartering (particularly obvious on the inside). On either side of these armorials the divided date in white "1·5·/·9·1," above and below, a five-pointed, erased star. Rim embellished with almost completely rubbed gilt scale border with green dots, flanked by double rows of white and blue dots. The relevance of the armorials was first clarified by Robert Schmidt: "The *Humpen* was painted for Duke Johann Georg I of Anhalt, who ruled over the whole of Anhalt from 1586, and after the 1603 partition with his brother, only Anhalt-Dessau, dying in 1618. His first wife was Dorothee, daughter of Count Albert von Mansfeld-Arnstein, she dying in 1594." (1931, p. 44, no. 43)
Compare with an armorial *Humpen* which corresponds to the Wolf *Humpen* in color, form and scale border, also painted for Duke Johann Georg I von Anhalt-Dessau (1567–1618) and his second wife Dorothea, born a princess of the Pfalz (1581–1631) bearing the date 1611, in the Reiss-Museum, Mannheim (Saldern 1965, p. 30, fig. 4; see also above, p. 39, fig. 57). A further *Humpen* of 1608, painted for Johann Georg I of Anhalt-Dessau, and now in the Bayerisches Nationalmuseum, Munich, is decorated with the Anhalt arms only (Rückert 1982, I, no. 166, pl. 45).

This *Humpen* belongs to a group of armorial glasses from the Saxon Erzgebirge, which, on the one hand are either heraldically connected with Saxony, or on the other, atypical of Bohemian products in their greenish-yellowish tones and impure seeded glass.
Within this group, the Wolf *Humpen* appears to be one of the earliest examples. Then follows the group of glasses from Schloss Moritzburg, now in the Dresden Museum für Kunsthandwerk, Schloss Pillnitz, all dated between 1604 and 1612, and painted with various ducal Saxon coats-of-arms (Haase 1975, no. 2–5, ill.), in which group the armorial *Humpen* of Hans Georg, Duke of Sachsen-Merseburg (1585–1656, Elector from 1611) must also be included. Dating from 1604, the year of his marriage to Sibylle Elisabeth of Württemberg, it is now in the Collections of the Veste Coburg (Schmidt 1922, p. 199; Baumgärtner 1977, p. 42, fig. 11). See also the *Humpen* of Hans Richelman with a long "welcome" inscription, the arms of the town of Celle and date 1613 (Saldern 1965, fig. 197; Mosel 1979, no. 84, ill.).
Only differing from this group in the purer glass is an armorial *Humpen* for Johann Wilhelm von Sachsen-Weimar (1554–1573) in the Art Collections in Weimar (before 1573: Hörning o. J. [1979], no. 35, ill.), another for Count Schönburg-Waldenburg and his wife, born Schenk von Landsberg, in the Kunstgewerbemuseum, Cologne, (dated 1595: Cologne 1963, no. 238, ill.; 1973, no. 330, ill.; Baumgärtner 1977, pp. 42–43, fig. 10), one for Johann von Sachsen-Weimar (1573–1605) in the Gotha Museum (dated 1597: Schmidt 1922, p. 199), as well as one for the Pfalzgraf Otto Heinrich II von Sulzbach (1556–1604) in the Bayerisches Nationalmuseum, Munich (dated 1596: Saldern 1965, fig. 199; Rückert 1982, I, no. 162 and 163, pl. 43).

Lit.: Schmidt Ms 1931, p. 44, no. 43 (as "Central Germany").

## 50  EQUESTRIAN AND ARMORIAL HUMPEN

Saxony, dated 1601

Height: 34.7 cm; diameter at rim: 11.2 cm; thickness of glass: about 3–4.5 mm

Light-green, seeded glass with enamel and gilt decoration, unpolished pontil mark; gilding completely rubbed. Enameled inscription chipped in places.

Tall cylindrical body with kick to base and applied foot ring decorated with three rows of blue and white enamel dots, originally on a gilt band (rubbed off). The sides painted in colors with a gentleman in contemporary dress on a rearing bay horse, holding out in his right hand a covered *Humpen* with the monogram "CH" and a coat-of-arms. On the reverse the arms of the town of Halle (on a silver shield a crescent moon between two red stars, crest with moon and star and red-and-silver mantling) surmounted by the date "1601," in between a large silver-and-gold star-in-splendor. Above and below are inscriptions in white capitals flanked by gilt bands (erased) embellished with blue and white dots: the upper inscription reads "HOC · VITRVM · PRIMO · SI · MENSAE · ASSEDERIS · HOSPES," and the lower, "EBIBE · SIC · PATRIAE · LEX · SOCIALIS · HABET." The uppermost gilt band is in scale form with green dots.

The identification of the armorials was first noted by Ottfried Neubecker, Wiesbaden/Stuttgart, (see Otto Hupp, *Wappen und Siegel der deutschen Städte*, 3. Heft, Prov. Sachsen und Schleswig-Holstein, Frankfurt a. M. 1903, p. 32).
The director of the Halle town archives, Piechocki, must be thanked for his identification of the arms on the covered *Humpen* in the rider's right hand with monogram "C H." They are for the "old established Halle family of Herold. The councillor Carl Herold ... died on the 16 April 1637, aged sixty three" (by letter of 25 September 1984). In 1601 Halle played host for a *gemein Land- und Spahn-Vogelschiessen* from 3 August to 5 September. Fifty towns from Saxony and Thuringia and altogether three hundred and thirty people too part in this shooting competition. Carl Herold can be proved to have been a participant – and in-

deed a winner – an event which this *Humpen* no doubt commemorates (see Johann Christian Hendel, *Archiv für deutsche Schützengesellschaften*, vol. II, Halle an der Saale, 1801, pp. 87–132, viz. p. 130) – (further see above, p. 40, fig. 58).
Compare the form and characteristics of the decoration with a series of originally eight *Humpen* of 1617, each with single figures of the Holy Roman Emperor and mounted electors, in the Museum für Kunsthandwerk, Dresden, Schloss Pillnitz, on permanent loan from the Historisches Museum, Dresden (Saldern 1965, p. 77, fig. 75; Haase 1975, no. 6, ill.; Baumgärtner 1977, pp. 41–42, fig. 7).

...NSÆ ASSEDERIS HOSPE...

· 1 · 6 · 0 · 1 ·

...SOCIALIS HABET...

...HOC VITRVM PRIMO...

...EBIBE SIC PATRIA...

## 51 COVERED HUMPEN WITH VIEW OF SCHLOSS COSWIG ON THE ELBE

Saxony, Jugel Glasshouse (?), dated 1676

Height: 41 cm (with cover), 31.2 cm (without cover); diameter at rim: 12 cm; thickness of glass: about 3 mm *(Humpen)*, 2 mm (cover)

Pale, yellow-brownish glass with enameled and gilt decoration. Unpolished pontil mark; gilding partly rubbed.

Provenance: Collection of the Dukes of Anhalt-Dessau, Schloss Dessau.

Tall, cylindrical body with kick to base, with applied foot ring decorated with a white enamel, splash border. Sides painted in tones of red-brown, white, gray, and pale pink with black-line outlines, with a bird's-eye view of Schloss Coswig on the Elbe, showing the quadrangular building with inner paved courtyard with central fountain, facade with Renaissance gables, and hexagonal staircase tower. Reverse inscribed in white, angular calligraphy with eight-part inscription: "Mit massen Trincke mich, / So bin ich recht vor dich, / Die weisheit vnd die Sorgen, / Sindt in mir Verborgen, / Ich hege Lust vnd Leidt, / ich gebe fried vnd streidt, / Vnd mache soll ichß melden, / Viel betler vnd viel Helden, / 1676," with gilt lozenges embellished with enameled swirls above and below. Cover with everted rim also decorated with gilt lozenges and finial supported on a ribbed flattened knop.

In view of the decorative subject matter, this *Humpen* was probably intended for the Hofkellerei at Schloss Coswig. After the destruction of the old castle at Coswig during the campaign of the league of Schmalkald, rebuilding had commenced from 1555 onwards, and a further program of extension and modernization, following the old ground plan, took place from 1667–1677. The terrace on the banks of the river connecting the two massive corner pavillions was obviously finished by 1676, as is indicated on the glass itself. Except in a few details, such as the omission of the fountain, the view of the castle on the glass corresponds to an engraving (see above, p. 41, fig. 60) in Johann Christoph Beckmann, *Historie Des Fürstenthums Anhalt Von Dessen Alten Einwohnern und einigen annoch verhandenen Alten Monumenten ...*, Zerbst 1710, p. 310 onwards. This information was kindly supplied by Hans-Joachim Krause of Leipzig (by letter, 21 February 1986 and 14 May 1986). To him I am also indebted for the information concerning the gallery, still in existence, which was built over the terrace, connecting the corner pavillions. This was constructed at the time of the castle's conversion to a prison in 1874 (see also Ernst Werner, *Geschichte der Stadt Coswig in Anhalt*, Coswig 1929, 3rd revised ed., pp. 55–56).

See also other views of castles on Saxon *Hofkellereihumpen* in: the Focke Museum, Bremen (with Veste Königstein, dated 1638: Baumgärtner 1977, fig. 20); the Museum für Kunsthandwerk, Schloss Pillnitz (with Veste Königstein, dated 1638: Saldern 1965, fig. 370; another with the castle at Dresden, dated 1688: Saldern 1965, fig. 371 and Baumgärtner 1977, fig. 27 as well as one with Schloss Torgau, dated 1688: Haase 1975, no. 49, ill.). In contrast to the afore-mentioned examples, the Wolf *Humpen* lacks the conspicuous light green used in their decoration. On each, the coat-of-arms has been left out, and the subsidiary decorative motifs more sparingly applied.
This would certainly suggest a different painter, and possibly also a different glasshouse from the chronologically closely-related examples at Pillnitz.
The *Hofkellerei* glasses painted with a view of "Bergkvehstung Königstein" mentioned above, and bearing the mark of the owner of the Jugel Glasshouse, Christoph Löbels von Platten (CLvP), are dated 1638, and in view of the earlier date can only be loosely connected from a stylistic point of view, with the glasses above (Baumgärtner 1977, pp. 46–48).

Mit maßen Trincke mich,
So bin ich recht vor dich,
Die weißheit vnd die Sorgen,
Sindt in mir Verborgen,
Ich hege lust vnd leidt,
ich gebe fried vnd streidt,
Vnd mache soll ichs melden,
Viel betler vnd viel Helden.

1 6 7 6.

## 52 TWO ENAMELED HALLOREN GLASSES

Saxony, dated 1695

a) Height: 39.3 cm (with cover), 30.9 cm (without cover); diameter at rim: 10.5 cm;
b) Height: 38.9 cm (with cover), 29.7 cm (without cover); diameter at rim: 10.6 cm;
thickness of glass: a) about 2–3 mm (*Humpen*), about 1.5–2 mm (cover)
b) about 2 mm (*Humpen*), about 1.5–2 mm (cover).

Colorless glass with enameled and gilt decoration. Unpolished pontil mark. a) Cracked base. Gilding considerably rubbed.

Provenance: Collection of the Dukes of Anhalt-Dessau, Schloss Dessau.

Tall, cylindrical body slightly swelling towards the rim, with kicked-in base and doubled, everted foot with border of vertical white stripes below a foliate wreath. The decoration of the sides is divided into three zones by colored line borders. The lowest one is infilled with a band of pendant anthemia below a swirling foliate band; the middle section is painted in colors with the arms of the Salt-panners Guild of Halle, supported by two salt workers crowned with flowers, and dressed in short white tunics, behind them crossed shovels painted yellow and the date in white "1695." On the reverse stands a standard bearer in black doublet and gray hose, bearing a blue-and-white flag with the arms of Brandenburg, above, gilt lozenges embellished with swirls in white. The uppermost zone is decorated with a continuous townscape of Halle itself in imbricated gilding, now only partially visible. Low cover with everted rim and band of white radials, and with multiple white line borders, with pendant anthemia and a band of red, blue, and yellow lily of the valley florettes. Knopped finial also decorated with white radials.

This belongs to group "3" within Robert Schmidt's suggested classification of Halle glasses, a group which is dated between 1693 and 1708 (Schmidt 1922, p. 207). Compare with a very similar glass, also dated 1695, in The Corning Museum of Glass, Corning (Saldern 1965, p. 211, cat. no. 83, ill.). W. Spiegl's hypothesis that the Corning glass is a late nineteenth-century copy cannot be substantiated, as the black and white pattern books of Fritz Heckert of Petersdorf, discovered in the Bayerisches Nationalmuseum, give no guide to color (Spiegl 1980, p. 258, fig. 274). Also his reference to the incorrect date of "31. (sic!) Juni," previously noted by Robert Schmidt, on two Halle glasses of this type, one formerly in Berlin (Schmidt 1922, fig. 112) and in Chicago (Schmidt 1926, no. 96; Strasser 1979, no. 27, ill.) still does not disprove the authenticity of this glass. Mistakes in spelling and numbers were frequent in the seventeenth and eighteenth centuries. The "31. Januarius" which appears on a parallel example published by W. Bernt (1950, no. 43a, ill.) can be shown to be a mistake (it should read "Junius"), as the annual corporate festival in Halle, in which the Salt Panners took part – marching to the "Thalamtshaus" at Pentecost – which usually falls in June.

Any doubts as to the genuineness of the cover, which might arise from comparison with a parallel example, dated 1697 in anonymous ownership (Saldern 1968, no. 160, ill.) as well as Robert Schmidt's list of characteristics for the third group of Halle glasses (1922, p. 207), should be allayed when a comparison is made with the similarly-decorated cover of a 1708 dated example in The Corning Museum of Glass, Corning, Strauss Collection (Strauss 1955, no. 175, with col. pl.) and the one formerly in the Krug Collection, Baden-Baden (Klesse 1973, no. 529, ill.; Sotheby's Krug II, lot no. 288, with col. pl.).

Lit.: Schmidt 1922, p. 207 ("Dessau, Schloß")

## 53   TUMBLER WITH BEAR HUNT

Franconia, possibly Fichtelgebirge, last quarter 17ᵗʰ century

Height: 7.3 cm; diameter: 8.2 cm;
thickness of glass: about 2 mm

Colorless glass with white enamel and *Schwarzlot* decoration. Unpolished pontil mark.

Provenance: Friedrich Neuburg Collection, Dresden/Leitmeritz.
Previously Dr. Max Strauss Collection, Vienna.

Slightly-flared, low sides with small kick to base; painted with a continuous scene of a bear hunt in a wooded landscape, the animal brought to bay, surrounded by hounds, a huntsman at his feet, whose spear he is breaking, while another huntsman attacks from the rear. A third huntsman blows a horn for help, and a mounted huntsman dashes toward the scene with drawn sword. Small, yellow painted patch overpainted with a bird in flight.

The hunting motifs, for which as yet no direct engraved source has been found, are in style and content very close to the bear-hunting prints of Virgil Solis.
This tumbler is one of a distinct group of small, cylindrical glasses of beaker type with white enameled decoration, stylistically connected and possibly from the same workshop, for which see: a beaker in the Kunstgewerbemuseum, Prague (Saldern 1965, fig. 271) with similar stylized trees, the terrain formed of similar small regular mounds. Another in the Bayerisches Nationalmuseum, Munich (Rückert 1982, I, no. 190, pl. 56) is decorated with a bear hunt among trees of similar form. There is a beaker with bear hunt dated 1679 in the Kestner Museum, Hanover (Mosel 1957, no. 86, and 1979, no. 91, ill.). The beaker form, known to Nuremberg *Hausmalers* and engravers of the second half of the seventeenth century suggests a Franconian origin (see also Drahotová 1982, fig. 54).
A more indirect comparison is with a double-handled, armorial *Humpen* with enameled stag and bear hunt in the Museum of Fine Arts, Boston (JGS II, 1960, p. 142, no. 23, ill.) as well as two conical beakers, also decorated in white with black outlines, one with bear

hunt frieze beneath fruit festoons in the Kunstgewerbemuseum, Prague (Prague 1970, no. 86, ill.), the other with boar hunt within an oval medallion dated 1691 in the Museum für Kunsthandwerk, Frankfurt a. M. (Ohm 1973, no. 340, ill.). For the origins of the Frankfurt beaker, Sabine Baumgärtner has put forward a convincing argument for the glasshouse of Steindöbra near Klingenthal in the Saxon Vogtland (1977, p. 51, fig. 37), an area which borders on the Franconian glassmaking region.

Lit.: Robert Schmidt among others, *Kunstschätze der Sammlung Dr. Max Strauss in Wien*, Vienna 1920, pl. 18; Auction cat. *Dr. Max Strauss, Glückselig und Wärndörfer*, Vienna, Jan. 1922, lot 13, ill.; Schmidt Ms. 1931, p. 49, no. 55 (described as "German, second half 17ᵗʰ century").

## 54  CHINOISERIE GOBLET

Central Germany or Venice, first third 18th century

Height: 14.5 cm; diameter at rim: 6 cm;
thickness of glass: about 1 mm

Colorless glass with gilt, highlighted, cold painting
and shallow, matt engraving. Unpolished pontil mark.
Cold painting and gilding partly rubbed.

On a conical foot with folded rim, decorated on the
upper side with cold-painted, foliate wreath and line
border in gilt (partly rubbed) over bole-red and olive
green, molded hexagonal pedestal stem and funnel
bowl decorated in the same tones with three chinoise-
rie figures with pink faces, and wearing green robes,
on a continuous band, the rim with foliate and floral
border below an engraved zig-zag band.

From a distinct group which includes goblets, beakers,
cups and saucers and other wares with unmistakable
decoration of Negroes, Indians and Turks in chinoise-
rie style in tones of muddy green, red and brown highlighted in gilt.

Compare with similar glasses in: the former Friedrich
Neuburg Collection, Dresden/Leitmeritz (Schmidt Ms.
1931, no. 71; from the Consul Rosenberg Collection:
Auction cat. Lepke, Berlin, 1919, lot no. 660); the Victoria and Albert Museum, London (with von Questen-
berg arms: Auction cat. Sotheby's, London, 26 June
1978, p. 42); formerly in the Erskine Sharpe Collection (Auction cat. Sotheby's London, 26 June 1978,
lots 27–28, ill.); the Kunstgewerbemuseum, Prague
(Inv. no. 10050, from the Freiherr Adalbert von Lanna
Collection).
From the same workshop comes a flask at one time in
the art market (formerly Mühsam Collection: Schmidt
1926, no. 114, ill. p. 32); two beakers in the Victoria
and Albert Museum, London, and another formerly in
the Erskine Sharpe Collection (auction cat. Sotheby's,
London, 26 June 1978, pp. 42–43, lot no. 29 with col.
ill.); a cup and saucer in the Museo Vetrario, Venice
(Lorenzetti 1953, p. 47, pl. XXXIIIa); a beaker in the
Metropolitan Museum of Art, New York (Inv. no.
91.1.1437); another beaker in the Strasser Collection,
Pelham Manor, N. Y.; three cups in the Kunstgewerbemuseum, Prague (from the Freiherr Adalbert von
Lanna Collection: Inv. No. 458, 10045 and 10046);
and a teapot and faceted beaker in the Österreichisches Museum für angewandte Kunst, Vienna (Inv.
no. G1 1346 and G1 1338).
A glass from this group was first mentioned by Robert
Schmidt in the second volume of his publication of the
Mühsam Collection 1926, p. 26, no. 114). With reference to a glass in the Neuburg Collection, he discuss-
es the complex problem of attribution (Ms 1931,
pp. 54–55). He finds his earlier conjecture, that these
glasses might have originated in Austria, strengthened
on the grounds of the arms of the Austrian noble family of Althann painted on the New York cup mentioned
above. The further appearance of armorials on glasses
in London and Vienna has not affected this theory. A
Thuringian origin was suggested for the three examples in the Erskine Sharpe Collection, in view of the
stem formation (Auction cat. Sotheby's, London, 26
June 1978, pp. 42–43). As yet no convincing hypothesis for the origins of this group has been formula-
ted (for the closest parallels see above, pp. 42–43,
figs. 61–64).

## 55   BOWL WITH GILT-METAL MOUNTS
## AND PAPER CUT-OUTS

South Germany, second quarter 17th century

Height: 6.5 cm; diameter: 36.2 cm;
thickness of glass: about 2 mm (single wall), 4 mm
(double wall)

Colorless glass panels with beveled edges and painted
paper insertions; gilt bronze mounts with glass beads.
Two panels cracked; a few paper insertions disfigured
by damp; gilt bronze filigree mount broken in one
area; a few beads missing.


On low, gilt-metal foot, octagonal bowl with upturned
rim, consisting of a central rosette of panels within a
broad octagonal band of octagonal panels, all of two
beveled layers of glass with cut-out paper insertions
painted in polychrome; the central octagonal panel
with Orpheus beneath a tree, playing the violin to an
audience of animals; the surrounding arched panels,
each with a single bird and flower or fruit spray; the
outer trapezoidal panels with alternate flower sprays
with butterflies or large bowls of fruit flanked by furry
animals or birds, the interstices with butterflies,
beetles, and other insects. Flat rim composed of a net-
work of scrolls with eight, small, oval glass panels, and
various colored applied glass beads arranged at casual,
rythmical intervals.

Compare with a similar, but much richer bowl in the
Kunsthistorisches Museum, Vienna (Inv. no. 926). In
this case, the panels are of rock crystal, also with paper
insertions painted with flowers. These are more delicate than those on the Wolf bowl, and on more graceful thin stems, while small animals are included only
on the outer border. The silver-gilt framework is
much broader and more elaborate, as well as being
partly enameled and set with one hundred and twelve
rubies and two hundred pearls.
Rudolf Distelberger has kindly pointed out (in a letter
of 3 December 1985) that an early seventeenth century commentary of the Vienna bowl by Philipp Hainhofer in Innsbruck, has survived (O. Döring, *Des
Augsburger Patriziers Philipp Hainhofer Reisen nach
Innsbruck und Dresden*, Vienna 1901, p. 43).

The notable similarities between these two pieces, in the use of the rare technique of paper insertions sandwiched between transparent panels, and the combination of rosette and octagon framework, suggests the possibility that the Wolf bowl was a simplified imitation of the piece from the Imperial Collection. Rudolf Distelberger also suggests a dating within the second quarter of the seventeenth century on stylistic grounds. As the Vienna bowl was in Innsbruck by that time, it is probable that the maker of the Wolf bowl would have been based in South Germany.

See also a number of smaller, simpler, and unmounted glass plates with applied flowers of painted and cut-out paper, among others, in the Germanisches Nationalmuseum (Inv. no. Gl 3 – labeled "German or Bohemian, circa 1600").

## 58 ENAMELED AND GILT SCENT BOTTLE WITH EXOTIC BIRD

England, possibly London, about 1765–1770

Height: 8.5 cm (with gold cap);
thickness of glass: about 2.5 mm (at rim)

Deep-blue tinted glass, cut, enameled, and gilt. Gold mount partly enameled in white. Small chips to enamel on flask. Enamel on cap partly missing.

Provenance: Steuben Antique Collection, New York City.

Compressed, rectangular, shouldered body with polished, flat base and small, cylindrical neck with inner fitted stopper and chased, gold screw cap, inscribed in white enamel round the base in capitals "J'AIME ... LA VERTU." Entire surface cut with shallow diamonds with superimposed enamel and gilt decoration in white, orange, red, and violet. One side is painted with an exotic crane-like bird flanked by trees and flowering shrubs, in the background two floating "islands" with church and houses; the reverse with large gilt flower spray, a butterfly hovering above it. Shoulders and stopper with gilt leaves.

See parallels with similar exotic birds in: The Corning Museum of Glass, Corning (D. C. Davis and K. Middlemas, *Coloured Glass*, London 1968, ill. p. 101, described as "probably Bristol"); the Victoria and Albert Museum, London (Thorpe 1929, I, p. 226, II, pl. CXXXIV, ascribed to Bristol; Savage 1965, fig. 127, as "Bristol, about 1780"; Wills 1968, section "18th Century Coloured Glass," p. 8, fig. 6 as "Bristol blue"). The stylistic similarities in the enameled details, particularly the birds and butterflies, trees, shrubs and little islands, as well as the gilding, strengthen the likelihood that these bottles were decorated in the same atelier as the Wolf example.
R. J. Charleston has argued on convincing grounds that the manufacture of these cut scent bottles, as well as other small toilet accessories belonging to the same group, can be pinpointed to Birmingham (1984, p. 189). On the other hand his opinion of the characteristics of the enameled decoration inclines rather to a London origin.

The atelier of James Giles in London obviously received the undecorated, cut blue flasks from the same source; either Birmingham or London (see Newman 1977, ill. p. 111; R. J. Charleston, "James Giles as a decorator of Glass," part II, in: *The Connoisseur*, 162, no. 653, July 1966, pp. 176 ff., figs. 19–26; see also Charleston, 1984, pp. 189–191). Compared to this, the examples from Giles's workshop decorated with gilding alone, as suggested by R. J. Charleston, display a more elegant and more mechanical style, despite superficial similarities such as exotic birds, twiggy trees and luxuriant flower sprays. Giles himself expressly mentions the use of enamel as well as gilding in his advertisement: "curiously enamelled in figures, Birds, Flowers & c., and ornamented with Mazarine and Sky Blue and Gold ..." (quoted from W. B. Honey, "The Work of James Giles," in: *Transactions of the English Ceramic Circle*, I, no. 5, 1937, p. 10), still the decisive stylistic similarities with this group of scent flasks are lacking. On the other hand, it is highly likely that one must seek their origins somewhere close to the atelier of James Giles.

## 59  BEAKER WITH GYPSY PROCESSION

Nuremberg, Johann Schaper, signed and dated 1666

Height: 10.5 cm; diameter at rim: 8.8 cm;
thickness of glass: about 2 mm

Colorless glass with black and transparent colored
enamels. Unpolished pontil mark.

Provenance: formerly Richard von Passavant-Gontard
Collection, Frankurt a. M.; prior to that Freiherr Adalbert von Lanna Collection, Prague.

Cylindrical, almost straight-sided body supported on
three flattened, hollow, bun feet. Sides painted with a
continuous gypsy procession comprising two front riders, one with a child up behind him in the saddle, followed by a musketeer on foot leading a single,
mounted, female gypsy and small children, followed
by two further mounted gypsy mothers with children
and household utensils. At one point a stunted tree at
the base of which is inscribed in Roman capitals
"JOH. SCHAPER 1666"; landscape and horses in
tones of gray and brown; garments in strong tones of
red, blue, violet, yellow, and green, with isolated
touches of turquoise.

The printed source for this scene is taken from the
series of engravings *Lés Bohemiens* (The Gypsies)
by Jacques Callot, published in 1621 (Lieure 375,
Meaume 668; see above, p. 47, fig. 66). Schaper has reversed the engraved source and heightened the artistic
effects by emphasizing the details of costume and
headdress. He has also omitted the intrusive small figures which occupy the background in the Callot engraving, thus creating a calmer, more two-dimension-
al blackish-brown landscape effect, in which the nuances of gray and brown of the horses act as a magnifi-
cent foil to the colored gypsy costumes, in particular
the cloak-like draperies of the women.
In the 1660s, Schaper used a number of motifs from
Callot's gypsy series. The beaker formerly in the Biemann Collection, Zurich (Klesse/Saldern 1978,
pp. 11–12, ill., no. 70 with col. pl.; Sotheby's Biemann, lot no. 94, ill.) is decorated with a different
grouping of figures from the Lieure page 374 (Meaume

667), while another in the Museum für Kunsthandwerk, Leipzig (Kämpfer 1966, fig. 133, 134 with text;
Schade 1968, pp. 54–55, 215 pl. 35) is also in polychrome, and in the flat brushwork is stylistically closest to the Wolf beaker.

Lit.: Auction cat. Lanna 1911, no. 838, pl. 67 and D; Pazaurek
1925, pp. 8 and 10; G. Swarzenski, *Sammlung R. von Passavant-
Gontard*, Frankfurt a. M. 1929 (Third opening of the Staedelschen
Kunstinstitut) no. 280, pl. 78; Klesse/Saldern, 1978, p. 126; Bosch,
1984, no. 60, col. pl.

## 60 SCHWARZLOT COVERED BEAKER DECORATED WITH BIRD-CATCHERS

Nuremberg, possibly Hermann Benckert, about 1677–1681

Height: 18.7 cm (with cover), 10.3 cm (without cover); diameter at rim: 8.9 cm; thickness of glass: about 2 mm

Colorless glass with *Schwarzlot* decoration. Unpolished pontil mark. Body with multiple cracks and small section restuck at rim. Cover decorated by the same hand, but not original.

Provenance: formerly in the Friedrich Neuburg Collection, Dresden/Leitmeritz; formerly Dr. Spitzner Collection, Dresden (lit. Pazaurek 1925 and Schmidt 1931, not included in auc. cat. 1918).

Cylindrical, straight-sided body supported on three, hollow, flattened, bun feet. Sides decorated in black fading to gray wash enamel with a scene of bird-catchers: a continuous scene in a hilly landscape; in the foreground a seated couple with a girl standing behind them with a bird in her hands and wicker birdcage. Also two men hidden behind trees with wicker cage and ropes attached to large nets in the valley below. On one side on the base an imbricated monogram " J. Sch." and on the other in capital letters "IOH. SCHAPER." Domed cover with everted rim, painted with a rope band embellished with fruiting vine. Knopped finial.

The bird-catcher motif is taken from a series of engraved hunting scenes after Matthäus Merian the Elder (1593–1651) published in 1616/17 (Wüthrich, 1966, I, p. 52, no. 235, fig. 114; see above, p. 48, fig. 68). The groups of figures on either side of this composition were borrowed by Merian from two different hunting scenes by Antonio Tempesta from a hunting series of 1600 (B. 1063 and 1073; see *The Illustrated Bartsch*, vol 36, New York 1983, ill. p. 307 and 317).

Both the monogram and full signature are considered later additions with the view to deceive. Concerning such pseudo-Schaper signatures there has already been a reference made by August Demmin (*Das Glas, dessen Geschichte und Werkweise*, Keramik-Studien IV, Leipzig 1883, p. 56). Pazaurek (1925), Schmidt (1931) and Bosch (1984) have all doubted the monogram-signature. While Pazaurek supposes there could have been a contemporary monogrammist "J. Sch." who could be shown on stylistic grounds to have nothing to do with Johann Schaper, and Schmidt (1931) suggests that this monogram stands for "an as yet unknown follower of the Nuremberg artist," for Bosch the monogram is simply "from a later period." This last opinion would seem all the more likely, when it is noted that the letters, instead of being intertwined as in the genuine Schaper signature, are each separated by a period, a nineteenth century calligraphic stylistic. Bosch attributes the decoration to Hermann Benckert, a suggestion which has much to recommend it. Benckert's style is conspicuous in its use of the standing female figure, which appears on the "bird-catchers" beaker. The fruiting vine motif on the cover was also another favored by Benckert, in contrast to other Nuremberg painters (compare illustrations and similar examples above, p. 48, figs. 67–69).

Lit.: Pazaurek 1925, I, p. 7, notes, and p. 22; Schmidt Ms 1931, pp. 113–114, no. 107; Bosch 1984, no. 118, ill.

Bohemia or Silesia, in the manner of Ignatius Preissler, about 1730

Height: 11.8 cm; length: 9.9 cm;
thickness of glass: about 2–3 mm

Colorless glass with cutting, gilt and yellow-enamel highlighted *Schwarzlot* painting. Pontil mark polished.

Provenance: Friedrich Neuburg Collection, Dresden/Leitmeritz.

Octagonal foot with canted corners cut with basal rosette and *Schwarzlot* scroll border. Faceted baluster stem flanked by collars and painted with scrolls and pendant husks. Boat-shaped bowl with concave and convex panels. Sides painted with rich scrolls and ribbonwork (*Laub- und Bandlwerk*) inhabited by stags pursued by hounds, vases of flowers surmounted by birds, at each end framing a cartouche enclosing a couple at a table, the man playing a viol, the lady a viola, and a mounted huntsman with rifle over his shoulder beneath a baldequin.

Compare with a similar example with different vignettes in: the Victoria and Albert Museum, London (Buckley Collection: Schmidt 1927, p. 32, pl. 53A).

For similar scenes of music-makers on flasks of differing form, see examples in: the former Krug Collection, Baden-Baden (Klesse 1965, no. 143, ill.; Sotheby's Krug I, lot no. 78, ill.; Sotheby's Biemann, lot no. 97, ill.) and one formerly at Nagy-Csákány, Count Ivan Batthyány Collection (Pazaurek I, 1925, fig. 202).

Lit.: Schmidt Ms 1931, p. 124, no. 117 ("... which is stylistically very close to Ignaz Preissler ...").

## 70  HOLLOW-BALUSTER GOBLET ENGRAVED WITH DANIEL IN THE LIONS' DEN

Nuremberg, Hermann Schwinger, signed, about 1670

Height: 30 cm; diameter at rim: 10.5 cm; thickness of glass: about 2.5 mm

Colorless to slightly greenish glass with matt and small areas of polished wheel engraving. Unpolished pontil mark. Rings above the baluster damaged and cemented. Vertical crack at rim in the decorative field as well as small concavities (typical of the glass sickness of Nuremberg glasses).

Provenance: Friedrich Neuburg Collection, Dresden/Leitmeritz; prior to that Collection of Duke of Sachsen-Anhalt, Schloss Dessau.

Wide circular foot with folded rim. Stem with hollow baluster shaft below hollow, flattened knop interspersed with collars. Ovoid bowl with continuous engraved scene of Daniel seated in the lions' den with arched ruins and masonry in the background, the reverse with hilly landscape, in the foreground, reapers harvesting a cornfield, as well as a saint raised aloft by an angel. Signed on the base to the right of the lions' den "He. Schwinger."

The scene of the lions' den has been reversed and somewhat simplified after an engraving by Matthäus Merian the Elder, from illustrations for the Bible of 1627 (Book of Daniel, Chapter 6; see above, p. 55, fig. 81). Hermann Schwinger has only diverged from the Merian original in the shape of Daniel's head and his stance as well as a few architectural details. The glass engraver has also, for lack of space, omitted the background group of King Darius and his false councillors sealing up the entrance to the den.

Of the fifteen signed glasses of Hermann Schwinger published by Meyer-Heisig (1963), this is the only one decorated with a religious scene, except for the well-known St. Christopher goblet formerly in the Mühsam Collection, now in the Metropolitan Museum, New York (Schmidt 1914, no. 81, pl. 11; Meyer-Heisig 1963, WT 83, ill.). Not only on iconographical, but also on stylistic grounds, the Wolf goblet appears close in date to the 1669 St. Christopher goblet, as Robert Schmidt has already suggested (Ms 1931).

Lit.: Hampe 1919, p. 33; Schmidt 1922, p. 249; Idem Ms 1931, pp. 193–194, no. 181; Bernt 1933, p. 44; Meyer-Heisig 1963, p. 57, W 90.

J. Herman Schwinger.
Crÿstall-schneider.

Vivat
Leopoldus
Vivat.

## 72 HOLLOW-BALUSTER GOBLET WITH PORTRAIT OF THE WURZBURG PRINCE-BISHOP

Nuremberg, possibly Heinrich Schwanhardt, about 1684

Height: 29.2 cm; diameter at rim: 9.3 cm; thickness of glass: about 2 mm

Colorless glass with matt and polished engraving as well as diamond-point engraving. Unpolished pontil mark. Foot broken and cemented. Bowl slightly crizzled.

Provenance: Theodor Wiskott Collection, Breslau.

Wide, conical foot with folded rim. Upperside decorated with meander of fruiting vine, inscribed round the rim "Aus diesem Pokal trank Fürstbischof Robert beim Mittagmahl im Hause Th. Wiskott, Breslau d. 21. Februar 1884." Tall stem with lower, inverted, hollow baluster and two higher, flattened, hollow knops separated by triads of collars. Bowl with slightly-flared sides and rounded base. Decorated on one side within an oval cartouche embellished with scrolls with a bust portrait in three-quarter profile to dexter of the Prince-Bishop Johann Gottfried von Guttenberg, on the reverse, within a tied palm-frond cartouche, the arms of Guttenberg flanked by the mirror monogram GJEH (Godefridus Joannes Episcopus Herbipolensis) beneath a princely crown and crossed sword and crozier.

The portrait was possibly taken from a contemporary engraving by the court and university engraver Johann Salver (1670–1738), which was mentioned later in the portrait collection of Anton Reinhard Franz Höfflings' *Philosophia Herbipolensis aeternae Episcoporum, S.R.I. Principum et Franciae Orientalis Ducum memoriae devota ...*, Würzburg 1712 (p. 69r) (see above, p. 57, fig. 86). The Diocesan archivist Erik Soder has pointed out that the princely crown of the Wurzburg Bishops represents their position as *Herzögen von Ostfranken* (Dukes of Eastern Franconia) (letter of 22 December 1983): "Crozier and sword symbolize the spiritual and temporal lordship of the Prince-Bishop, the latter most important as the Wurzburg Prince was also ducal incumbent of an Imperial *Landgericht* (provincial court), hence the expression: *Herbipolis sola iudicat ense cum stola.*"

Johann Gottfried von Guttenberg was born on 6 November 1645 at Schloss Marloffstein (diocese of Bamberg), and studied at the Universities of Wurzburg, Louvain, Vienna and Bamberg. In 1665 he was a member of the Imperial *Kammergericht* (law court) at Speyer, and on 16 October 1684 he was elevated from cathedral capitulary to Bishop of Wurzburg. He is remembered with gratitude for the number of new churches he built. He has also come down in history as a great mariolotrist. He died on 14 December 1698.

Taking into account the relevant dates, it follows that this goblet was commissioned between 1684 and 1698. Certain pronounced similarities with the Ampringen goblet by the elder Schwanhardt dated 1665 in the Kurpfälzisches Museum in Heidelberg (Schmidt 1922, fig. 136; Meyer-Heisig 1963, WT 51) make possible an attribution for this goblet to his son, Heinrich Schwanhardt who died in 1693 (see above, p. 57, fig. 87). However, the lack of signed pieces by Heinrich Schwanhardt prevents a firmer attribution.

The later commemorative inscription added to the foot of the Wolf goblet in 1884, refers to the Prince-Bishop of Breslau, Robert Herzog, in office from 1882–1886 (born 17 February 1823 in Schönwalde bei Frankenstein, died 26 December 1886 in Breslau, buried in Breslau Cathedral: E. Brzoska, *Neunhundertfünfzig Jahre Bistum Breslau*, Königstein i. T. 1951, p. 58). Perhaps the celebration took place in the Wiskott home on the occasion of the gathering of German Catholics in Breslau, reported in the 21 Febuary 1884 edition of *Der Volksfreund für Stadt und Land*, (13th annual vol., no. 9).

## 73 HOLLOW-BALUSTER GOBLET WITH PORTRAIT OF LEOPOLD I

Nuremberg, Johann Wolfgang Schmidt, about 1690–1700

Height: 43.4 cm (with cover), 30 cm; (without cover); diameter at rim: 10.8 cm;
thickness of glass: about 2.5 mm (bowl), 1.5 mm (cover)

Colorless to smoky glass with matt, and in parts lightly-polished engraving and polished ovals. Unpolished pontil mark. Small crack at the fourth uppermost collar. Cover not original. Marked on the base of foot in diamond point "No. 18."

Provenance: Friedrich Neuburg Collection, Dresden/Leitmeritz; before that Freiherr von Einem Collection, Hildesheim.

Wide conical foot with folded rim, decorated on the underside with an engraved wreath. Stem with hollow inverted baluster and flattened, hollow knop flanked by pairs of collars. Flared bowl with rounded base engraved on one side with a bust portrait of the Emperor Leopold I in profile to dexter, marshall's baton in his right hand, Order of the Golden Fleece on his breast, and a wreath crowning his long wig. The reverse with double-headed Imperial Eagle, with lightly-indicated haloes, and orb, sceptre and sword. On its breast a polished lens; the entire composition flanked by crossed palm and laurel fronds. Low cover with everted rim engraved with wreath, finial with hollow, flattened knops separated by triads of collars.
The profile of Leopold I (Emperor 1658–1705) is perhaps based on a coin or medallic likeness. A *Taler* of 1693 and an undated *Doppeltaler* undated from the Nuremberg Mint display considerable similarities – if reversed – in the stylized physiognomy (see above, p. 58, fig. 89; see also Hans-Jörg Kellner, *Die Münzen der Freien Reichsstadt Nürnberg*, Grünwald 1957, no. 154 and 181, ill.). Perhaps these, in their turn, are based on a medal by Philipp Heinrich Müller, struck on the occasion of Leopold's marriage in 1676 to Eleonore of the Pfalz (Drahotová 1972, p. 219, fig. 10).
The attribution to Johann Wolfgang Schmidt is based on comparison with a similar hollow-baluster goblet, which is very close in style and composition, engraved with a portrait of the Margrave Ludwig Wilhelm of Baden within a laurel wreath, in an Upper Franconian private collection, and bearing the diamond-point signature "I W S" (Saldern 1968, no. 173, ill.; idem 1970, pp. 103–105, figs. 1–4). A further signed glass with a portrait of Max II Emanuel of Bavaria in Corning, dating from the 1690s, reinforces this attribution (JGS 22, 1980, p. 107, no. 26, ill.) (see above, p. 58, fig. 90).
Compare also two parallel goblets which correspond to the Wolf goblet in the Imperial Eagle on the reverse, except for the raised marshall's baton in: the Bayerisches Nationalmuseum, Munich (Meyer-Heisig 1963, WT 75, incorrectly attributed there to Heinrich Schwanhardt; Rückert 1982 II, no. 486, pls. 144–145) and in the Strasser Collection, Pelham Manor, N.Y. (formerly Max Strauss Collection, Vienna: Robert Schmidt, *Kunstschätze der Sammlung Dr. Max Strauss in Wien*, Vienna 1922, pl. 16; JGS 21, 1979, p. 121, no. 11, ill.). It is not imposssible that Schmidt used as a prototype for his Leopold goblets an important goblet skillfully engraved with a portrait of Leopold, the reverse with the Imperial Eagle, formerly in the Schiftan Collection, and attributed to Heinrich Schwanhardt (Auction cat. 439, Dorotheum, Vienna, 27–29 Feb. 1936, lot no. 524, pl. XVI).
For this type of portrait in a wreathed medallion, compare with other portrait goblets by Schmidt in: a private collection, Upper Franconia (portrait of Max Emanuel of Bavaria: Saldern 1968, no. 174, ill.; idem 1970, pp. 105–106, figs. 5–8); a private collection, Franconia (portrait of the Emperor Charles VI: Saldern 1968, no. 178, ill; idem 1970, p. 108, figs. 11–12, described as atelier of J. W. Schmidt).

Lit.: Schmidt Ms 1931, p. 193, no. 185 (described as "Nuremberg, workshop of H. Schwinger, about 1680").

## 76  HOLLOW-BALUSTER GOBLET WITH NAVAL BATTLE

Nuremberg, Johann Wolfgang Schmidt, about 1685–1700

Height: 38 cm (with cover), 26 cm (without cover); diameter at rim: 9.3 cm; thickness of glass: about 2 mm (bowl), about 1–1.5 mm (cover).

Colorless glass with matt and polished wheel-engraving. Unpolished pontil mark. Cover not original.

Provenance: Collection of the Dukes of Anhalt-Dessau, Schloss Ballenstedt (according to Alfred Wolf's records).

Wide foot with folded rim decorated with foliate wreath on the underside. Tall stem with hollow baluster and flattened, hollow knop separated by pairs of collars. Ovoid bowl engraved in the round with a continuous naval engagement between full-riggers in various stages of burning, exploding, and sinking, two with the arms of France on the stern, as well as cannon smoke. Low cover with everted rim, engraved foliate wreath, and hollow-knopped finial.

The engraved motif may possibly have been taken from an illustrated broadsheet (see above, p. 60, fig. 98). These broadsheets were influential at that time in disseminating information about the most important events in contemporary politics or war. They would have played an important part in spreading information about the many naval engagements between the English, Dutch and French in the seventeenth century (see Wolfgang Harms (editor), *Deutsche illustrierte Flugblätter des 16. und 17. Jahrhunderts*, Tübingen 1980 onwards). Not enough heraldic information is supplied by the engraver to enable one to judge whether a specific battle is indicated on this goblet.
For the motif of a sea battle see a glass in a private Franconian collection (Saldern 1968, no. 176, ill.; idem 1970, pp. 106–107, fig. 9–10) as well as the ruby-glass beaker, cat. no. 77.
A. von Saldern has already correctly attributed the goblet in a private Franconian collection to the Nuremberg glass engraver Johann Wolfgang Schmidt (1970, pp. 106–107). This attribution, which is based on close motif and stylistic similarities as well as superior artistic and technical qualities, can be applied without hesitation to the Wolf goblet. Nautical subjects appear frequently in Schmidt's repertoire (Meyer-Heisig 1963, WT 162–164) and, as A. von Saldern has suggested, were probably engraved between 1685 and 1700.

remberg engraving. It is possible that the engraver had access to an earlier edition containing this emblem by another author. This possibility is supported by the appearance of another emblem, also from the *Devises et Emblemes anciennes et modernes*, (pl. 50, no. 9: Amor fashions two hearts into one on an anvil with the inscription "Je fais de deux un") engraved possibly by the same metic on a beaker dated 1686 for the Imhof family, and which was attributed by Robert Schmidt to Heinrich Schwanhardt (died 1696) (1922, p. 246, fig. 138).

For the decorative subject matter compare with almost identical versions at Schloss Arnstadt (different silver-gilt mounts with Nuremberg mark) and in the antiques trade, Heide Hübner, Wurzburg (possibly with later mounts: Auction cat. *English and Continental Glass*, Sotheby's, London, 30 June 1980, lot. 232, col. pl.), as well as a ruby-glass tankard with cover (with silver-gilt mounts by Severinus Konrad Weiss, Nuremberg, Master 1696, died 1708) in the Schatzkammer of the Residence in Munich (Meyer-Heisig 1963, WT 62).

This tankard belongs to a distinct group of gold-ruby glasses, all with emblems taken from *Devises et Emblemes anciennes et modernes*, all possibly by the same hand – possibly Heinrich Schwanhardt – engraved in Nuremberg (Klesse 1976, pp. 65–70, pl. 20, 1–5 and 21, 1–8). Besides those already mentioned, there is a ruby-glass tankard in the Kunstgewerbemuseum, Cologne (Cologne 1963, no. 286, ill. and 1973, no. 358, ill.; Meyer-Heisig 1963, WT 63), a ruby-glass covered beaker with silver-gilt mounts in the Hermitage, Leningrad (B. A. Shelkovnikov, among others, *Art Glass* (in Russian), Hermitage Museum, Leningrad 1967, fig. 46), a ruby-glass beaker formerly in the Biemann Collection, Zurich (Klesse/Saldern 1978, pp. 37 onwards, no. 99, ill.), and a ruby-glass beaker with silver-mounted rim in a private collection (Cologne 1980, no. 408, col. ill.).

For shape see cat. no. 79 and footnote.

## 79 RUBY-GLASS TANKARD DECORATED WITH FRUIT FESTOONS

South Germany, about 1700

Height: 21 cm (with cover), 17 cm (without cover); diameter at rim: 9.1 cm; thickness of glass: about 4–4.5 mm

Deep gold-ruby glass, lightening towards the base, with matt wheel-engraving and polished circles. Unpolished pontil mark. Base of handle broken and cemented. Silver-gilt mounts unmarked.

Baluster body with wide, cylindrical neck and small everted foot bound with a silver ring mount with chased lappet border. Applied loop handle with silver mounted, hinged cover. Body decorated for the most part in matt wheel-engraved decoration, the shoulder with three pendant drapes and three luxuriant bunches of fruit and flowers including polished bunches of grapes, the neck with band of stylized flowers and fruiting vine embellished with polished ovals. Low silver cover with chased gadroon border and laurel wreath around the central medallion of Cupid watering flowers within the inscription "Die Bewesserung befärdert (!) das Wachstum." Spherical, mellon-ribbed thumbpiece, hinged to the handle with a foliate clasp.

For shape compare with cat. no. 78 and footnote for similar examples (all with wheel-engraving).
Compare further parallel examples, mostly undecorated and silver-gilt mounted in: the Reichenheim-Oppenheim Collection, formerly Berlin (Nuremberg mounts: Schmidt 1914, B. G., pl. 17, no. 8); the Art Institute, Chicago (former Mühsam Collection; Augsburg mounts by Tobias Baur: Schmidt 1914, no. 183, ill.; idem 1914, B. G., pl. 18, no. 1; Strasser 1979, no. 43, ill.); the Museum für Kunsthandwerk, Frankfurt a. M. (Ohm 1973, no. 474, ill.); Rosenborg Castle, Copenhagen, (a series of tankards with Augsburg silver mounts, some by Tobias Baur: Heine 1912, ill. p. 132; J. Hein, *Venetianske Glas*, Rosenborg, Copenhagen 1984, no. 139, ill.); the art market (silver mounts with illegible marks, Spiegl 1983, p. 50, fig. 1); Victoria and Albert Museum, London (one tankard unmounted, another with Augsburg mounts of the Master "DB": Charleston 1977, p. 204); private collection (Augsburg mounts by Marx Weinhold: Seling 1980, I, col pl. XVIIIb); private collection (mounts somewhat later, unmarked: Cologne 1980, no. 423, ill.); Württembergisches Landesmuseum, Stuttgart (formerly part of the "cabinet of curiosities" of the Dukes of Württemberg: Schack 1976, fig. 118); The Toledo Museum of Art, Toledo, Ohio (with wheel-engraving and mounts by Tobias Baur: Toledo Museum, *Art in Glass*, 1969, ill. p. 64); the James A. de Rothschild Collection, Waddesdon Manor (Augsburg mounts of Tobias Baur: Charleston 1977, no. 54, ill.).
The bunches of fruit are distinguished here by their large size; the more frequent type is found on cat. no. 80. Nevertheless, stylistically it is still unmistakably South German.

## 80  RUBY GLASS FLASK
## WITH ENGRAVED FESTOONS

South Germany, Freising or Munich, last quarter 17th century

Height: 14.2 cm;
thickness of glass: 3–4 mm

Deep gold-ruby glass, decorated with matt wheel-engraving. Unmarked silver mounts. Lappet on footring missing.

Piriform body with tapering neck, strongly-gadrooned base and everted foot bound in silver with a repoussé rope and lappet border. Silver cap with plain neck band, hinged lid with gadrooned border and scales. Body decorated in matt wheel-engraving with alternate linked large and small fruit festoons.

Compare with close parallels in: the Kunstmuseum, Düsseldorf (without decoration: Jantzen 1960, no. 123; Heinemeyer 1966, no. 298, ill.); Museum der Stadt, Regensburg (with continuous stag hunt: Baumgärtner 1977 R, no. 169, ill.); one formerly in the Biemann Collection, Zurich (without gadroons: Klesse/Saldern 1978, no. 100, with col. pl.).
Compare also with further variants, certainly from the same glasshouse, with similar decoration, but with more extended neck in: Kunstgewerbemuseum, Berlin (now lost, Schmidt B. G. 1914, pl. 18, no. 2; idem 1922, fig. 184); the Museum der Stadt, Regensburg (Baumgärtner 1977 R, no. 168 with col. pl.); private collection (Cologne 1980, no. 418, with col. pl.).
The fact that ruby-glass was so popular in Southern Germany, and so frequently decorated with fruit festoons (with or without perching birds) of stereotyped form and indifferent quality, having little to do with incomparably richer and finer examples of known Nuremberg masters (see Meyer-Heisig 1963, WT 86, 173, 174, 178) would suggest that the engravers themselves were to be found in and around the centers of ruby-glass production (in Munich or Freising). This subject has already been extensively discussed in other publications (Klesse 1976, p. 70, note 18; Klesse/Saldern 1978, p. 163, no. 100). In Munich the glass-engraver Veit Limer working in the glasshouse managed by Hans Christoph Fidler is mentioned in contemporary documents, and it is known that the Munich glasshouse, immediately after its founding in 1677, had, besides a complete set of glassmaking equipment, a cutting apparatus from Freising (Berliner 1924, p. 118). On the other hand the report of Johann Chr. Orschall in 1684 in which he says "... bis auf den heutigen Tag zu Freysingen genug dergleichen verfertiget ... wird," (until now enough of it [i. e. gold-ruby glass] will be produced), (ibid., pp. 118–119, note 21), implies that ruby glass and its embellishment with engraved decoration was already being intensively produced before the setting up of the glasshouse in Munich.

## 83  BEAKER WITH MERCURY
##     AND FRUIT FESTOONS

Nuremberg, possibly Paulus Eder, about 1700–1710

Height: 12.6 cm; diameter at rim: 10.3 cm;
thickness of glass: about 4–5.5 mm

Colorless heavy-blown glass with matt wheel-engraving. Small unpolished pontil.


Cylindrical, straight-sided body supported on three hollow, flattened, bun feet. Engraved with a continuous hilly landscape with trees, a huntsman and hound, as well as Mercury playing a shawm, with cows in the background, ruins and a town on the horizon. Beneath the rim, rich ribbon-tied fruit festoons accentuated with large flowers, globular fruit of melon type, grapes, and finely-detailed veining on the leaves.

The rendering of Mercury and the cows could refer to his role as god of herds and pasture, as well as the episode where Jupiter, besotted with Io, turns her into a cow. Missing, however is Argus, appointed by watchful Juno to guard the herd, and lulled to sleep by the music of Mercury's shawm. It is possible that this amusing myth was represented in its complete form on one or several similar beakers.

The rich fruit festoons with finely accentuated details are characteristic of Paulus Eder (see Bernt 1950, pl. 51; Meyer-Heisig 1963, WT 173 and 174), although those on the Wolf beaker are not consistently as finely drawn. Also typical of Eder is the contrast between the large festoons and the small-scale landscapes (see above, p. 63, fig. 106). This beaker could well have been decorated by Paulus Eder with the help of an experienced apprentice.

## 84 HOLLOW-BALUSTER GOBLET WITH IMPERIAL EAGLE

Nuremberg, late 17th century

Height: 46 cm (with cover), 30.3 cm (without cover);
diameter at rim: 11.9 cm;
thickness of rim: about 2.5 mm

Green and colorless glass with matt and polished wheel-engraving. Unpolished pontil mark. Stem damaged and repaired with silver collars, originally taller. Underside of foot painted in sealing-wax red with a ducal crown and number "92."

Provenance: Friedrich Neuburg Collection, Dresden/ Leitmeritz; previously Collection of the Dukes of Anhalt-Dessau, Schloss Dessau.

Wide, green-tinted foot with folded rim, below a stem in clear glass with hollow baluster and knop (now missing) separated by triple collars. Green-tinted, ovoid bowl engraved on one side with the Imperial, double-headed eagle, crowned and holding polished Imperial insignia in its talons, on its breast the shield of Austria, all flanked by fronds. Reverse with inscription in Roman capitals "CONSILIO / ET / INDUSTRIA," also framed by fronds. Low, green-tinted cover with everted rim decorated with engraved palm and laurel wreath, colorless knopped finial with triple collars and crowning knop in green.

For a parallel example compare with cat. no. 85.
For the decorative motif compare with other Nuremberg *Reichsadler* goblets in: the Bayerisches Nationalmuseum, Munich (Rückert 1982, II, no. 490, pl. 147); one formerly in the Biemann Collection, Zurich (signed and dated "Mäuerl 1723": Klesse/Saldern 1978, no. 103 A, ill.; Sotheby's Biemann, lot 84, ill.).
For this type of part-colored, hollow-baluster goblet see examples in: Barrington Haynes 1959, pl. 33d; Strauss 1955, no. 196, ill. (with cut decoration); Cologne 1963, no. 294; 1973, no. 361, ill. (with cut decoration); Corning 1965, no. 72, with col. pl.; Auction cat. Parpart, fig. 997 (with cut decoration); Heinemeyer 1966, no. 326, ill. (undecorated).

Lit.: Schmidt Ms 1931, p. 194, no. 186 (as "Nuremberg, about 1675").

## 85   HOLLOW-BALUSTER GOBLET WITH IMPERIAL EAGLE

Nuremberg, about 1690–1700

Height: 19.3 cm; diameter at rim: 7.3 cm; thickness of glass: about 3.5–4 mm

Green and colorless glass with matt wheel engraving, small polished circlets and small amounts of diamond engraving. Unpolished pontil mark.

Wide, conical foot with folded rim in green, decorated with three delicate insects on the upper surface. Colorless stem with a series of four hollow drop knops and three collars. Green-tinted, slightly-flared bowl with rounded base engraved on one side between crossed laurel sprays with the Imperial double-headed eagle with polished haloes, surmounted by a crown and clasping sceptre and orb in its talons. Reverse with three-part inscription in Roman capitals "CONSILIO / ET / INDUSTRIA" flanked by crossed palm fronds. Interstices decorated with fruiting vine with diamond-engraved tendrils, polished bunches of grapes and small insects.

Compare with larger and finer engraved parallel, cat. no. 84 and its footnote.

## 86 COVERED HOLLOW-BALUSTER GOBLET ENGRAVED WITH PASTORAL SCENE

Nuremberg, late 17th century

Height: 41.5 cm (with cover), 31.2 cm (without cover); diameter at rim: 11.4 cm; thickness of glass: about 2 mm

Pale, yellowish-gray tinted glass with matt and slightly-polished wheel engraving. Unpolished pontil mark. Small stress crack in the engraved area (under the head of the sheepdog). Cover possibly decorated by another hand.

Provenance: Friedrich Neuburg Collection, Dresden/ Leitmeritz; previously Philipp Schwarz Collection, Stuttgart; before that von Drach Collection.

Wide, conical foot with folded rim. Stem with hollow baluster and hollow flattened knop between collar triads. Bowl with slightly-flared sides and rounded base engraved with a continuous landscape frieze. In the foreground beneath a small tree two shepherds, sheepdog, and flock of grazing sheep; in the background, behind areas of water, hilltop castles. Cover with everted rim and encircling forestscape with two figures on foot; finial with hollow knops and trios of collars.

Lit.: Schwarz 1916, p. 76, ill. p. 79; Auction Cat. Philipp Schwarz Collection, Stuttgart, "Alte Gläser in künstlerischer Veredlung," Helbing Munich, 25 October 1916, lot no. 239 with paper impression, pl. 10; Schmidt Ms 1931, p. 194, no. 183 (as "Nuremberg, in the manner of H. Schwinger, about 1680.").

## 87   ENGRAVED FLASK AND PAIR OF TUMBLERS

Glass: Central or Southern Germany, second quarter 18<sup>th</sup> century;
engraving: Nuremberg, about 1735–1740

Height: 19.8 cm (flask), 8.3 and 8.6 cm (tumbler a and b); diameter: 7.2 cm (tumbler);
thickness of glass: about 2.5 mm (flask), 1 mm and 1.5 mm (tumbler a and b).

Colorless glass with matt and polished wheel engraving. Pontil mark on flask unpolished; polished out on tumblers.

Flask: flattened globular body with everted neck and small, flared foot. Body engraved on one side with the female robed figure of Concordia, carrying bound reeds, and with one foot on the prostrate figure of Discordia, in the background a landscape with hilltop settlements, all flanked by palm trees and the inscription "CONCORDIA RES PARUAE CRESCHNT (sic!) / DISCORDIA MAXIMA DILABUNTUR." Reverse with two coats-of-arms acolée (to sinister, three balls on a chief, below, two opposed rampant hounds on a mount; to dexter three castellated towers), surmounted by coronet and baldequin, and supported on socle flanked by baskets of fruit. Neck decorated at base with stiff-leaf border and sprays of lily of the valley and forget-me-nots.

Tumbler: possibly a marriage tumbler. Bell-shaped bowl on small everted foot decorated with wheel engraving.
a) Base of foot with unpolished pontil mark. Engraved on one side with two coats-of-arms acolée surmounted by coronet and baldequin (repeated on the flask) surrounded by scrollwork and trelliswork base, flanked by palms. Reverse with a couple flanking the central figure of Concordia with linked hands, flanked by cornucopia, above the inscription in Roman capitals "UNIONE ANIMORUM THORUS (sic!) FELIX" .
b) Pontil mark on base engraved with florette. One side engraved with arms (as on flask and other tumbler) flanked by allegorical figures of Caritas and Spes.

Reverse with double medallions acolée bearing the polished mirror monograms ICVT and STVT (or SFVT) on a matt ground, flanked by angels blowing trumpets.

Ottfried Neubecker, Wiesbaden/Stuttgart, identified the arms as those of the Thurm family (three castellated towers: see Burgher Families, Siebmacher, 2, p. 58, pl. 97; E. Zimmermann, *Augsburger Zeichen und Wappen*, no. 2602) and v. Schnurbein (opposed hounds beneath three balls; see E. Zimmermann, ibid., no. 4529/4530/6029; Revised Siebmacher, III, 7, pp. 7–8, VI, 11, p. 55, pl. 31; M. Gritzner, *Standes-Erhebungen und Gnaden-Acte Deutscher Landesfürsten*, Görlitz 1881, p. 364, 698).

Both families are from Augsburg. One Christie Thurm, a merchant, is mentioned in 1685. One Balthasar von Schnurbein, born in Augsburg, was ennobled in 1696, while his uncle Gottfried von Schnurbein, secret war councillor in Hesse and Saxony, was raised to the rank of Imperial Freiherr on 10 July 1742. It has not been possible so far to determine a date of marriage between members of these families in the first half of the eighteenth century.

The flask with everted neck would seem to be without parallel.

Rückert points out that this type of tumbler has its origins in Thuringia, and was often used by Nuremberg metics, particulary when embellished with Augsburg silver mounts, in the fitting up of traveling compendia. Following Robert Schmidt, Rückert suggests that the beaker with the initial "K" in the Bayerisches Nationalmuseum, might have been engraved by the *Glasspiegelschneider* (mirrormaker) and *Zieratschneider* (ornament engraver) (Johann) Leonard Keil (Käul), working in Nuremberg between 1722 and 1739 (1982, no. 501; see Hampe 1919, p. 48). Against R. J. Charleston's theory that in view of the frequent instance of Augsburg mounts, the decoration was possibly also executed there (1969, p. 105), Rückert is justified in pointing out that there are no indications to support this theory.

Compare the following tumblers of similar form (with various engraved decoration) in: Schmidt 1914, no. 88; idem 1926, no. 124, 126, pl. 15; Schlosser 1956, fig. 133; 1965, fig. 218; Heinemeyer 1966, nos. 329 and 330, ill.; R. J. Charleston in *Årbok Oslo*, 1969, p. 105, fig. 10–11, 13–15; Baumgärtner 1977 R, no. 186, ill.; Klesse 1973, no. 555, ill.; Cologne 1980, no. 400, ill.; Rückert 1982, II, no. 501–502, pl. 157, no. 574, pl. 166.

## 90  COVERED HOLLOW BALUSTER GOBLET WITH ENGRAVED BOAR HUNT

Possibly Bohemia, late 17th century

Height: 37.2 (with cover), 26.2 cm (without cover); diameter at rim: 11.6 cm;
thickness of glass: about 2.5 mm (bowl and cover)

Colorless glass with polished wheel engraving. Unpolished pontil. Second collar below the knop damaged.

Wide foot with folded rim. Tall stem with hollow baluster and flattened knop flanked by a series of collars. Wide ovoid bowl decorated within an encircling wooded landscape with a boar hunt: on one side a rider attacks a boar with a spear while, on the other, two huntsmen on foot spring from a thicket with guns and lance to attack another one. Depressed cover with everted rim engraved with a deer hunt with hunter and hound. Finial with flattened hollow knop flanked by collars. Decoration of cover and bowl by the same hand.

Although this type of goblet is closely connected with Nuremberg, the sides are thicker and heavier. The style of decoration and the polished engraving also point stylistically to Bohemia.

## 91 COVERED HOLLOW-BALUSTER GOBLET WITH IMPERIAL EAGLE

Bohemia, late 17th century

Height: 48.8 cm (with cover), 37 cm (without cover); diameter at rim: 12.4 cm;
thickness of glass: about 4 mm (bowl), 2 mm (cover)

Colorless glass with polished ovals and matt wheel engraving. Unpolished pontil mark.

Provenance: Friedrich Neuburg Collection, Dresden/Leitmeritz; formerly Freiherr von Einem Collection, Hildesheim.

Wide, conical foot with folded rim engraved with a wreath of crossed laurel fronds. Tall stem with hollow baluster and two flattened, hollow knops separated by three triads of collars. Wide ovoid bowl engraved on one side with crowned *Reichsadler* grasping sceptre and sword in its talons, and flanked by palm fronds and polished ovals, the reverse with trophies on a base. Flattened cover with everted rim decorated with foliate wreath. Baluster and knop finial.

Although not of the quality of typical North Bohemian *Reichsadler* goblets influenced in form and decoration by Nuremberg (see cat. nos. 84 and 85); for which see examples formerly in the Krug Collection, Baden-Baden (Klesse 1965, p. 24, fig. 24, no. 186, ill.; Sotheby's Krug IV, no. 701, ill.) and another formerly in the Bremen Collection in the Rheinischen Landesmuseum, Bonn (Bremen 1964, no. 212, ill.), there is no doubt concerning its origins. It is closest in style to a goblet with the Imperial Arms in the Bayerisches Nationalmuseum, Munich (Rückert 1982, II, no. 601, pl. 181) which Rainer Rückert pinpoints to South Bohemia.

Lit.: Schmidt Ms 1931, no. 188 (described as "Nuremberg or Bohemia, late 17th century.").

## 94 COVERED GOBLET WITH STAG HUNT

Glass: North Bohemia or Saxony, first third
18th century
decoration: Saxony, first third 18th century

Height: 24.8 cm (with cover), 17.2 cm (without cover);
diameter at rim: 7.4 cm;
thickness of glass: about 4 mm

Deep blue-tinted glass with matt wheel engraving.
Unpolished pontil mark. Base of foot and rim of cover
inscribed "No. 1" in diamond point.

Provenance: Friedrich Neuburg Collection, Dresden/
Leitmeritz; formerly Freiherr von Einem Collection,
Hildesheim.

Conical foot, stem with inverted baluster shaft and
shoulder knop flanked by collars. Deep conical bowl
with shallow, matt wheel-engraved decoration: a
hunter shooting a stag in a landscape with trees inscribed above "Ich bin ein iäger/ undt steh von fern/
ich schische (sic!) wildtbradt / undt / vögel gern." Low
cover decorated with foliate circlets and flowers. Finial
with flattened knop flanked by collars and spire knop.

The blue-tinted glass and the form of goblet are characteristic of the cobalt-rich Erzgebirge region situated
on the borders of north Bohemia and Saxony. Stylistic
pointers, such as the stiff landscape "base" and type of
calligraphy, indicate a Saxon origin.

Lit.: Schmidt Ms 1931, no. 228 (described as "Central or northern
Germany, first half 18th century").

## 95 PAIR OF COVERED GOBLETS WITH BLUE KNOPS

Bohemia, about 1710–20

a) Height: 26.5 cm (with cover), 18.4 cm (without cover); diameter at rim: 8.3 cm;
thickness of glass: about 5 mm (bowl), 4 mm (cover)
b) Height: 26.5 cm (with cover), 18.7 cm (without cover);
diameter at rim: 8.4 cm;
thickness of glass: about 5 mm (bowl), 4 mm (cover)

Colorless and cobalt-blue glass with cutting and matt wheel engraving. Unpolished pontil mark. a) Rim chipped; b) chip on rim of cover cemented.


Flattened, conical colorless foot with faceted cobalt-blue, inverted baluster stem flanked by colorless-glass collars. Conical faceted bowl decorated with vertical panels of floral scrolls with sunflower heads, part matt, part polished, alternating with polished, stylized foliate motifs (a) with starlets (b) with ovals and circlets. Low covers cut with ten facets, polished flutes alternating with sunflower sprays (a) and smaller flowers (b) Blue faceted spire finial on a colorless collar.

As opposed to the more frequent use of ruby-glass threads on the bowl or to accentuate the knops on this classic type of Bohemian goblet, the use of blue glass in this combination is very rare. (Compare a goblet with similar cover only, formerly in the Krug Collection: Klesse 1973, no. 568, ill.; Sotheby's Krug IV, lot no. 704, ill.).
The simple, stylized flower decoration appears again in similar form on somewhat later blue-tinted covered goblets and sweetmeat glasses, possibly of North Bohemian origin. See in this connection cat. no. 101.

## 96 GOBLET WITH ALLEGORY OF TRANSIENCE

Riesengebirge, late 17th – early 18th century

Height: 21.3 cm; diameter at rim: 7 cm; thickness of glass: about 2 mm

Colorless glass with polished ovals and wheel engraving. Pontil mark polished out.

Provenance: formerly F. v. Parpart Collection, Schloss Hünegg.

Wide foot with folded rim. Massive stem consisting of irregular knops and cysts between collars. Tall, conical bowl embellished with polished ovals and polished, engraved, oval medallion framing a child, seated on a large, polished ball in a flowery meadow, blowing bubbles. Rim decorated with three large, polished floral sprays, a tulip between two narcissi, as well as rosettes.

The motif of the child blowing bubbles, reversed in this version, originates in Emblem no. 4, depicting symbols of worldly Vanity and Transience, of Wolfgang Helmhard von Hohberg's *Lust- und Artzeney-Garten des Königlichen Propheten David*, illustrated by Georg Christoph Eimmart (1638–1705), and published in Regensburg in 1675 (see above, p. 68, fig. 115).

Lit.: Auction cat. Parpart 1912, lot no. 1083.

## 97  COVERED GOBLET WITH ALLEGORY OF THE SEASONS

Riesengebirge, early 18th century

Height: 28 cm (with cover), 18.9 cm (without cover); diameter at rim: 8.5 cm;
thickness of glass: about 2 mm (bowl), 1.5 mm (cover)

Colorless glass decorated predominantly with polished wheel engraving and polished ovals. Unpolished pontil mark. Ducal crown and number "78" in sealing-wax red on base of foot.

Provenance: Friedrich Neuburg Collection, Dresden/Leitmeritz; formerly Collection of the Dukes of Anhalt-Dessau, Schloss Dessau.

Wide, conical foot with folded rim decorated with palm frond circlet. Stem comprising compressed, teared baluster flanked by flattened knops and collars. Wide, conical bowl decorated with four oval medallions framed in different fruit, floral, and foliate wreaths, each engraved with a child and respective symbol of the Four Seasons: Spring with basket of flowers, Summer with sheaf of corn, Autumn with bunch of grapes, Winter with faggots. Interstices with bunches of fruit and flowers. Low cover with everted rim decorated with foliate wreath incorporating polished fruits, finial with hollow knop supported on collars.

The engraved sources for the Four Seasons are derived from the title page of Johann Ulrich Krauss's 1687 German/French Augsburg version of André Félibien's engravings after Charles Lebrun's Gobelin series "Les Quatres Elemens," made for Louis XIV and originally published in 1665 (title of the Augsburg edition from Henkel/Schöne 1976, p. LXI, no. 300: *Tapisseries du Roy, où sont representez les quatre elemens et les quatre saisons de l'année ... Königlich Französische Tapezereyen, auf welchen die Vier Elementen samt den Vier Jahr Zeiten vorgestellt werden ... an den Tag gegeben und verlegt durch Johann Ulrich Krauss, Kupferstecher in Augsburg ... 1687*), (see above, p. 69, fig. 117).
The glass engraver has followed the original engraving exactly. In the original, the symbols are reinforced in

the surrounding landscape: Spring with two flowering shrubs, Summer with a cornfield, Autumn with a vine stock, and Winter with a leafless tree-stump. The children's meager clothing, consisting of a brief cloth tied round the middle of their pudgy stomachs, corresponds to the original, as does Winter, who wears a knee-length garment.
Compare with a Silesian goblet of a generation later formerly in the Krug Collection (Klesse 1965, no. 211, ill.; Sotheby's Krug IV, lot no. 784, ill.) decorated with allegories of the Seasons from the same source (here not in medallion but on socles surmounted by baldequins alternating with vases of flowers).
For the use of the same engraved source by other glass engravers see also cat. no. 202 and 203.

Lit.: Schmidt Ms 1931, p. 268 and 269, no. 254 (described as "Bohemian, about 1700").

## 98  GOBLET DECORATED WITH SATYR HERM AND DANCING PEASANT

Bohemia, first quarter 18<sup>th</sup> century

Height: 15 cm; diameter at rim: 8.8 cm;
thickness of glass: about 1.5 mm

Wide, plain foot supporting a hollow, conical stem with vine-leaf border round the shoulder continuing onto the funnel bowl. Bowl decorated in polished wheel engraving on one side with a dancing peasant flanked by small trees, the reverse with satyr herm playing pan pipes within an oval medallion of fruiting vine.

The figure of the satyr herm derives from an ornament engraving by Jean Berain I of the god Bacchus (see above, p. 70, fig. 119). In its quality of detail and engraving technique this motif is undoubtedly by a different hand from that on the reverse.

The shallow-cut figure of the dancing peasant corresponds exactly in style to the decorative engraving on a large table service consisting of goblets and beakers in Schloss Favorite in Rastatt (see above, p. 70, fig. 121). Schloss Favorite was built with terrific haste as a summer residence about 1710 by the Margravine Franziska Sibylla Augusta of Baden-Baden (1675–1733). She was born the daughter of Duke Julius Franz of Sachsen-Lauenberg, and grew up in the North Bohemian castle of Schlackenwerth, and a considerable proportion of the furnishings for Schloss Favorite stemmed from this region.

The 1762 *Inventarium über die in der hochfürstlichen Favorite sich befindlichen Meubles* (Inventory of the furnishings in the princely Favorite) mentions: "Alle dieße vorgemelde Gläßer bestehn aus dem feinesten Böhmischen Glaß, alle fein und künstlich geschliffen;" (All the aforementioned glasses are of the finest Bohemian glass, all beautifully and artistically engraved); (Rudolf Sillib, *Schloß Favorite und die Eremitagen der Markgräfin Franziska Sibylla Augusta von Baden-Baden*, Heidelberg 1914, p. 96; Dietrich Rentsch, *Kunstschätze in Badischen Schlössern*, Bildhefte des Badischen Landesmuseums Karlsruhe, Karlsruhe 1972, p. XII). The attribution of the Wolf goblet to Bohemia is therefore hardly in question, even though there are as yet no further stylistically related pieces, except those in Schloss Favorite, which are definitely of Bohemian origin.

## 99  GOBLET ENGRAVED
## WITH MYTHOLOGICAL SCENES

Glass: Bohemia, early 18th century
Engraving: Riesengebirge, Hirschberger Tal, early 18th century

Height: 18.8 cm; diameter at rim: 8.4 cm; thickness of glass: about 3.5–4 mm

Colorless glass with cutting, matt and polished wheel engraving and small areas of diamond-point engraving. Unpolished pontil mark.

Provenance: Friedrich Neuburg Collection, Dresden/Leitmeritz.

Wide, flattened foot decorated with foliate circlet on the upper surface. Columnar stem with two flattened, faceted knops separated by collars and short plain sections. Conical bowl cut with sixteen vertical facets and decorated with polished wheel engraving: on one side, within an oval foliate wreath, is portrayed the nymph Philyra with Saturn (Chronos) in the form of a stallion, bearing a small winged figure carrying his scythe, thus confirming his identity. On the reverse, the nymph Melantho preceeded by a flying putto with garlands of flowers, being carried off to an island by Poseidon in the form of a dolphin. In the flanking sections stand bacchinalian figures crowned and overgrown with fruiting vine, the tendrils executed in diamond point.

The two scenes from Greek mythology are obscure incidents in the loves of the gods and are very seldom depicted. They are mentioned briefly in Ovid's *Metamorphoses* (Book VI, verse 120 and 126). Saturn (Chronos) turned himself into a stallion on being surprised by his wife Thea with the nymph Phylira. Out of this union came the centaur Cheiron, who fulfilled the role of wise educator of the greatest heroes in Greek mythology. Melantho, daughter of Deucalion, and especial lover of dolphins, was ravished by Poseidon in the guise of a dolphin and gave birth to Delphos after whom Delphi was named.
As the printed source the glass engraver has used plates no. 89 and 90 of the *Verwandlungen des Ovidii/In*

*Zweyhundert und sechs- und zwantzig Kupffern* with dedication by Johann Ulrich Krauss of Augsburg, undated, but probably finished in 1694 (see above, p. 71, figs. 125 and 126). He could also have used the "Metamorphoses d'Ovide en Rondeaux ... die Verwandlungen des Ovidii in ... Rundgedichten ... überall mit schönen Figuren ... gedruckt bey Andreas Knortzen Seel. Wittib" already published by Johann Hoffmann in Nuremberg in 1689, which refer back to the same compositions, but larger and coarser than those of Krauss. Both were editions for a German-speaking clientele of the original illustrations by Le Brun which originally appeared in 1676, complete with the two relevant love sagas. (*Metamorphoses d'Ovide en Rondeaux imprimez et enrichis de figures par ordre de sa majesté, et dediez à Monseigneur Le Dauphin. A Paris de l'Imprimerie Royale 1676*, with a letter from M. Le Brun to M. de Benserade of the 1 November 1674 as preface).
Stylistically, this goblet belongs to the same group as cat. no. 100. See corresponding footnote.

Lit.: Schmidt Ms 1931, pp. 268–269, no. 257 (described as "Bohemian, about 1700"); Rückert 1982, II, p. 256 (in connection with no. 771, pl. 228, 229).

## 100  COVERED GOBLET WITH ALLEGORICAL FIGURE OF FORTUNE

Glass: Bohemian, second decade 18th century
Decoration: Riesengebirge, Hirschberger Tal, second decade 18th century

Height: 31.9 cm (with cover), 20.3 cm (without cover); diameter at rim: 10 cm; thickness of glass: about 4 mm (bowl and cover)

Colorless glass with cutting and mainly matt wheel engraving. Small chips to uppermost stem collar, rim, and cover finial.

Flattened foot with wreath composed of four joined garlands of rosettes. Stem with faceted baluster shaft and knop between collars. The twelve-faceted conical bowl decorated mainly in matt wheel engraving: on one side, the standing allegorical figure of Fortune with floating veil suspended above a winged ball, all within elaborate symmetrical scrollwork inhabited by small monkeys, baskets of flowers and foliate masks. Reverse with crossed palm-frond medallion enclosing crowned monogram "TS" or "ST," within similar foliate scrolls embellished with baskets of flowers and birds. The fields in between decorated with vertical foliate panels with storks in medallions. Rim decorated with band of rosettes. Cover with broad band of foliate scrolls and masks, and rosette festoons; spire finial and faceted knop.

A beaker in the Art Institute, Chicago, (formerly Mühsam Collection: Schmidt 1926, pl. 23, no. 133) is decorated with an almost identical unclothed figure of Fortune, probably from the same workshop.
Together with cat. no. 99, this goblet belongs to a group of goblets and beakers of the early 18th century, with decoration composed of a *horror vacui* of small foliate scrolls and details such as coats-of-arms, monograms, symbolic, emblematic, or allegorical subjects, all of which has its stylistic roots in the latter part of the previous century. In the steps of Robert Schmidt, Olga Drahotová has put forward a convincing case for an origin in the Hirschberger Tal for this group, still uninfluenced by the arabesques of Jean Berain as pub-

lished in the engravings of Paul Decker, whose origins are also close to the group of so-called Koula glasses and the deeply-cut scenes on the Silesian relief-carved glasses of the Hermsdorf workshop of Friedrich Winter (1965, pp. 340–343). Sophie Charlotte Bauer's theory (1975, pp. 150–156) that this group stems from the South Bohemian Helmbach glasshouse of Michael Müller in Winterberg, based on documents published by D. Šrýtrová (1966, pp. 35–38, and 1969, pp. 201–203) contradicts the argument of Sabine Baumgärtner (1984, pp. 2012–2017) who points out with justification that glasses attributed to the Helmbach glasshouses differ stylistically both as to figural and foliate decoration. Rainer Rückert also supports the theory that this group originated in the Hirschberger Tal, pointing out that in form (already drawn attention to by O. Drahotová, 1982, on pl. 74) as well as in ultraviolet fluorescence, the glass itself might be of Bohemian origin.
Compare with goblets in many collections belonging to this group in: Rijksmuseum, Amsterdam (Van Gelder 1955, p.44, pl. XXVIII, 2 and 3); one formerly in the Krug Collection, Baden-Baden (Klesse 1973, no. 564, ill.; Sotheby's Krug I, lot no. 161, ill.) Musées Royaux d'Art et d'Histoire, Brussels, *Trois Millénaires* 1958, no. 636, ill.); Nordböhmisches Gewerbemuseum, Liberec (Reichenberg), (Pazaurek 1902, pl. 15a–c, 24b; Prague 1970, no. 392, ill.); British Museum, London (London 1968, no.247, ill.); Victoria and Albert Museum, London, Buckley Collection (Schmidt 1927, p. 31, pl. 52A); Bayerisches Nationalmuseum, Munich (Rückert 1982, II, no. 771, pl. 228–229); Kunstgewerbemuseum, Prague (Drahotová 1965, ill. p. 342; *idem* 1982, pl. 74). A comprehensive list of this group of glasses is to be found in Rückert 1982, II, note to no. 771.

## 103 SCHAFFGOTSCH GOBLET CARVED IN HIGH RELIEF

Silesia, Hermsdorf, Friedrich Winter, about 1700

Height: 19.7 cm; diameter at rim: 10.2 cm; thickness of glass: about 5–5.5 mm

Colorless, light straw-tinted glass with matt and polished high-relief carving and deep engraving. Unpolished pontil mark.

Provenance: Friedrich Neuburg Collection, Dresden/Leitmeritz.

Wide, conical foot with cameo-carved circlet of acanthus leaves and radial engraved tulip sprays in between. Stem with basal node carved with stiff leaves, short baluster section decorated with arcaded circlets below a shoulder knop in very high relief with double acanthus volutes from which springs the conical bowl. Bowl divided into three tapering, vertical zones, each with shell-crowned, high-relief cartouche over strapwork socle flanked by cornucopiae and foliate scrolls – enclosing respectively 1) a fir tree in high relief surmounted by the engraved inscription "Aucun temps ne le Change," 2) in a polished engraved landscape herdsmen and peasants approach a hilltop castle, 3) also in a polished, engraved landscape a mounted horseman poised on the rim of a wheel. Rim embellished with groups of polished circlets.

The significance of the fir tree as part of the crest on the Schaffgotsch family coat-of-arms was first explained by H. Seydel (1919, p. 255). Here he cites Johann Sinapius who explains the name of the mountain castle, Schloss Kynast belonging to the Counts Schaffgotsch as originating from "den Kiefer-Bäumen, als von dem Kyhn und Ast" (*Schlesische Curiositäten, darinnen die Gräflichen, Freyherrlichen und Adelichen Geschlechter*, part II, Breslau and Leipzig, 1728, p. 205). This motif is an important factor in attributing these relief carved goblets to the workshop of Friedrich Winter who was employed on 5 August 1685 at Schloss Kynast by Count Christoph Leopold Schaffgotsch as *Korporal und unterthäniger Glasschneider* (corporal and apprentice glass engraver).

The fir tree motif with surrounding motto "Aucun temps ne le Change" is found more frequently on slightly later Winter-type goblets with lightly faceted bell-shaped bowls (see Schmidt 1914, pl. 14, no. 101; Schmidt 1922, fig. 148; auction cat. 439, Dorotheum, Vienna, 27–29 February 1936, lot no. 545, pl. XVII; Bernt 1950, p. 60, pl. 67; Cologne 1963, no. 318, and 1973, no. 385, ill.; Mosel 1979, no. 161, ill.; Rückert 1982, II, no. 769, pl. 227 and 228 with further comparisons).

See also two further goblets comparable in form and type of high relief carving, one formerly in the Krug Collection, Baden-Baden (Auction cat. 439, Dorotheum, Vienna, 27–29 February 1936, lot no. 542, pl. XVII; Klesse 1965, no. 205, ill.; Sotheby's Krug IV, lot no. 818, col. pl.) and the other in the Kunstgewerbemuseum, Prague (Inv. no. 16706; see above, p. 73, fig. 130).

The form of this goblet, with its bowl seemingly "wedged" into the massive wrythen leaf-decorated collar, is typical of the products of the workshop of Friedrich Winter, even though so few examples have survived. One finds in Winter's *œuvre* motifs of shell, flower and a foliate scroll simultaneously expressed on the bowl in sculptural form (see Vávra 1954, fig. 191; Barrington Haynes 1959, pl. 43b). In later developments, the bold three-dimentional collar is reduced to an acanthus-leaf scroll at the base of the funnel bowl, which is placed on a wrythen knop or plain conical shaft rather than a baluster (compare, for example Schmidt 1922, fig. 148; Vávra 1954, fig. 191 and 198).

Lit.: Schmidt Ms 1931, p. 275, no. 280 (as "work of Friedrich Winter, Hermsdorf, Silesia, beginning of the 18th century").

## 104 TWO-HANDLED BOWL
## WITH LANDSCAPE VIGNETTES

Silesia, Hermsdorf, workshop of Friedrich Winter, about 1700

Height: 6.5 cm; diameter: 9.7 cm; width: 13.5 cm; thickness of glass: about 6 mm

Colorless glass with cutting, matt, high-relief carved detail and polished wheel engraving. Pontil mark obscured with polished circlets. Base with digits "87" in sealing-wax red. Lip with small chips.

Provenance: Collection of the Dukes of Anhalt-Dessau.

Massive domed foot with carved, dentillate, faceted rim, underside with polished rosette. Shallow, conical body of circular cross-section with exceptionally thick walls. Decoration divided into two zones by opposed, applied scroll handles. Basal area decorated with raised, acanthus-leaf border and vertical, ornamented panels flanking the shaped panels; one side engraved with a riverscape with a solitary boatman, flanked by wooded banks, and a castle in the background on the left; the other with meadowscape flanked by rocky hills, in the foreground a boat-shaped chariot, on which is perched an eagle with wings outspread, is pulled by a female figure (possibly allegorical), in the background a castle. Rim embellished with polished circlets.

Despite its unusual form, this glass is nevertheless typical of the Winter workshop in its use of framed, relief-carved motifs and scenes in polished wheel engraving. Also typical is the female figure, her costume and hairstyle in the style of the late seventeenth century (see for instance cat. no. 103; see above, p. 74, figs. 131–132).
A beaker from the Winter workshop, now in the Kunstgewerbemuseum, Prague, is also decorated with a basal acanthus frieze and upper band of polished circlets (Drahotová 1982, fig. 72).

## 105 GOBLET ENGRAVED WITH SCENES OF DANCING

Silesia, Hermsdorf, possibly Jeremias Feister, about 1720–30

Height: 21.5 cm; diameter at rim: 9.5 cm; thickness of glass: about 2–3.5 mm

Colorless glass, in parts manganese tinted, with cutting, matt and polished high-relief details and matt wheel engraving. Pontil mark polished out. Rim of foot and bowl with tiny chips.

Provenance: Friedrich Neuburg Collection, Dresden/Leitmeritz; formerly Schöller Collection, Berlin.

Foot with relief-carved, acanthus-leaf border round the rim and stiff-leaf collar at base of stem. Baluster stem with polished, stiff leaves, flanked by collars. Bell-shaped bowl, the rounded base embellished with petal flutes and acanthus leaves in relief. Sides relief-carved with a continuous exterior scene with fanciful park buildings (an acanthus-decorated grotto framed by columns and a pavillion with herm caryatids) in the foreground dancing gallants and their ladies (two couples dancing and two sitting on the grass). On one side in the background two trumpeters and a gardener surmounted by an elaborate floral festoon. On the other side, below a fountain surmounted by a figure of reclining Neptune and a flying putto holding up a baldequin, an engraved cartouche enclosing the arms of the Silesian family of von Seidlitz (blazon with three fishes, one beneath the other) with monogram "F / I. S. / VS." and the inscription "A toutte / épreuve."

Concerning this goblet, Robert Schmidt comments (1931, pp. 276–277): "The piquant dancers, their costumes reminiscent of a French ballet, as well as the fantastic architectural backdrop, indicate an unusual talent at work in the special art of relief carving. The goblet cannot be earlier than 1730, as the initials F. J. S. V. S., kindly identified by Prof. Erwin Hintze, Breslau, most likely stand for Ferdinand Julius Sigismund von Seidlitz. As he was not born until about 1730, it is unlikely to have been made for him, unless possibly as a christening present. It is possible therefore that it

was commissioned or donated by his father Julius Sigismund, and that the 'F' stands rather for 'Freiherr' (baron). Julius Sigismund von Seidlitz was a high official and councillor of the Consistory Council, and owned several estates of which the chief were Ober-Pailau and Nieder-Pailau in the Eulengebirge."

Although different in subject matter, the high-relief decoration is still in the Winter workshop tradition and possibly originated in Hermsdorf. As a follower of Winter "Der Hermsdorfsche Glas- und Steinschneider Jeremias Feister" (the Hermsdorf glass and gem cutter Jeremias Feister) is mentioned in a directive from Count Schaffgotsch on the 29 February 1712 (Seydel 1919, p. 253 and 257). Perhaps the small group of goblets with continuous figural scenes exclusively in high relief, of which the Wolf goblet is one, were executed under Feister's aegis. In this connection compare it with a goblet in the K. H. Heine Collection, Karlsruhe (with riders: Baumgärtner 1971, no. 66, ill.) and one in the Dr. Karl Ruhmann Collection, Vienna (with pastoral scenes: Schlosser 1956, fig. 104, and 1965, fig. 186; Dreier 1965, p. 74, fig. 22). Apart from the fact that they are all decorated in the same pure high-relief, there are virtually no stylistic comparisons among these three goblets owing to the differences in the subject matter.

Lit.: Auction catalog Schöller Collection, Berlin; Schmidt 1922, p. 267; idem Ms 1931, pp. 276–277, no. 283 (as "Hermsdorf in Silesia, about 1725") (see also above, p. 74, fig. 133 a–c).

## 106 GOBLET WITH HUNTING SCENES

Silesia, possibly Hermsdorf, about 1730

Height: 22.2 cm; diameter at rim: 9.4 cm; thickness of glass: about 3–4.5 mm

Colorless glass with cutting and matt and polished relief and intaglio engraving. Pontil mark replaced by polished circlets. Small chips to rim of foot and bowl.

Underside of foot decorated with polished rosette, upperside with faceted rim embellished with stiff-leaf border. Cut baluster stem with basal collar and faceted shoulder cyst. Flared bowl with everted base cut with petal flutes below a band of raised diamonds. Sides divided into eight vertical panels, alternate wider panels decorated in wheel engraving, narrower ones in high relief. First a panel engraved with scrollwork and mirror monogram "CJVM" within the inscription (in angular calligraphy) "Rechte wahre freundtschafts- pflicht, ändert sich abwessendt nicht," beneath it a vignette with shepherd and his flock. Reverse with country house, parterre and deer fountain; remaining wheel-engraved panels with deer- and boar-hunting scenes as well as fishing scene with traps and nets. The high-relief panels filled mainly with scrollwork, a trumpeter, drummer, and flower spray.

This goblet belongs to a group of glasses with bowls with swelling bases, with alternate panels in high-relief detail and wheel-engraved decoration. Robert Schmidt comments on this group. "... continuation of the earlier *Hochschnitt* group ... which were produced up to around 1720 in the Hirschberger Tal" (1922, p. 293). This provenance is additionally confirmed by the repeated appearance on this type of glass of the Schaffgotsch fir tree device and the motto "Aucun temps ne le change." A goblet dated 1729 in the Düsseldorf Kunstmuseum indicates that this group of glasses were still being made up to around 1730.

For comparable goblets see examples formerly in the Schlossmuseum, Berlin (Schmidt 1922, fig. 167, center); in the Metropolitan Museum, New York, formerly Mühsam Collection (Schmidt 1926, pl. 18, no. 139); in the Kunstmuseum, Düsseldorf (Jantzen 1960, no. 88, pl. 24; Heinemeyer 1966, no. 348, ill.; Saldern 1968 D, no. 31, ill.); Kestner-Museum, Hanover (Mosel 1957, no. 149, pl. 48, and 1979, no. 165, pl. 44); Städtisches Reiss-Museum, Mannheim (Schmidt 1922, p. 294); formerly V. Schick collection, Prague (Bernt 1950, p. 60, pl. 68; Vávra 1954, fig. 197; and formerly in the Dr. Ruhmann Collection, Vienna (Schlosser 1956, fig. 109, and 1965, fig. 192).

Compare with footed beakers with similar decoration in: formerly Schlossmuseum, Berlin (Schmidt 1922, fig. 167, left); Kunstmuseum, Düsseldorf (Heinemeyer 1966, no. 349, ill.); Kunstgewerbemuseum, Cologne (Cologne 1963, no. 329, ill., and 1973, no. 392, ill.); Nordböhmisches Museum, Liberec (Reichenberg), Pazaurek 1902, fig. 8b; formerly V. Schick Collection, Prague (Bernt 1950, p. 60, pl. 69); Württembergisches Landesmuseum, Stuttgart (Inv. No. G 11, 268); Österreichisches Museum für angewandte Kunst, Vienna (Schlosser 1956, fig. 118, and 1965, fig. 202).

## 107 COVERED SWEETMEAT GLASS WITH BEAR HUNT

Silesia, possibly Hermsdorf, about 1730–1740

Height: 20.4 cm (with cover), 13 cm (without cover); diameter at rim: 9.9 cm; thickness of glass: about 4 mm

Colorless glass with cutting and matt and polished high relief detail and engraving. Pontil mark polished out. Small chip on rim.

Provenance: Otto Schilling Collection, Berlin.

Underside of foot decorated with polished rosette. Upper side with faceted rim embellished with wheel-engraved scrollwork border. Faceted baluster stem flanked by collar. Base of oval bowl, the ogee base cut with vertical flutes embellished with stiff-leaf border below a band of raised diamonds. Upper portion with convex sides divided into eight panels alternately decorated with wheel engraving and relief cutting. The broad sides decorated with a bear-hunting scene and a lady playing a lute. Narrow ends decorated with wheel-engraved panels of scrollwork with parkscapes and fountains. The four intermediate panels with high-relief scrolls with bunches of flowers and foliate ornament. Cover with matching alternate panels in wheel-engraving and high relief carving decorated with miniature landscapes, flowers and musical instruments. Cut artichoke finial.

The glass engraver has taken the motif of the bear hunt in a reversed and simplified form from the engravings of hunting scenes by Antonio Tempestas published in 1609 (*The Illustrated Bartsch*, vol. 37, New York, 1984, p. 45, no. 1147[a]; see above, p. 75, fig. 135). In doing so, he has left out all the background figures not directly connected with the killing of the bear and reduced the pack of hounds to two. At the same time the hunting outfits of the century-old prototype were updated.

The richly-contrasting combination of high-relief carving and engraving, a continuation on goblets and beakers of the decorative tradition of the Hermsdorf workshop of Friedrich Winter, with its distinctive vertical alternation of wheel-engraved figures and high-relief ornament, is encountered relatively seldom on the bowls of sweetmeat glasses.

Compare variants in: the Bayerisches Nationalmuseum, Munich (Rückert 1982, II, no. 772, pl. 229); the Österreichisches Museum für angewandte Kunst, Vienna (Schlosser 1956, fig. 115, and 1965, fig. 198); one formerly in the Schiftan Collection, Vienna (Auction cat. 439, Dorotheum, Vienna, 27–29 February 1936, lot no. 535, pl. XV).

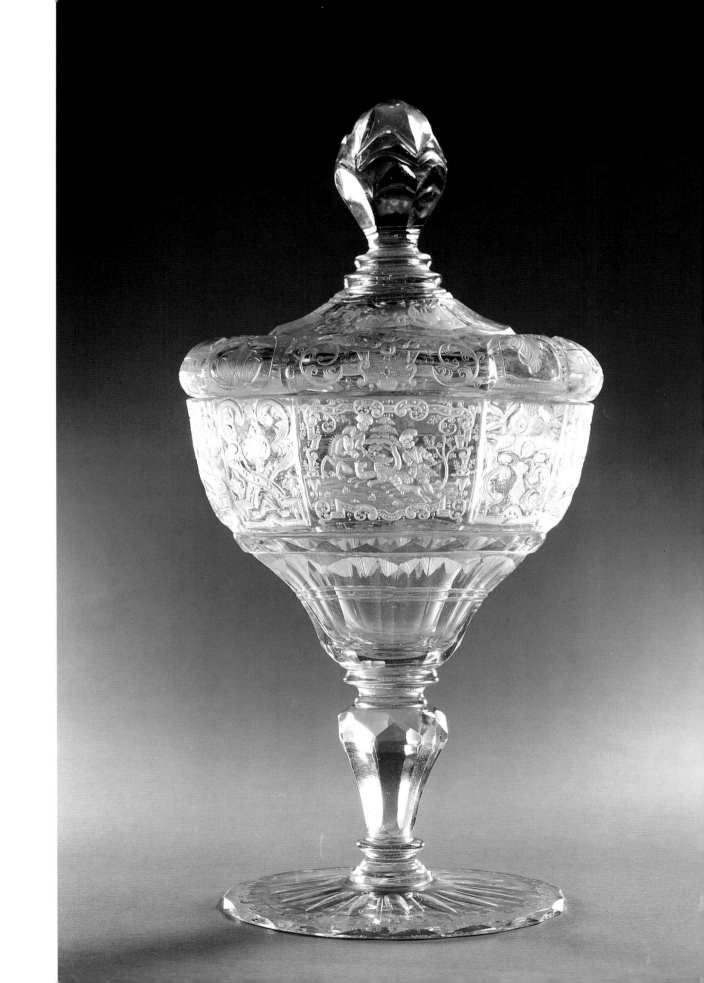

## 108  A PAIR OF GOBLETS WITH ALLEGORIES OF RELIGIOUS FREEDOM

Silesia, about 1720–1725

Height: 23.3 cm (a and b);
diameter at rim: 9.2 cm and 9.5 cm;
thickness of glass: about 2–2.5 mm

Colorless glass with ruby-glass thread inclusions, cutting and wheel engraving. Unpolished pontil mark.

Provenance: Collection of the Dukes of Anhalt-Dessau (according to Alfred Wolf papers).

Wide foot decorated with circlet of opposed foliate scrolls on the upper side. Stem with wrythen baluster and knop enclosing red threads, flanked by collars. Constricted base of the bell-shaped bowl decorated with facets. Everted base of bowl decorated on a) with honeycomb facets and on b) with arched panels. Sides decorated with a scrollwork cartouche enclosing a) an allegorical figure of Hope sitting on a snail, inscribed "Die Hoffnung besrer Zeiten" and "WENN KOMMT SIE." b) Allegorical figures of Chastity and Justice flanking an obelisk surmounted by a shield inscribed "ZÜCHTIG / GERECHT / GOTTSE / LIG," behind the seated figure of Faith, inscribed below "Sie. fragt nach guten Leuthen" / "WO SIND SIE."

The scenes are taken from both sides of a medal by Kaspar Neumann, as has been discovered by Olga Drahotová (1972, pp. 220–221) comemmorating the Agreement of the Alt-Ranstädt Convention of 1707 (see Johann Christian Kundmann, *Die Heimsuchungen Gottes in Zorn und Gnade über das Herzogthum Schlesien in Müntzen*, Leipzig o. J. (about 1742), pp. 390 onwards, table IV, 27; K. Domanig, *Die deutsche Medaille*, Vienna 1907, no. 843, pl. 97), whereby the religious freedom of the Evangelical-Lutheran Church was reconfirmed to the Silesian princes of the Augsburg Confession (Dukedoms of Brieg, Liegnitz, Münsterberg, and Öls) as well as the City of Breslau. This took place as a result of the intervention of the Swedish King Charles XII and was ratified by the Emperor Joseph I in 1709.

The glass engraver has followed almost exactly the medallic prototype. In each case he has removed the inscription from the frame, thus creating a simpler, more spacious composition. The engraving of each side of the medal, on two different glasses, which have survived together for two-and-a-half centuries, is unusual.

For decoration using both sides of Neumann's commemorative medals on front and back of the same glass, either Silesian or Bohemian, see examples in: former Krug Collection, Baden-Baden (Klesse/Saldern 1978, discussed under no. 110; Sotheby's Krug IV, lot no. 633, ill.); formerly in the Museum schlesischer Altertümer, Breslau (Czihak 1891, p. 261); Museum für Kunsthandwerk, Dresden (Schloss Pillnitz, Haase 1984, no. 64, ill.); Victoria and Albert Museum, London, Buckley Collection (Schmidt 1927, p. 32, pl. 52 C); W. L. Buchecker Collection, Lucerne (Lucerne 1981, no. 732, ill.); Kunsthandlung K. Brunnarius, Obershagen (*Weltkunst* 55, part 7, 1 April 1985, ill. p. 867); Kunstgewerbemuseum, Prague (Drahotová 1972, p. 220, figs. 12–13); Museum der Stadt, Regensburg (Baumgärtner 1977 R, no. 221, ill.); Württembergisches Landesmuseum, Stuttgart (Inv. No. 29.25); one formerly in the Biemann Collection, Zurich (Klesse/Saldern 1978, pp. 51–52, no. 110, ill.).

## 109 GOBLET DECORATED WITH ATALANTA AND HIPPOMENES

Silesian, possibly Warmbrunn, about 1730

Height: 23.6 cm; diameter at rim: 9.9 cm; thickness of glass: about 5–6 mm

Colorless glass with cutting and mainly matt with a small amount of polished wheel engraving. Small unpolished pontil mark.

Underside of foot with polished, star-shaped rosette, rim with stiff-leaf border. Cut baluster stem flanked by collar and faceted cyst. Everted base of conical bowl decorated with cut, arched panels. Sides of bowl divided into six vertical panels and decorated with the continuous scene of the race between Atalanta and Hippomenes with spectators in a landscape with trees.

The source for the mythological scene is an engraving of Crispyn de Passe after a drawing of Martin de Vos for the *Metamorphoses of Ovid* published in 1607 (see above, p. 76, fig. 138). The glass engraver has faithfully followed the original, and only in the interest of maintaining the compositional balance has left out two spectators who were obscured by the cloak of the winning Hippomenes, thus avoiding over-cutting which would render the glass engraving muddled. As the bowl allowed for more room, he included two additional figures, a standing youth and at his feet a kneeling female figure, possibly also connected with other illustrations of Ovid. There are also three animals, seemingly unconnected with the mythological scene, a lion, a running stag, and a hound, whose possible significance remains unexplained.

For a comparison of the engraved decoration (without vertical divisions) see an almost identical goblet formerly in the Krug Collection, Baden-Baden (Klesse 1973, pp. 38–40, figs. 45–46 and no. 595, ill.; Sotheby's, Krug II, lot no. 404, ill.). The Krug goblet is attributed to the best-known Warmbrunn engraver of the second third of the eighteenth century, Christian Gottfried Schneider (1710–1773). In view of certain superior artistic qualities exhibited by the Wolf goblet, an attribution to the same hand cannot be made without further justification, all the more so since a comparison with the well-known paper impressions (see Chrzanowska 1963 and Dreier 1965), believed to be his late works, reveal little to compare with these large athletic figures.

## 110 GOBLET WITH HUNTING FANFARE

Silesia, about 1725–1730

Height: 20 cm; diameter at rim: 8.5 cm;
thickness of rim: about 3.5–4 mm

Colorless to light manganese-tinted glass with cutting,
matt and small amount of polished engraving. Pontil
mark polished out. Rim with small chips.

Provenance: Friedrich Neuburg Collection, Dresden/
Leitmeritz.

Underside of foot decorated with polished rosette, upperside with matt scroll-and-strap border. Faceted
baluster stem with angular cutting. Everted base of
the conical bowl with cut, arched panels and bands of
horizontal facets. Conical bowl wheel engraved with a
continuous scene in a forest glade with a group of six
tall huntsmen playing a fanfare, four with horns and
two with shawms, among them, and in the background hounds and deer. An oval shield with the arms
of von Schiffer (a bird with a ring in its mouth, repeated on the crest) and the monograms "CHS / FVS"
hanging from a tree.

Robert Schmidt (1931) first identified the arms.

The finely-executed and extremely unusual hunting
motif must certainly be based on a graphic source,
such as plate 16 of Johann Elias Ridinger's 1729 series
of etchings *Die edle Jagdbarkeit*. Depicted there are
horn-blowing huntsmen at the end of the hunt "wenn
die Hunde ihr Recht bekommen" (when the hounds
receive their due), while the scene on the glass definitely refers to the beginning of the hunt. Unfortunately, the exact source used by the glass engraver has
not yet been identified.

It has also not been possible to relate the Wolf goblet
to any similar corpus of glass engraving where the figures are delineated with the same felicity and sureness
of touch or with the same vivacity of movement. In
this respect one can only see this glass as a forerunner
connected in the simplest terms with the group of

Silesian goblets, their bowls with everted bases, closely related in date, and decorated with relatively-large
figural scenes of children. See cat. no. 113 and its footnote.

Lit.: Schmidt Ms 1931, no. 286 (as "Silesian, about 1725").

## 111  BEAKER WITH CHILDREN AT PLAY

Silesia, Hermsdorf or Warmbrunn, about 1720–1725

Height: 12.3 cm; diameter: 9.2 cm;
thickness of glass: about 4–5 mm

Faintly manganese-tinted glass with cutting, matt high-relief carving and matt wheel engraving with small areas polished. Pontil mark polished out. Small chips on rim.

Provenance: Friedrich Neuburg Collection, Dresden/ Leitmeritz.

Base of the everted foot polished flat and decorated with central circlet within zig-zag cutting. Upper side of foot rim with matt, stiff-leaf border. Lower section of conical bowl with frieze of slanting, stiff, matt leaves over polished shell facets. Sides decorated above with a continuous frieze wheel-engraved with children at play among trees; on one side a child holding up a goblet in one hand, the other stretched toward a basket of fruit surrounded by five other children, the other side with four children playing on a see-saw, one holding a whirlygig.

As graphic sources the glass engraver has used two etchings from the 1657 series of children at play *Les jeux et plaisirs de l'enfance* by Jacques Stella (1596–1657), (see above, pp. 79–80, figs. 142 and 144). For the scene with the see-saw he has followed the print "La balançoire," giving one of the children an additional whirlygig. For the other scene he has followed equally faithfully the composition of the game *La marelle à cloche-pié*, a form of hopscotch. However, there is a slight reinterpretation here in that the skipper is furnished with a goblet and a basket of fruit and flowers at his side, so that he appears as a hero within the circle of his admiring comrades. Stylistically, there is indeed a clear relationship with the two other goblets with scenes of children (cat. nos. 112 and 113). However the execution of the faces, the handling of the hair and foliage is somewhat different so that an attribution to the same hand does not appear to be completely justifiable. The crisply profiled acanthus frieze in high relief as well as the stiff-leaf borders be-

tray the unmistakable mark of the Winter workshop in Hermsdorf.

The motif of large children at play within the Silesian glass engraver's repertoire possibly derives from Friedrich Winter himself (see for instance Drahotová 1982, fig. 72; Klesse 1965, pp. 27–30, figs. 28, 30, no. 206, ill.). Among other examples, he may have been inspired by the lively engravings of children's games after Wenzel Hollar. For a number of decades thereafter this theme was often used by the Silesian glass engraver.

Lit.: Schmidt Ms 1931, p. 276, no. 282 (as "Hermsdorf in Silesia, about 1720–1725").

## 112 COVERED GOBLET WITH CHILDREN'S GAMES

Silesia, Hermsdorf or Warmbrunn, about 1730

Height: 26 cm (with cover), 17.5 cm (without cover); diameter at rim: 8.9 cm; thickness of rim: about 4–4.5 mm (bowl and cover)

Colorless glass with cutting, matt and lightly-polished wheel engraving. Pontil mark polished out. Small chips to foot and bowl rims.

Provenance: Friedrich Neuburg Collection, Dresden/Leitmeritz; before that Consul Rosenberg Collection, Berlin.

Flat octagonal foot with chamfered corners. Underside with polished rosette; upper rim with matt, stiff-leaf border. Cut baluster stem between collars. Tapering base of bowl cut with oval flutes as on the foot, but with stronger diagonal emphasis. Bowl divided into vertical panels, the three panels on the longer side with wheel-engraved scenes: at the base of all three a miniature stag hunt, above, large children at play, on one side the game of "catch the ring and the beaker," on the other side a game of skittles. Rim of low cover with baskets of flowers in strapwork frames. Cut finial matches the baluster stem.

For the motif of the ring and beaker, the glass engraver has used in reversed form the etching "Le cercle et le bilboquet" from Jacques Stella's 1657 series of children's games (*Les jeux et plaisirs de l'enfance*), and for the game of skittles the four central figures from the plate "La marelle à cloche-pié" from the same series, and also reversed (see above, p. 79, figs. 141 and 142).
Stylistically the scenes with children have obvious parallels with cat. no. 111. Perhaps both glasses are from the same workshop, particularly in view of the same use of a rare series of engravings, although quite probably by two different hands.

Lit.: Auction cat. Consul Rosenberg, Lepke, Berlin, 1919, lot no. 658; Schmidt Ms 1931, no. 297 (as "Silesian, about 1730").

## 113   COVERED GOBLET WITH SCENES OF CHILDREN

Silesia, Hermsdorf or Warmbrunn, about 1730

Height: 29.5 cm (with cover), 20 cm (without cover);
diameter at mouth: 8.7 cm;
thickness of glass: approx 4 mm (bowl and cover)

Colorless glass with cutting as well as matt and a little
polished wheel engraving. Pontil mark polished out.
Small chip to lightly-trimmed rim.

Provenance: Friedrich Neuburg Collection, Dresden/
Leitmeritz; before that Consul Rosenberg Collection,
Berlin.


Underside of foot with star-formed, polished circlet
and zig-zag cutting; on the upper side leaf-and-strapwork border. Faceted baluster stem flanked by collars.
Tapering base of bowl embellished with band of
raised, oval panels below flutes and a frieze of arched
panels enclosing classical warrior heads, female busts,
and scrollwork motifs. Conical bowl with vertical in-
dentations forming four panels of children at play and
animals in wheel engraving: four children in a forest
glade catching a stag (a seated child with his dog on
the steps of a portico) three children in a meadow with
fruit and a child shepherd, two children under a tree
with a billy goat. Rim of cover embellished with circlet of large polished ovals below an engraved wooded
landscape including a child lying at ease and a boar
encircled by hounds. Cut artichoke finial. Cover decorated by a different hand from the bowl.


Only the printed source for the pair of children arm-
in-arm has been found so far, having been taken from
the frame of an emblematic motif from the *Amorum
Emblemata* of Otto van Veen which appeared in 1608
in Antwerp (see above, p. 81, fig. 146). The metic has
simplified the remaining children, at the same time
leaving out their wings, but otherwise following the
source exactly.
Compare also with scenes of children on cat. nos. 111
and 112, and see footnotes.

Lit.: Auction cat. Consul Rosenberg, Lepke, Berlin, 1919, lot
no. 673; Schmidt Ms 1931, no. 296 (as "Silesian, about 1725").

## 114 AN ENGRAVED COVERED GOBLET WITH MUSICAL MOTIFS AND PRUSSIAN ARMS

Silesia, possibly Casper Gottlieb Langer, Warmbrunn, about 1742–1745

Height: 28 cm (with cover), 20 cm (without cover); diameter at rim: 8.3 cm; thickness of glass: approx 2.5 mm

Colorless glass with cutting and lightly-polished wheel engraving. Unpolished pontil mark. Cover probably not original.

Provenance: Friedrich Neuburg Collection, Dresden/Leitmeritz; formerly von Bardeleben Collection, Jena (according to Schmidt 1931).

Under side of foot with polished rosette, upper side with partly latticed leaf-and-strapwork border. Cut baluster stem flanked by collars. Tapering base of conical bowl with band of petal flutes below an arcade of small panels decorated with alternate heads of classical warriors, female busts, and scrolling motifs. Sides of bowl with fourteen vertical facets decorated in delicate engraving with the arms of Prussia flanked by wild-men supporters over an ornamental socle, the remaining surface with architectural features flanking a garden terrace with a dance scene; in the center a dancing couple, to the left four musicians with violin, 'cello, shawm (or chalumeau) and hunting horn, to the right three cavaliers, seated at a table drinking and smoking, above them two lines of music in $^3/_4$ time inscribed "Polonese." Rim with matt stiff-leaf border. Twelve-faceted cover with engraved leaf-and-strap border and foliate scrolls. Faceted artichoke finial.

Thanks to Heiner Spicker of the Cologne School of Music, the music has actually been found to be a polonaise. Perhaps the piece was dedicated to a musical friend as a present.

The polonaise, a lively three-beat "Polish dance" was originally based on a strutting long-paced dance for couples, and was first danced at a court ball at the Saxon Court of Augustus the Strong in 1709 as a processional dance. Originating at the beginning of the eighteenth century, it enjoyed its greatest popularity in the second quarter of the eighteenth century, so

that it is to be found in every musical publication of the period, and it was played not just at the festivities of the nobility but in the lower ranks of society as well (see *Musik in Geschichte und Gegenwart*, Kassel-Basel-London-New York, vol. X, 1962, col. 1427–1431).

For the motif of musicians with obvious musical notation, see two Silesian goblets from more or less the same period in: the Museum für Kunsthandwerk, Frankfurt a. M. (with minuet, Ohm 1973, no. 397, ill.) and in the Metropolitan Museum of Art, New York (formerly Mühsam Collection: Schmidt 1926, pl. 20, no. 147).

Both these goblets display not only the same Silesian characteristics as the Wolf goblet but similarities in the style of engraving as well (see above, pp. 82–83, fig. 148–152). Perhaps these three musical goblets were engraved by the same hand. The convivial cavaliers are also found on the glass in New York (fig. 152). It is particularly this motif which links the musical goblets with the only fully-signed Silesian glass of this period, the 1749 goblet of the Leipzig *Kaufmannschaft* (mercantile union), preserved in the Museum für Geschichte der Stadt Leipzig, and engraved by the Warmbrunn glass engraver Casper Gottlieb Langer (see above, p. 83, fig. 153). The stylistic similarities are so great that without hesitation one can attribute all three musical goblets to this engraver, who would have produced them sometime between 1730 and 1745. On account of the Prussian coat-of-arms the Wolf goblet was probably engraved after 1742 in which year Silesia was annexed by Prussia.

Lit.: Schmidt Ms 1931, no. 285 (as "Silesian, about 1725").

## 115 GOBLET WITH FLASK COVER AND TROPHIES

Silesia, about 1730–1740

Height: 28.5 cm (with cover), 20.5 cm (without cover); diameter at rim: 10.4 cm; thickness of glass: about 3–3.5 mm (bowl)

Colorless glass with cutting and matt wheel engraving. Pontil mark polished out. Foot rim with small chip.

Provenance: Friedrich Neuburg Collection, Dresden/ Leitmeritz.

Under side of octagonal foot with polished rosette, upper rim with matt scrollwork border. Faceted baluster stem flanked by collars. Tapering bowl of oval convex/ concave section. Cover in the form of a small flask with matching lobes, neck with screw joint and faceted knop stopper. Vertical panels divided into two zones by horizontal lines in the center and at the rim. Opposed central convex panels engraved with trophies, soldiers and riders in medallions; the side panels with motifs including masks, eagles, lions, and busts among foliate strapwork. Cover with matching smaller trophies and foliate strapwork.

Compare with a similar goblet with cover in the form of a flask formerly in the Krug Collection, Baden-Baden (Klesse 1965, no. 209, ill.; Sotheby's Krug I, lot no. 196, ill.); and in the Museum für Kunsthandwerk, Dresden (Messner 1965/66, fig. 14; Haase 1984, no. 69, ill.); in the Heine Collection, Karlsruhe (Baumgärtner 1971, no. 67, ill.); Kunstgewerbemuseum, Cologne (Cologne 1963, no. 307, and 1973, no. 374 ill.); the Buchecker Collection, Lucerne (Lucerne 1981, no. 733, ill.); and in the Metropolitan Museum of Art, New York (formerly Mühsam Collection: Schmidt 1914, pl. 19, no. 126).

Lit.: Schmidt Ms 1931, no. 288 (as "Silesian, about 1725").

## 116 GOBLET WITH THE ARMS OF VON SCHLIEBEN

Silesia, probably Warmbrunn, about 1730–1740

Height: 17.5 cm; diameter at rim: 7.4 cm;
thickness of glass: about 2.3–2.5 mm

Colorless glass with cutting, matt and polished wheel engraving. Pontil mark polished out.

Provenance: Helfried Krug Collection, Mülheim a. d. R./Baden-Baden.

Under side of foot with polished rosette, upper side with circlet of finely-engraved foliate scrolls and border of small matt dots. Faceted baluster stem between collars. Flared bowl with tapered base cut with flutes below an arcaded frieze of forest animals and foliate motifs. Sides engraved with the arms of the von Schlieben family beneath a baldequin flanked by two female allegorical figures seated before columns, each holding a sword and palm frond. The reverse with the figure of Caritas with three children flanked by elaborate scrollwork frame inhabited by putti, eagles, and miniature hunting, park and landscape scenes.

Ottried Neubecker, Wiesbaden/Stuttgart, first identified the arms (in a letter, 1969).
The von Schlieben belonged to one of the oldest noble families in Brandenburg, with the rank of count of the Holy Roman Empire. A grant of the title of count from the Prussian Kingdom was made to Adam Georg von Schlieben on 12 July 1704, "Märkischer Linie zu Tucheband, kurbrandenburgischer Geh. Rat" (died 1708 without male issue) and again on the 9 August 1718, for Georg Adam von Schlieben, of a junior line, Royal Prussian Master of the Hunt (see E. H. Kneschke, *Neues allgemeines Deutsches Adelslexicon*, vol. VIII, p. 209). Only the last-named could have commissioned this glass.

Lit.: Klesse 1973, no. 580, ill.; Sotheby's, Krug II, lot no. 405, ill.

## 119 FOOTED BEAKER WITH PASTORAL SCENE

Silesia, Warmbrunn, possibly workshop of Christian Gottfried Schneider, about 1745

Height: 14.3 cm; diameter: 8.7 cm; thickness of glass: about 3.6 mm

Colorless to light manganese-tinted glass with cutting and matt and a little polished wheel engraving. Pontil mark polished out. Small crack at the rim.

Provenance: Friedrich Neuburg Collection, Dresden/Leitmeritz; before that Spitzner Collection, Dresden (not included in 1918 auction catalog).

Under side of foot with polished rosette, polygonal faceted foot rim with matt stiff-leaf border on the upper side. Conical bowl with tapering base cut with petal flutes. Sides divided into sections by vertical panels of high-relief decoration: on one side a parkscape with seated shepherdess being offered a basket of fruit and flowers by a shepherd, in the background a standing shepherdess pointing to a wall fountain, below, a cartouche with miniature landscapes. On the reverse, a large polished palmette in relief with shell-like ornamentation on the lower half, from which issue leaves engraved with a rich variety of miniature landscapes, on the central leaf the monogramm "FR" with Prussian eagle, trophies, and flags, as well as to the sides under the palmette.

Compare with cat. no. 120 and variants in: the Art Institute, Chicago (formerly Mühsam Collection: Schmidt 1914, no. 149, with illustrated paper impression); Auction cat. Lepke, Berlin, March 1914, lot no. 93, ill. with impression); Museum für Kunsthandwerk, Dresden (Messner 1965/6, fig. 23; Haase 1984 no. 84, ill.); Kunstmuseum, Düsseldorf (Heinemeyer 1966, no. 371, ill.); and formerly in the art trade, Munich (Bernt 1950, p. 60, pl. 70).
The parallels in Chicago, Dresden, and Munich have been attributed to Christian Gottfried Schneider. A comparison with paper impressions of traditional pastoral scenes by this metic (see above, p. 85, fig. 159) shows more animated and graduated details of figures

and ornament, so that one cannot think of this glass as being by the same hand. However, the very similar handling of the trees and parkscapes suggests that the Wolf glass is a product of the workshop of Christian Gottfried Schneider. If Robert Schmidt hesitated over an attribution in 1931, it was perhaps over the question of master or apprentice.

Lit.: Schmidt Ms 1931, no. 314 (as "Silesian, about 1740–1745").

## 120  BEAKER WITH ALLEGORICAL AND PASTORAL SCENES

Silesia, Warmbrunn, workshop of Christian Gottfried Schneider, about 1745

Height: 13.4 cm; diameter: 9 cm;
thickness of glass: about 3.5 mm

Colorless glass with cutting and wheel engraving with polished circlets. Pontil mark polished out. Bowl rim considerably chipped. Foot rim with small chips.

Everted foot with faceted rim below faceted basal collar supporting the flared bowl with tapering base cut with petal flutes. Sides with wheel engraving: on one side the allegorical figures of Pax and Justitia as an embracing couple on a scrolled base, the reverse with scrollwork cartouche enclosing inscription "Es grün / und blüh / die Schlesische / Redligkeit." The spaces in between infilled with pastoral scenes in a park setting, on one side a seated shepherdess feeding a lamb, and further off a shepherd; on the other side a seated shepherdess with two shepherds, to whom a gallant is offering a basket of fruit and flowers.

For the motif of the gallant offering fruit and flowers see cat. no. 119 and corresponding footnote.

This beaker certainly comes from the same workshop as cat. no. 119, however the engraving here is coarser and more schematic, so that it cannot be attributed to the same hand (see also above, p. 85, fig. 161).

# 121 COVERED BEAKER
## WITH VON SCHWEINICHEN ARMS

Silesia, about 1735–1740

Height: 21.5 cm (with cover), 13.2 cm (without cover);
diameter at rim: 8.2 cm;
thickness of glass: about 3.5 mm (bowl),
2.5 mm (cover)

Colorless to light manganese-tinted glass with cutting
and wheel engraving. Pontil mark polished out.

Provenance: Friedrich Neuburg Collection, Dresden/
Leitmeritz.

Foot with polygonal facets and matt, stiff-leaf border,
supporting a faceted, flattened knop and flared bowl
tapering at the base. Sides decorated with the arms of
the Silesian family of von Schweinichen (blazon: a
leaping boar; crest: a demi-boar) flanked by foliate
mantling and the mirror monogram "GSvS" surmounted by a coronet, both above foliate socles.
Flanking scenes with mounted cavaliers with drawn
swords. Rim with matt, stiff-leaf border. Flattened
cover with four different foliate motifs. Finial with
faceted collar and spire knop.

Robert Schmidt first identified the arms (1931).
The mounted cavaliers are taken from dressage prints
of *Haute école* riding, as first appeared in the series
published by Antoine de Pluvinel in Paris in 1627 *Instruction du Roy en exercise de monter a cheval*, popular in the seventeenth and eighteenth centuries. One of
the mounted figures is taken in a reversed form from a
plate titled *Changieren rechts* from the series *Neue
Reit Schul* of Johann Elias Ridinger, published in
Augsburg in 1734 (Thienemann 641; see above, p. 86,
fig. 163).
For the relatively rare dressage motif compare with an
example after Philipp Rugendas in Pazaurek 1902,
pp. 11–12, fig. 9, pl. 11c (there with reference to further related examples); as well as variants in Schmidt
(1914, no. 136, text ill.), and Saldern (1968, no. 204,
ill.).

Lit.: Schmidt Ms 1931, no. 307 (as "Silesian, about 1730").

## 122 COVERED GOBLET WITH SCENES WITH GALLANTS AND ARMS OF VON MAXEN

Silesia, Warmbrunn, about 1750–1760

Height: 27.3 cm (with cover), 19.9 cm (without cover); diameter at rim: 8.5 cm; thickness of glass: about 3 mm (bowl and cover).

Colorless to light manganese-tinted glass with cutting, matt, semi-polished, and polished engraving. Pontil mark polished out. Rim of foot and bowl chipped. Cover probably not original.

Under side of foot with polished rosette, upper side with matt, stiff-leaf border round the rim. Cut baluster shaft flanked by collars. Tapering base to conical bowl with ring of polished palmettes in high relief below a circlet of polished, foliate scrolls. Sides with richly ornamented scrollwork cartouche enclosing the coat-of-arms of the Prussian noble family of von Maxen (shield: three lime leaves; crest: a hat with three feathers) and monogram "AvM". Reverse with miniature landscapes enclosed by polished palmettes and opposed shell scrolls. The sides decorated above crossed flower sprays with delicate island bases, one supporting a music-making couple beneath a tree, the other a seated couple, the gallant holding a bird's nest. Rim embellished with foliate scroll border. Low cover cut with petal flutes, two large and two small high-relief polished palmettes with foliate scrolls in between; faceted artichoke finial.

The coat-of-arms has been identified by Ottfried Neubecker, Wiesbaden/Stuttgart (in a letter of 13 April 1984). The family von Maxen, originally from Saxony (*Maxen bei Pirna*) was settled in Niederauslitz from the fifteenth to the nineteenth century. The final expansion of their estates took place towards the end of the eighteenth century, and in particular in the region of Züllichau-Schwiebusisch, where the last Alexander von Maxen owned Klein-Dammer, Keltschen, and Walmersdorf until 1772, and Carl Andreas von Maxen until 1774 (Siebmacher, *Großes und allgemeines Wappenbuch*, vol. VI, sect. 5, Nuremberg, 1880, p. 59). The monogram "AvM" therefore probably refers to Alexander von Maxen.

Compare the motif of the music-making couple with four other glasses with the same motif by the same hand in: the Kunstgewerbemuseum, Prague (footed beaker: Vávra 1954, pl. 82, fig. 203); Kunstgewerbemuseum, Zurich (goblet: Billeter 1969, fig. 112); one formerly in the Biemann Collection, Zurich (footed beaker: Klesse/Saldern 1978, pp. 52–53, figs. 117 and 120, ill.; Sotheby's, Biemann, lot. no. 109 and 110, ill.); and former Beck Collection, (footed beaker, Auct. cat. Sotheby's, London, 23 November 1964, lot no. 24, ill.).

This glass engraver, who could be known as the "Master of the gallants-in-a-park scenes" has repeated the same motifs on the Wolf glass as on the others, if on a reduced scale, so that there is no doubt of the same authorship. A further beaker with the subject of a promenade, formerly in the Biemann Collection, Zurich (Klesse/Saldern 1978, pp. 52–53, fig. 118, no. 121, ill.) can also be attributed to this metic. Certain details in the treatment of foliate and fantastic ornament lead one to believe that the artist could have been a pupil of Christian Gottfried Schneider, and certainly one of the most accomplished engravers of the later generation of the third quarter of the century.

## 123 SWEETMEAT GLASS WITH ARMS OF VON SAURMA-JELTSCH

Silesia, Hirschberger Tal, second quarter 18th century

Height: 12.5 cm; width: 9.1 cm;
thickness of glass: about 3.5–4 mm

Colorless glass with cutting, matt, and polished engraving. Pontil mark polished out.

Provenance: Friedrich Neuburg Collection, Dresden/Leitmeritz; before that Dr. Spitzner Collection, Dresden (not included in 1918 auction cat.).

Under side of foot with polished rosette, upper side with polygonal, faceted rim and matt, stiff-leaf border. Faceted baluster between collars. Boat-shaped bowl with splayed, palmette-shaped panels rising towards the curvilinear rim, smaller, pendant palmettes at the ends, one pulled up into a curving handle. Leaves of the palmettes engraved with: on one side the arms of the Silesian family of von Saurma-Jeltsch (pale, to dexter, or, a crowned lion rampant, to sinister, or, a spread-eagle) within a scrolling frame, on the reverse, in identical frame a terrace with fountain. Spout decorated with a seated Chinaman and a dog. All panels embellished with finely-executed foliate and strapwork scrolls.

The original identification of the arms by Robert Schmidt (1931) is confirmed by Ottfried Neubecker, Wiesbaden/Stuttgart (in a letter of 13 April 1984); see M. Gritzner and Ad. M. Hildebrandt, *Wappenalbum der gräflichen Familien Deutschlands und Österreich-Ungarns etc.*, vol. IV, Leipzig 1890, pl. (s.p.); A. Frhr. von Krane, *Wappen- und Handbuch des in Schlesien einschließlich der Oberlausitz landgesessenen Adels*, Görlitz 1901–1904, pp. 109–111).

This glass was possibly commissioned for Leuthold, Freiherr von Saurma-Jeltsch. This is based on the contempory statement of Johann Sinapius: "Jetziger Zeit: Herr Leuthold, Freyherr von Sauerma von und zu der Jeltsch, Herr auf Laßkowitz, Jeltsch, Gnichwitz, Schlantz etc. in Breßlauischen, und auf Reichenwalde und Pohlnisch Hündorff im Hirschbergisch-Jauri-

schen, ward als Haeres Fidei-Comissarius in possessionem der Güter Laßkowitz den 11. May 1723 durch die Königl. Hof-Gerichte introduciret ..." (*Schlesische Curiositäten darinnen die Gräflichen Freyherrlichen und Adelichen Geschlechter*, Leipzig and Breslau 1728, vol. II, p. 425).

For the form of this sweetmeat glass compare with other examples in: the Nordböhmisches Museum, Liberec (Reichenberg), (Pazaurek 1902, pl. 24a and c); the British Museum, London (London 1968, no. 248, ill.); and formerly in a private collection (Bernt 1950, p. 61, pl. 71).

A glass of identical form in the Kunstmuseum, Düsseldorf (Heinemeyer 1966, no. 362, ill.), with the Schaffgotsch fir-tree device and the motto "Aucun temps ne le change" is a reproduction from the late nineteenth century, as is a variant formerly in the Krug Collection, Baden-Baden, Sotheby's, Krug III, lot no. 610, ill.).

Lit.: Schmidt Ms 1931, no. 315 (as "Silesia, about 1740–1745").

Silesia, Hirschberger Tal, second quarter 18th century

Height: 12.9 cm; width: 9.4 cm;
thickness of glass: about 4.5–5.5 mm

Colorless glass with cutting and wheel engraving. Pontil mark polished out. Small chips on rim of bowl and foot.

Provenance: Friedrich Neuburg Collection, Dresden/ Leitmeritz; before that Dr. Spitzner Collection, Dresden (not included in 1918 auction cat.).

Under side of foot cut with polished rosette. Upper side with polygonal, faceted rim embellished with matt engraved, stiff-leaf border. Cut baluster stem flanked by collars. Boat-shaped bowl with polished, high-relief band of lappets round the base, long sides with polished, high-relief, pendant palmettes and one at the "stern" drawn up into a handle. Area below the spout engraved with an as yet unidentified coat-of-arms (a seated child holding a spray of lily of the valley) in a rich foliate-scroll and strapwork frame. Each leaf of the palmettes on the long side embellished with miniature landscapes and foliate motifs. Handle palmette undecorated.

For shape and decoration, see comparable examples in: formerly Schlossmuseum, Berlin (Schmidt 1922, fig. 165 left); Heine Collection, Karlsruhe (Baumgärtner 1971, no. 76, ill.); Victoria and Albert Museum, London (Buckley Collection: Schmidt 1927, pl. 52 B); Bayerisches Nationalmuseum, Munich (Rückert 1982 II, no. 776, pl. 231); Kunstgewerbemuseum, Prague (Vávra 1954, fig. 204); one formerly in the Biemann Collection, Zurich (Klesse/Saldern 1978, no. 132, ill.; Sotheby's, Biemann, lot no. 117, ill.); see also cat. no. 125.

Lit.: Schmidt Ms 1931, no. 316 (as "Silesian, about 1740–1745").

## 125  SWEETMEAT GLASS
## WITH RELIEF PALMETTES

Silesia, Hirschberger Tal, second quarter 18th century

Height: 13 cm; width 8.8 cm;
thickness of glass: about 4–4.5 mm

Colorless glass with cutting, matt and polished wheel
engraving and high-relief carving. Pontil mark polished out.


Under side of foot decorated with polished rosette, upper side with polygonal, faceted rim and matt engraved, stiff-leaf border. Cut baluster stem flanked by
collars. Boat-shaped bowl of oval section decorated
with high-relief carved elements, at the base a band of
tongue-shaped lappets; on the long sides two pendant
palmettes, a palmette drawn up into a handle at the
"stern," the rim following the contours of the palmettes. Spout decorated with an empty scrollwork cartouche flanked by trophies, the side palmettes embellished with engraved, miniature landscapes and foliate
motifs continued on the intervening spaces.

See cat. no. 124, and corresponding footnote.

## 128  COVERED BEAKER WITH ARMS OF BRANDENBURG-SCHWEDT

Potsdam-Berlin, Gottfried Spiller, 1689–1698

Height: 22 cm (with cover), 12.2 cm (without cover); diameter at rim: 9.2 cm; thickness of glass: about 7–8 mm

Colorless glass with slight straw tint with polished cutting and matt and polished high-relief carving and engraving. Pontil polished out with circlets. Inner rim of cover with small chips.

Provenance: Friedrich Neuburg Collection, Dresden/Leitmeritz; before that Collection of the Dukes of Anhalt-Dessau, Schloss Dessau and the Gotisches Haus at Wörlitz.

Flat base with central circlet and everted rim cut with a band of polished ovals below a raised band of acanthus leaves. Sides engraved with opposed medallions over crossed cornucopiae on which perch putti supporting the surmounting crown, one medallion with the arms of Brandenburg, the other with the mirror monogram "PWMVB" (Philipp Wilhelm, Margrave of Brandenburg-Schwedt). Side panels decorated with a dancing child with bunches of grapes and fruit. Rim with band of polished ovals. Terraced cover with two bands of raised acanthus leaves flanking a deeply-engraved band of fruit. Cut and polished pine-cone finial.

Robert Schmidt writes about this beaker (Ms 1931, p. 223): "I have already illustrated this splendid beaker, decorated in Spiller's rich style, in the *Brandenburgische Gläser*, pl. 11,3; there I did not decipher the monogram correctly and could not identify the owner. I now believe the initials PWMVB definitely refer to Philipp Wilhelm, Margrave of Brandenburg-Schwedt. He was a son of the great Elector and his wife Dorothee von Holstein-Glücksberg, born on 19 May 1669, and married the daughter of Duke Johann Georg II von Anhalt-Dessau on the 25 January 1699, and died on 19 December 1711. His marriage to a princess of Dessau would explain its appearance in Anhalt."
Philipp Wilhelm became Margrave of Brandenburg-Schwedt in 1689. As there is no reference to a mar-

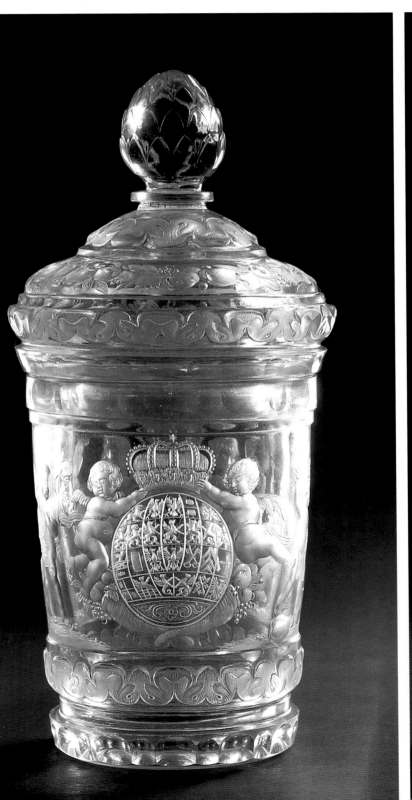

riage on the beaker, this would suggest it was commissioned before that event, thus between 1689 and 1698. Margrave Philipp Wilhelm was an enthusiastic collector of fine glasses, as is confirmed by the contents of a number of inventories from 1682, 1713 and 1771, which have been systematically analyzed by Walter Stengel (1948, pp. 5–8, 36, 51–55).

Compare with a beaker, very similar in form and decoration, engraved with the arms of the Elector Friedrich III of Brandenburg, half-brother of Philipp Wilhelm of Brandenburg-Schwedt, in The Corning Museum of Glass, Corning (Charleston 1980, no. 62, with col. pl.; see above, p. 93, figs. 170–171). Judging from the dates of his reign, this beaker must have been commissioned between 1688 and 1700. The decoration on the Corning beaker is closely related to a glass in the Württembergisches Landesmuseum in Stuttgart (Pazaurek 1927, fig. 28; see above, p. 93, fig. 172), which bears the arms and monogram of the Electress Christine Eberhardine of Saxony, of the house of Brandenburg-Bayreuth. This glass is also contemporary with the above mentioned glasses, as the Electress was married in 1693 and died in 1697. It is therefore possible to assume that the beaker in the Wolf Collection dates from the 1690's.

Compare the motif of the children from the same period of Spiller's *œuvre* with a group of beakers decorated with bacchanalian children, already discussed by Pazaurek (1927, p. 48), among which the example in the Green Vaults, Dresden (Schmidt 1914 B. G., pl. 8; Schade 1968, fig. 66; Menzhausen 1982, color plate p. 97) and the one in the Victoria and Albert Museum, London (Schmidt 1914 B. G., pl. 7, nos. 2 and 3) are the best known.

Lit.: Schmidt 1914, p. 74, pl. 11, no. 3; Pazaurek 1927, p. 47; Schmidt Ms 1931, pp. 223–224, no. 199; Stengel 1948, p. 51.

## 131 GOBLET WITH PRUSSIAN COAT OF ARMS

Potsdam-Berlin, about 1715 (after 1713)

Height: 25.5 cm; diameter at rim: 12.4 cm;
thickness of glass: about 3.5 mm

Colorless glass with cutting, as well as matt and polished relief detail and wheel engraving.

Foot, baluster stem, and base of conical bowl with matt relief acanthus-leaf borders. Flattened collars of stem with stiff-leaf wreath and circlet borders. Sides decorated within a medallion with the Prussian coat-of-arms (lower quarterings omitted) surmounted by crown and backed onto mantling with wild-men supporters and eagles, the wild men holding pennants inscribed "FWR" (*Fridericus Wilhelmus Rex*). Reverse with crowned, strap-work cartouche inscribed with the monogram "FWR" flanked by trophies and weapons. Rim embellished with cabochon-and-circlet border.

The Prussian coat-of-arms is seldom depicted within a round shield, unless as a marriage goblet, for instance a goblet with the arms of Frederick William I and his wife Sophie Dorothea (see Klesse 1973, no. 618, ill.; Sotheby's Krug I, lot. no. 100, with col. pl.).
Compare with examples with the more usual armorial rendering from the later reign of Frederick I and the early part of Frederick William I's reign in: the Herbert Dreja-Nilges Collection, Arnoldshain (Saldern 1968, no. 219, ill.); one formerly in the Kaiser-Friedrich-Museum, Görlitz (Schmidt 1914 B. G., pl. 19, no. 2, dated 1707); Nordbömisches Gewerbemuseum, Liberec (Reichenberg) (Pazaurek 1902, pl. 32b); the collection of Count Schönborn, Pommersfelden (Saldern 1968, no. 218); the Jobst von Zanthier Collection, Schloss Schmachtenberg (Saldern 1968, no. 215, ill.).

## 132 COVERED GOBLET WITH CHILDREN WITH FRUIT

Glass: Silesia, Hermsdorf, Friedrich Winter workshop, about 1710
decoration: Berlin, about 1720–1725

Height: 29.7 cm (with cover), 20.7 cm (without cover); diameter at rim: 9.8 cm;
thickness of glass: about 4.5 mm (bowl), 3 mm (cover)

Colorless, light, manganese-tinted glass with cutting, matt high-relief detail and matt and polished wheel engraving. Unpolished pontil mark.

Upper side of foot, baluster stem, base of bell-shaped bowl, and rounded cover decorated with relief matt acanthus leaves on polished, arched borders. Conical sides with wheel-engraved decoration with small, polished details: fruit festoons embellished with small cornucopiae and birds, linked by ribbons held in place by flying putti. Rim with border of polished circlets. Cover decorated with ribbon scrolls and fruit. Knop finial cut with matt leaves.

For this type of goblet with high-relief foliate borders placed at regular intervals on the body, see parallels as well as variants from the Winter workshop, among others in: formerly Krug Collection, Baden-Baden (Klesse 1973, no. 563, ill.; Sotheby's Krug I, lot no. 201, ill.); the Kunstgewerbemuseum, Staatliche Museen Preußischer Kulturbesitz (ibid. p. 30); in the Museum für Kunsthandwerk (Ohm 1973, no. 385, ill.); Kunstgewerbemuseum, Prague (Vávra 1954, pl. 77, fig. 189); and one formerly in the Biemann Collection, Zurich (Klesse/Saldern 1978, no. 108, ill.).
Ever since Robert Schmidt first researched this subject it has been known that Silesian, as well as Bohemian, Saxon, and Thuringian blanks and partly-decorated glasswares were imported into Brandenburg, despite repeated efforts of successive electors to stem the tide by means of trade restrictions, and they were a considerable and continued source of competition for the Brandenburg glasshouse. (Schmidt 1914 B. G., pp. 5–6, 11–13, 44).

The engraved decoration was certainly carried out subsequently by a Berlin glass engraver. This supposition is not just based on stylistic grounds and the motif of the *Früchtekinder* (children with fruit) so characteristic of the Berlin work of Martin Winter and Gottfried Spiller, but also that the engraver of this glass must have seen an example from the Spiller workshop. An early Potsdam goblet engraved with the arms of the Elector of Trier, Hugo, Freiherr von Orsbeck (reigned 1676–1711) has exactly these motifs of children and fruit. It has five putti, and Pazaurek ascribes it to Spiller himself (1927, pp. 50–52, fig. 30–31). Sadly, this glass, on temporary loan from the Judicial Councillor A. Wiest of Landstuhl to the Historisches Museum der Pfalz in Speyer from 1912 onwards, disappeared around 1928 (or later?). This information was kindly supplied by F. X. Portenlänger of that museum in a letter of 4 January 1984). (See *Führer durch das Historische Museum der Pfalz*, 4th edition, Speyer 1914, p. 74; Friedrich von Bassermann-Jordan, *Führer durch das Weinmuseum im Historischen Museum der Pfalz zu Speyer am Rhein*, 1928, p. 21). Due to the poor quality of the Pazaurek illustration, it is not possible to make any comparative evaluation. However, this goblet, originating from before 1711 (Pazaurek dates it around 1680–1690) must be earlier than the Wolf goblet. The engraved decoration would appear to be superior to that on the slightly later Wolf goblet.
At the same time, there is no basis for a comparison with the children-and-fruit engraved much later by Elias Rosbach (see for example Schmidt 1914 B. G., pl. 33, no. 1 and 3 ; pl. 34, no. 2; Drahotová 1982, fig. 82) executed in a style more gracious, decorative, and above all with surer anatomical accuracy.

## 135 GOBLET WITH BACCHANALIAN SCENE

Potsdam-Berlin, about 1720–1730

Height: 18.1 cm; diameter at rim: 9.4 cm;
thickness of glass: about 4 mm

Colorless glass with cutting, as well as matt and polished high-relief detail and wheel engraving. Pontil cut with circlets.

Conical foot and base of conical bowl decorated with matt high-relief, stiff-leaf collars, stem with large, shoulder knop flanked by flattened knops, all cut with bands of polished circlets. Sides of bowl wheel engraved with polished details with a continuous meadow scene with the youthful Bacchus, crowned with fruiting vine, lying near a billy-goat, holding up a goblet in his right hand to be filled from a carafe by an acolyte: the reverse with two further children with grapes and a basket of fruit. Rim embellished with matt, cabochon border, above a border of polished circlets.

Compare with goblets decorated with similar bacchanalian scenes, one in a private anonymous collection (Schlosser 1956, fig. 142, and 1965, fig. 229), another formerly in the Julius Schülein Collection, Munich (Ludwig F. Fuchs, *Ein signierter Pokal von Elias Rosbach,* in: *Belvedere* 8, 1929, pp. 437–438, figs. 25 and 25a). For the bacchanalian motifs compare also with cat. no. 136.

## 136 GOBLET WITH INFANT BACCHANALE

Potsdam-Berlin, about 1735

Height: 17.1 cm; diameter at rim: 8.8 cm;
thickness of glass: about 2.5 mm

Colorless glass with cutting and matt and polished
high-relief detail and engraving. Unpolished pontil.

Conical foot with matt, stiff-leaf collar in relief. Short
stem with honeycomb facets merging into arched panels decorated with vertical rows of cabochons reserved
on a matt ground. Drawn conical bowl decorated with
a continuous woodland and meadow scene with the
infant Bacchus, crowned with fruiting vine, and lean-
ing against a barrel, in his raised right hand a shell being filled from a carafe by an acolyte. Near him on the
grass a seated shawm-player with two dancing children, and finally the goddess Diana with lunar headdress and quiver, reclining scantily-draped among her
hounds and being invited to the dance by the small
figure of Amor. Rim embellished with cabochon and
dot borders.

For a discussion of the motif of the children's bacchanale see also cat. no. 135.

## 142 COVERED GOBLET WITH ARMS AND MONOGRAM OF AUGUSTUS THE STRONG

Dresden, 1731

Height: 41.5 cm (with cover), 25.2 cm (without cover), diameter at rim: 9.8 cm;
thickness of glass: about 5–6 mm (bowl), 6–8 mm (cover)

Colorless glass with cutting, as well as matt and polished high-relief detail. Pontil mark polished out. Rim chipped.

Provenance: Friedrich Neuburg Collection, Dresden/Leitmeritz; before that von Bardeleben Collection, Jena.

Conical foot decorated with a collar of double scallops in relief. The massive stem and matching cover finial carved on the lower portion with the initials "AR" repeated three times in polished relief on a matt ground, the shoulder knop in the form of a crown with jeweled details. Conical bowl with collar of relief scallops at the base below the royal arms of Saxony-Poland and pendant Golden Fleece beneath a crown and framed by scrolled mantling and crowned eagles perched on acanthus scrolls, all carved in high relief, the reverse with the Polish Order of the White Eagle, also in relief. Cover in the form of an elector's cap with ermine fringe and vertical flutes. Elements of stem repeated on the finial which ends in a crown and orb.

This goblet is first mentioned in an account sent to King Augustus the Strong on the 10 December 1731 by Adam Heinrich Rauhe, clerk of the royal glasshouse at Dresden as:
"Auff Ihro Königl. Majest. in Pohlen und Churfürstl. Durchl. zu Sachssen, allergnädigsten hohen Mündl. Befehl sind aus dero Glass-Fabrique nachfolgende kostbare Gläser verfertiget und gelieffert worden, alss 1 gross stark Gesundheitsglass, unten am Fusse mit Muscheln, am Knopff A. R. in Triangel, darüber die Königl. Crone, am Kelch unten mit Muscheln und auf einer Seite das Pohl. und Sächss. Wappen, welche 2 Adler halten, unten am Wappen das goldene Fliess,

## 144 RUBY-GLASS TEAPOT

Glass: Dresden, about 1713–1718
Mounts: probably Dresden, about 1740–50

Height: 17 cm (with cover), 13.2 cm (without cover);
width: 19 cm;
thickness of glass: about 5.5–9 mm

Deep-red to purple, amethyst-tinted gold-ruby glass.
Pontil mark polished flat. Silver mounts partly gilt,
unmarked.

Terraced silver foot with *repousée* rococo scrolls supporting the depressed, globular body with small, everted foot ring and short neck in very thick, gold-ruby
glass. Curved spout in amethyst-tinted glass with basal, silver mount connected to the foot ring and neck
ring with a vertical, silver strap, another one connecting the scroll handle in the form of a satyr balanced on
an acanthus scroll, grasping an arrangement of flowers. Domed cover also decorated with scrolls and with
finial in the form of a kneeling Chinaman (screw
joint).

Together with cat. no. 145, this teapot belongs to a
group of unusually heavy and thick-walled teapots in
gold-ruby glass, of unusual but perfect proportions,
which are balanced by the strongly curved form of the
spout. All have in common the lack of an applied glass
handle which in each case has been supplied by the
silversmith and which connects the foot and neck
mounts. Three of these teapots are engraved with the
crowned "AR" monogram, the reverse with the Sax-
on/Polish arms (in the Staatliche Kunstsammlungen,
Grünes Gewölbe, Dresden: Fetzer 1977, no. 3, with
col. pl.; on the London art market: Auction cat. Sotheby's, 10 February 1986, lot no. 178, col. ill.; and in
Nuremberg, Germanisches Nationalmuseum: Baumgärtner, 1977, p. 83, fig. 120; see also above, p. 102,
fig. 188). Stylistically the shape, monogram, and arms
would seem to apply to Augustus the Strong. (The silver and silver-gilt mounts are almost in all cases of later date, those on the London and Nuremberg examples are by the master Schwerino Bergkstädt, who became a master in 1749 [see R³, no. 1811], thus dating
them to the middle of the eighteenth century.)

In contrast to the frequently-stressed statement concerning the Dresden ruby-glass production, that one is
dealing above all with overlay glass, the teapots would
seem to consist of completely colored glass. It seems
obvious that Johann Friedrich Böttger, the originator
of European porcelain, in his simultaneous development of gold-ruby glass at the Dresden Court,
would not just have made overlaid wares but also large
pieces in ruby-glass itself. R. J. Charleston is of this
opinion when discussing other ruby-glass pieces with
Dresden characteristics (1977, p. 214, notes to no. 59).

## 145 RUBY-GLASS TEAPOT

Glass: Dresden, about 1713–1718
Mounts: Dresden, about 1730–1740

Height: 9.6 cm (with cover), 7 cm (without cover);
width: 11 cm;
thickness of glass: about 3–4.5 mm

Deep raspberry-red to amethyst-colored, gold-ruby glass. Pontil obscured by shallow cut circlet. Unmarked silver-gilt mounts.

Raised silver-gilt foot ring with *repousée* scrolls and lappet border, supporting the depressed, globular body with everted, small foot and short neck in thick-walled, deep-red, gold-ruby glass. Silver-gilt scroll handle with seated putto linking the foot and neck rim. Domed cover with *repousée* fruiting vine and small ribbed melon knop.

For the question of origin see cat. no. 144.
In contrast to these well-blown, richly-colored, silver-mounted, Dresden, ruby-glass teapots, there is another group of ruby-glass pots, which are not only considerably larger, less elegant of shape, and less bluish in color, but are also recognizable by the consistently-applied glass handle. They are thought to be products of either Potsdam or South Germany. For relevant examples, see pieces in: Märkisches Museum, Berlin (*Das Märkische Museum und seine Sammlungen, Festgabe zum 100jährigen Bestehen*, Berlin, 1974, p. 57; Fetzer 1977, no. 8, col. ill.); Kunstgewerbemuseum, Cologne (Cologne 1963, no. 284, ill; 1973, no. 231, ill.; Klesse/ Mayr 1977, pp. 104–105, col. pl.); Schwerin Museum, Schwerin (with Augsburg mounts by Matthäus Baur, unpublished); in a private collection (with Augsburg mounts: Heine 1912, ill, p. 127; Mylius 1927, ill. p. 39); the James A. de Rothschild Collection, Waddesdon Manor (with Augsburg mounts by Matthäus Baur: Charleston 1977, pp. 208–209, no. 56, ill.).

## 146 ROTHENBURG ARMORIAL COVERED GOBLET

Saxony or Bohemia, probably about 1736

Height: 50 cm (with cover), 33 cm (without cover); Diameter at rim: 13.8 cm; thickness of glass:
about 3–4 mm (rim), 1.5 mm (cover)

Colorless glass with red and gilt thread inclusions, cutting, as well as matt and polished wheel engraving. Polished pontil mark. Screw threads damaged.


Upper side of conical foot decorated with engraved, foliate scrolls around the rim, and collar of polished petal flutes. Stem with three faceted knops interspersed with pairs of collars, the upper two knops having red and gold spiral thread inclusions, and are linked with a screw joint. Tall, bell bowl with faceted, incurving base. Sides engraved with a wreath medallion enclosing the arms of the Silesian counts of Rothenburg (to dexter a crowned lion rampant, to sinister three bendlets, crest: a millstone and peacock feathers) surmounted by a coronet and flanked by trophies and banners as well as two children with clubs, all framed within elaborate foliate scrolls and supported on scroll and palm-frond socle. Domed cover with everted rim cut with facets and band of scrolls and strapwork around the rim, and with finial an inverted version of the stem.

The coat-of-arms was identified by Ottfried Neubecker, Wiesbaden/Stuttgart (by letter, 2 April 1985). Among the various branches of the family of Rothenburg, who originated from the epomynous place in Lower Silesia in the area of Grünberg, the most important in the eighteenth century were those of Nettkow and Beutnitz. Nicolaus Friedrich von Rothenburg (1646–1716), a member of the Beutnitz line was a soldier in the service of the King of France, became *marechal de camp*, and was elevated with his son Conrad Alexander (1684–1735) to the rank of a count by Louis XIV. When the Beutnitz line died out, their estates passed to Alexander Rudolf von Rothenburg (1677–1758) of the Nettkow branch, District Administrator of Crossen, who was raised to the rank of a Prussian count on 14 April 1736. On his death in 1758, he entailed his considerable possessions to his son Johann Sigismund (Siebmacher, vol. VI sect. 8, *Der abgestorbene Adel der Provinz Schlesien und der Oberlausitz*, revised by K. Blazek, Nuremberg, 1887, pp. 89–90, pl. 65). It is possible that the glass was commissioned on the elevation of the family to the rank of Prussian counts in 1736.

Despite small variations, the form of this goblet is comparable in profile with large Saxon covered goblets, engraved by Johann Franz Trümper (see Klesse 1972, pp. 135 onward, figs. 41–45 and 48; idem 1973, pp. 56–58, figs. 72–75, 77, no. 641, ill.). Unusual in view of the Saxon provenance is the use of red and gold threads in the stem and finial, features usually found on Bohemian glasses. The scrollwork decoration also includes strong Bohemian features, evidence of its widespread influence on Saxon glass engraving in the first half of the eighteenth century. In these circumstances the question of origin must remain open.

## 147 COVERED GOBLET WITH ALLEGORICAL SCENES

Saxony or Silesia, about 1720–1725

Height: 30.5 cm (with cover), 20.5 cm (without cover);
diameter at mouth: 9.9 cm;
thickness of glass: about 2.5 mm (bowl),
1.5 mm (cover)

Colorless glass with red and gold threads, polished circlets, and wheel engraving. Unpolished pontil mark.

Conical foot engraved with foliate scrolls, supported on a baluster stem with red and gold, twisted thread inclusions flanked by collars. Bell bowl with everted base engraved with a cartouche and socle in scrollwork with a vignette of stag and hounds below, and an eagle with outspread wings flanked by the allegorical figures of Justice and Peace, and surmounted by a large shell. Reverse with large empty cartouche surmounted by a baldequin and flanked by cornucopiae of fruit and flowers. Rim decorated with matt scrolls punctuated by four alternate male and female bust medallions. Depressed cover with everted rim engraved with scrollwork, the finial corresponding to the stem.

Certain features of the engraving, for instance the feathery scrolls, stiff pendant flowers, and large support scrolls, as well as the bust medallions, would indicate a Saxon rather than a Silesian origin for this goblet. Compare for example with a goblet in formerly Klemperer Collection in Dresden, Museum für Kunsthandwerk (Haase 1975, no. 124, ill.) as well as Saxon examples with slightly varying decorative details (ibid., no. 111 and 112, ill.; and Baumgärtner 1977, figs. 65 and 67).

## 148 COVERED GOBLET WITH MOLDED PORTRAIT OF VIKTOR FRIEDRICH VON ANHALT-BERNBURG

Saxony, possibly Glücksburg, about 1760

Height: 37 cm (with cover), 24.5 cm (without cover), diameter at rim: 10.3 cm;
thickness of glass: about 4.5 mm (bowl), 2.5 mm (cover)

Colorless glass with cutting, wheel engraving, and molded glass. Unpolished pontil mark.

Provenance: Collection of the Dukes of Anhalt-Dessau, Schloss Ballenstedt.

Foot with crossed laurel and palm fronds. Tall, faceted baluster enclosing a tear, flanked by lightly-faceted collars. Conical bowl faceted at the base. Sides with an engraved oval cartouche with elector's cap and ermine baldequin, enclosing the applied molded-glass relief portrait of Duke Viktor Friedrich of Anhalt-Bernburg (1721–1765), supported by two bears; the reverse with the monogram "VFFZB" (Viktor Friedrich Fürst zu Bernburg) surmounted by prince's crown and flanked by crossed palm fronds. Rim inscribed in cursive: "Es lebe das hochfürstl: Haus / Anhalt Berrenburg." Depressed cover engraved with laurel and palm fronds, finial matching stem.

For this type of goblet with molded portrait see also cat. no. 130, as well as Schmidt 1922, p. 349 and Baumgärtner 1977, p. 63. The form points to a Saxon provincial center, possibly Glücksburg (see Baumgärtner 1977, fig. 139).
For other portraits of Duke Viktor Friedrich see comparable portraits on coins, for instance a sixth-of-a-thaler piece of 1758, the one-third-thaler coin of 1759, and the eight groschen piece of 1758 (Gisela Förschner, *Deutsche Münzen, Mittelalter bis Neuzeit, der münzprägenden Stände von Aachen bis Augsburg*, vol. 1, Melsungen 1984, no. 313, 301, 306, all ill.), (see also above, p. 103, fig. 190).

Lit.: Schmidt 1922, p. 349.

## 149 COVERED GOBLET WITH GALLANTS AND LADIES

Glass: Thuringia, mid 18th century
engraving: Saxony, mid 18th century

Height: 44.4 cm (with cover), 30.7 cm (without cover);
diameter at rim: 12.3 cm;
thickness of glass: about 3.5–4 mm (bowl),
2 mm (cover)

Colorless glass with cutting, matt and polished wheel engraving. Unpolished pontil mark.

Provenance: Collection of the Dukes of Anhalt-Dessau, Schloss Ballenstedt or Schloss Dessau.

Conical foot with folded rim. Stem with faceted shoulder and basal cysts flanking a molded pedestal stem with molded vertical ribs. Base of the conical bowl cut with a band of petal flutes below an engraved, continuous landscape scene, with polished details, inhabited by three couples, one playing the hunting horn next to a seated lady, a clown playing a shawm accompanied by a lady on a lute, and a courting couple. Small hatched border at the rim. Depressed cover with everted rim engraved with foliate scrolls around the central domed section cut with flutes, finial matching the stem.

The figural scenes are inspired by similar gallant scenes by Antoine Watteau, which were very popular at that time in all branches of the applied arts.

## 150 LEITGEB ARMORIAL INSCRIBED COVERED GOBLET

Saxon, possibly Glücksberg, probably about 1748

Height: 35.8 cm with cover), 26.8 cm (without cover);
diameter at rim: 11.1 cm;
thickness of glass: about 3 mm (bowl), 4 mm (cover)

Colorless glass with cutting, matt and polished wheel engraving. Pontil mark polished out.

Conical foot with engraved scrolls round the rim and chronostic inscription "EXConsVL VIVat LeVtgeb, qVIbIs MoDo praetor · Integer Astreae fortIter ense nItet" (=1741; Vivat the ex consul [former mayor] Leutgeb, who has been appointed to office for the second time. Colossal, he shines incorruptible with the sword of Astrea [goddess of Justice]). Stem with arcade-cut baluster and faceted knop flanked by collars. Conical bowl cut with bands of arched flutes round the base, engraved with the arms of Leitgeb (1st and 4th quarters, a man standing with a tankard, 2nd quarter, a star, 3rd quarter Fortune on her ball; crest with demiman holding tankard flanked by wings); on the opposite side a man standing with jug and goblet between two houses, each roof bearing the inscription "Annis" and the dates 1729–1732, 1741–1744 on one, and 1733–1736, 1745–1748 on the other, surmounted by the six-part verse: "Der Leutgeb, der bey denen Stäben / Den Burgern Nectar eingeschenckt, / Wird bey der Kugel sich bestreben / Wie er nun die mit Wermut tränckt, / So straeflich seynd. Von beyden Stellen / Wird also stäts sein Ruhm erhellen." Rim decorated with the same border as on the foot, and with pendant spandrels in the interstices. Low cover engraved on one side with a townscape of Vienna, on the other side a country house surrounded by vineyards. Rim encircled with another chronostic inscription: "Da VVIen Verkehrt heIst WeIn / so MVß eIn soLCher LeVtgeb seIjn" (=1737). Scroll border round the finial which matches the baluster shaft on the stem.

Thanks to the friendly cooperation of the Historisches Museum der Stadt Wien, and the Wiener Stadt- und Landesarchiv, Vienna (information supplied by letter of the 13 June 1984 and 19 June 1984) the arms have been identified as being those of a mayor of Vienna, Andreas Ludwig Leitgeb (born Klagenfurt 1683; died Vienna 1751). From 1720 he was an assessor of the City Court in Vienna, in 1724 a judgement scribe, in 1728 a member of the Inner Council of Vienna, from 1729–1732 town clerk, from 1732–1736 mayor, and at the same time, from 1734–1736 *Praeses der kaiserlichen Banco-Gefäll-Administration*, 1737–1740, senior town councillor, 1741–1744 town clerk, 1745–1751, again mayor (see Felix Czeike, *Wien und seine Bürgermeister*, Vienna 1974, p. 234).
The dates on the roofs of the two houses, refer to the periods during which he held two different offices, that of town clerk (1729–1732 and 1741–1744) and mayor (1732–1736 and 1741–1748). The glass was possibly commissioned to celebrate the sixty-fifth birthday of Mayor Leitgeb.

The rather mechanical execution of the view of Vienna might suggest thad the engraver followed a prototype on a medal or coin rather than an engraving. A possibility is the medal struck to commemorate the raising of the Siege of Vienna in 1683, on which the city walls beneath the church-tower landmarks are likewise indicated in sketchy fashion (see Exhibition catalogue: *Die Türken vor Wien*, Historisches Museum der Stadt Wien in the Künstlerhaus, Vienna, 1983, cat. no. 13/81–13/87; see also above, p. 104, fig. 193). Not only the clarity of the glass itself, but also the graduated bands of arched flutes on stem, bowl, and finial, would suggest a Saxon provenance, and other variants with similar decorative elements have been attributed to the Glücksburg Glasshouse (Baumgärtner 1977, pp. 91–92, fig. 134). See also the examples formerly in the Krug Collection, Baden-Baden (Klesse 1965, no. 285, ill., and 1973, no. 644, ill.; Sotheby's, Krug IV, lot nos. 625 and 645, ill.).

Compare also with a very similar goblet in the Landesmuseum Joanneum, Graz, (see above, p. 104, fig. 194).

# 151 COVERED GOBLET WITH INFANT BACCHANALE

Weimar, Andreas Friedrich Sang, signed and dated 1729

Height: 35.6 cm (with cover), 23.3 cm (without cover); diameter at rim: 9.8 cm; thickness of glass: about 3.5 mm (bowl), 6–7 mm (cover)

Colorless glass with cutting and matt and polished wheel engraving. Pontil decorated with a matt rosette. Stopper of the flask a modern replacement; cut hole in the center of the base of flask.

Provenance: Friedrich Neuburg Collection, Dresden/Leitmeritz; before that, Collection of the Dukes of Anhalt-Dessau, Schloss Dessau.

Domed foot with upper faceted section, sides with four scrolled cartouches enclosing children with symbols of the Four Seasons linked by feathery, foliate scrolls. Molded pedestal stem flanked by collars decorated with circlet of polished ovals. Base of the extended ogee bowl decorated with cut, arcaded flutes. Sides engraved with small cartouches which match those on the foot, enclosing small female allegorical figures (among them Hope and Love) from which hang fruit festoons and a shield surmounted by ducal crown and mantling and inscribed "AL" and the motto "VIVAT" beside it, as well as bunches of grapes and bunches of fruit. The lower area is decorated with a continuous meadow scene with encircling procession of children, at the head two musicians followed by children carrying fruit and a goblet, the last carrying a large wine jug decorated with Bacchus astride a barrel. The cushion cover (in the form of a flask) is decorated with a similar border of linked cartouches with children symbolizing the Elements. Domed upper section cut with flutes and facets, cut spire stopper. Base of the flask with matt ground inscribed in polished engraving with the circular signature "A * F * Sang * Año * 1729," within a ring of polished circlets.

The monogram "AL" is probably for Duke August Ludwig von Anhalt-Köthen (reigned 1728–1755).

Before they were added to the Neuburg collection, the goblet and flask/cover must have been separated for a long time, as only the cover (minus goblet) formerly at Schloss Dessau, is mentioned in former records. That they were made for each other is without doubt, in view of the matching cartouches on foot, bowl, and cover. Stylistically, the rendering of the putti corresponds very closely to that on the Sang goblet in Cologne dated 1725 (Cologne 1963, no. 350, ill., as well as 1973, no. 417, ill.; see also above, p. 105, fig. 196). For the decoration see a Potsdam goblet with similar music-making putti and bunches of grapes, where obviously the same engraved source, as yet unidentified, has been used (see Hörning o. J. [1979], no. 93, ill.).

Lit. (flask/cover): Schmidt 1922, p. 359; Ch. Scherer, "Die Hofspiegel – und Kartonfabrik zu Braunschweig (II)," in: *Der Kunstwanderer*, 1926, p. 186; G. E. Pazaurek, "Die Glasschneiderfamilie Sang", in: *Der Kunstwanderer*, 1930, pp. 389 onwards, figs. 3 and 4; Schmidt Ms 1931, pp. 240–241, no. 215; W. Schneidig, "Andreas Friedrich Sang, Fürstl. Weimarischer Hofglasschneider (Erfurt – Weimar – Ilmenau)," in *Glastechnische Berichte* 10, part 7, 1932, p. 383; H. Kühnert, *Urkundenbuch zur Thüringer Glashüttengeschichte. Beiträge zur Thüringer Geschichte 2*, Jena 1934, p. 302; L. F. Fuchs, "Jacob Sang, ein holländischer Glasschneider deutscher Nation," in: *Weltkunst* XXIV, 15 Aug. 1954, p. 3; Van Gelder 1958 I, p. 3; Janda 1962, pp. 77, 82, 84, cat. no. 187).

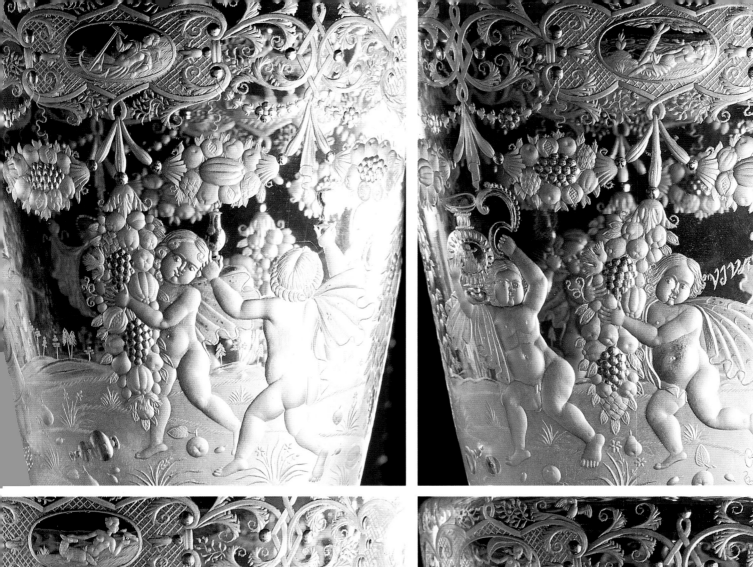

## 152 COVERED GOBLET WITH HUNTING SCENES

Weimar, Andreas Friedrich Sang, about 1730

Height: 35 cm (with cover), 23.4 cm (without cover); diameter at rim: 10 cm; thickness of glass: about 3–3.5 mm (bowl), 2 mm (cover)

Colorless glass with matt and polished facet cutting and matt and polished wheel engraving. Unpolished pontil mark. Inner edge of cover with small chips. Base of foot bears number "121" in sealing-wax red lacquer.

Provenance: possibly Collection of the Dukes of Anhalt-Dessau, Schloss Dessau or Schloss Ballenstadt (the red number "121" and remains of a crown is found on other glasses formerly in the Anhalt ducal collection).

Wide foot engraved with a continuous scroll-and-strapwork border punctuated by cartouches with small boar-hunting and hare-coursing vignettes. Upper section of foot decorated with a collar of matt scallops with a polished alternate rosette and diamond, these motifs repeated on the baluster stem. Shoulder knop consisting of a conical sleeve flanked by collars and decorated with stiff-leaf motifs, supporting the separate tall, cylindrical bowl with everted rim. Bowl divided at the eversion by a thin, light-yellow fillet. Lower section decorated above facets and scroll-and-strapwork border with four caryatids in the guise of female herms with butterfly wings, dividing the surface into panels decorated with bear-, stag-, wild boar- and deer-hunting scenes. Area above the fillet treated as a balustrade, above it, the head and shoulders of goddess Diana with sickle-moon diadem, bow, and hunting falcon, as well as the juvenile Bacchus, crowned with fruiting vine, with carafe and goblet, the interstices with bunches of grapes and floral motifs. Rim and cover decorated with scroll-and-strapwork borders echoing the foot, with miniature hunting vignettes as well as a tiny Bacchus on a barrel between a stag and deer. Upper portion of the cover also dec-

orated with matt petal flutes as on the foot. Finial matches baluster stem.

Certain decorative motifs are derived, possibly directly, or through an intermediate German engraver from a series of engravings of decorative ornamentation by Jean Berain I (see above, p. 106, fig. 200).

The attribution to Andreas Friedrich Sang is definite, and made not just on the basis of the general composition, but also the detail of the borders with cartouche inclusions. The delicate treatment of the features of Diana and Bacchus can be found again on the putti engraved on cat. no. 151, and particularly on the infant bacchanale on the Cologne goblet. Sang clearly shows an unusual preference on all three goblets for depicting delicately-cut miniature glasses held by the gesticulating figures, in this case Bacchus.

Probably as a result of a mistake, the engraver was compelled to replace the lower portion of the bowl, which was then fitted over the remains of the old shoulder knop. As the caryatids in the Berainesque prototype support a kind of balustrade on the capitals, it is probable that the original section was not decorated in any substantially different way from its replacement.

## 153 GOBLET WITH ARMS OF SAXON-EISENACH

Thuringia, possibly Eisenach, Georg Ernst Kunckel, about 1730–1750

Height: 17.7 cm; diameter at rim: 7.3 cm; thickness of glass: about 1.5 mm

Colorless glass with cutting, matt, and polished wheel engraving. Unpolished pontil mark.

Provenance: Collection of the Dukes of Anhalt-Dessau, Schloss Dessau or Schloss Ballenstedt (according to Alfred Wolf papers).

Conical foot with folded rim. Teared, molded pedestal stem with vertical ribs and diamonds at the shoulder below a flattened knop. Funnel bowl with solid base enclosing an air bubble. Sides decorated with the arms of Sachsen-Eisenach surmounted by a ducal crown and embellished with banners and scrolls. Rim decorated with foliate scrolls linked by swags of polished dots.

According to information kindly supplied by Ottfried Neubecker, Wiesbaden/Stuttgart, the glass is decorated with a "simplified version of the arms of the Dukedom of Sachsen-Eisenach quartering Saxony, Cleves, Jülich, the Saxon Palatinate, Homburg and Freusburg" (by letter of 13 April 1984). "The Dukes of Saxony claimed precedence over the Jülich-Klevisch inheritance (1609), claims which were unfulfilled as these areas remained under Brandenburg and Palatinate control."

The glass was perhaps dedicated to Wilhelm Heinrich von Sachsen-Eisenach (1728–1741) or Ernst-August von Sachsen-Weimar (1728–1748), from 1741 in Eisenach.

The attribution to G. E. Kunckel is supported by a signed glass in the Collections of the Veste Coburg (Schmidt 1922, fig. 204, center). Although Kunckel was in the service of Duke Friedrich II of Sachsen-Gotha as court glass engraver from 1721 until his death in 1750, he also worked for many other clients (Janda 1962, p. 132). As he settled in Eisenach no later than 1727, where he acquired citizenship in 1742, it would seem likely that he decorated glasses for the court there as well, particularly as no other glass made for the Duke of Sachsen-Eisenach except the Wolf glass, has come to light (see also Klaus J. Dorsch, "Glasschnittpokale von Georg Ernst Kunckel und aus seinem Umkreis im Germanischen Nationalmuseum," in: *Anzeiger des Germanischen Nationalmuseums 1984*, pp. 77–91).

Compare also with a related glass in the collections of the Veste Coburg with similar border to the rim (but also including richer motifs) which celebrates the marriage between Friedrich III of Sachsen-Gotha and Louise Dorothea von Sachsen-Meiningen in 1729 (Inv. no. a. S. 489).

## 154 SCHWARZBURG ARMORIAL COVERED GOBLET

Lauenstein about 1771

Height: 31.3 cm (with cover), 24.4 cm (without cover); diameter at rim: 9.5 cm; thickness of glass: about 4 mm (bowl and cover)

Colorless glass with a bluish tint, cutting, matt and polished wheel engraving and gilding. Pontil mark polished and engraved with the Lauenstein mark used from 1768: a lion rampant (Lauenstein = Löwenstein) and "C" indicating "Cristall" for glass of the first quality (see Scherer 1924, pp. 326 onwards; Dreier 1969, text to figs. 70–81). Small brownish incrusted marks on the foot.

High domed foot with wide folded rim. Upper section of foot and baluster stem faceted. Everted base of the bell bowl with polished diamonds flanked by arcaded blazes. Sides engraved with the arms of the Princes of Schwarzburg-Sondershausen flanked by a wild man and woman, the reverse with the monogram "CW" beneath the inscription in Roman capitals: "FUNFZIG IAHR WIE HEUTE," and crown, flanked by scrolls and palm fronds. Flattened cover with band of facets, finial matching the stem. Gilt rim to bowl and cover.

The arms and monogram refer to Prince Christian Wilhelm zu Schwarzburg-Sondershausen (1647–1721). He was elevated to the rank of *Reichsfürst* (Prince of the Holy Roman Empire) on 3 September 1693. The inscription would suggest a commemoration of his death fifty years before.

The arms correspond to those as defined in the diploma of elevation granted by the Emperor Leopold I on the 3 September 1697 to Sondershausen, and by the Emperor Joseph I on the 2 June 1710 to Rudolstadt (see Siebmacher, *Großes und allgemeines Wappenbuch*, I, 1, 3, revised by G. A. Seyler, Nuremberg 1916, pp. 81–88, pl. 79).

It is difficult to determine whether the arms are for Schwarzburg-Sondershausen or Schwarzburg-Rudolstadt, as the armorial differentiation depends upon small color changes difficult to indicate with engraving on glass. Ottfried Neubecker, Wiesbaden/ Stuttgart, suggests (in a letter of 13 April 1984) that the arms were for Schwarzburg-Rudolstadt and not Sondershausen, as the armorial colors are indicated, correctly although in monochrome, by means of lines and dots. So the shield has no dots for "or" (for Sondershausen) but a smooth ground suggesting "argent" (for Rudolstadt), (see E. Fischer, *Die Münzen des Hauses Schwarzburg*, Heidelberg, 1904, pp. LV, LIX; H. G. Ströhl, *Deutsche Wappenrolle*, Stuttgart 1897, pp. 57–61, fig. 87 and pl. XIV). In any case, the identity of the owner is resolved here by the monogram.

Taking cat. no. 155, which is obviously related to this goblet and is engraved with the same arms, the "field" is indicated by means of a light matt finish which is not armorially accurate, so that a certain amount of doubt remains as a result. This is reinforced by the pair of goblets, cat. no. 156, which are obviously products of the same glasshouse as the goblets mentioned above, nevertheless they bear the initials "CG" for Christian Günther von Schwarzburg-Sondershausen (1758–1794).

See also a variant (without faceting on stem and bowl) formerly in the Krug Collection, Baden-Baden (Klesse 1973, no. 635, ill.; Sotheby's, Krug I, lot no. 110, ill.).

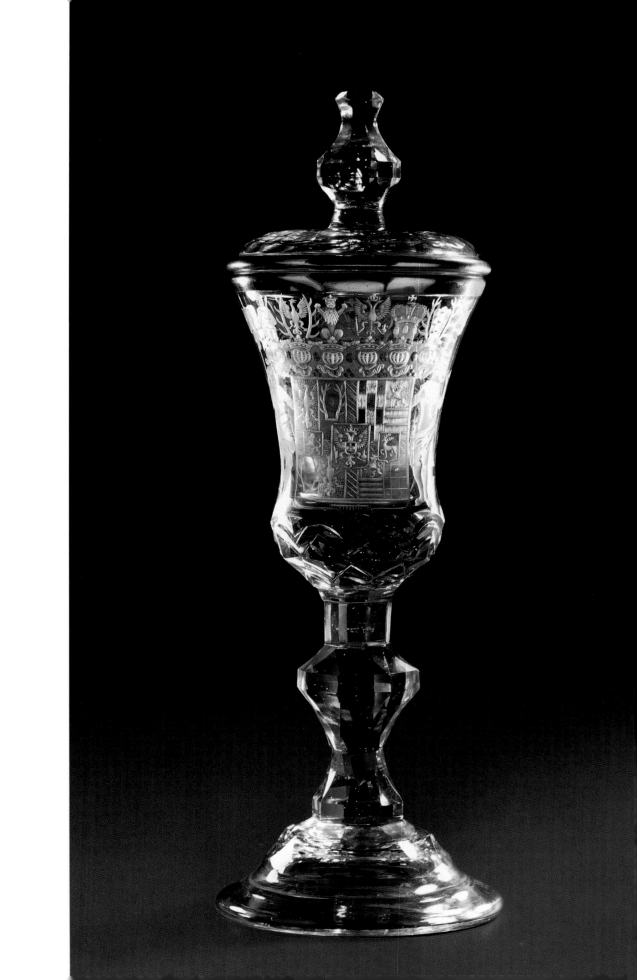

## 155 SCHWARZBURG ARMORIAL COVERED GOBLET

Lauenstein or Hesse, about 1770

Height: 34.5 cm (with cover), 24.8 cm (without cover); diameter at rim: 11.3 cm; thickness of glass: about 3.5–4 mm (bowl), 3 mm (cover)

Colorless glass with cutting, matt, and polished wheel engraving and gilding. Pontil mark polished out. Bowl and cover crizzled and clouded (early stages of crizzling).

Bell-shaped foot with broad, folded rim. Stem with large baluster enclosing an air tear. Stem and base of ovoid bowl cut with facets. Sides engraved with the arms of the Princes of Schwarzburg (-Rudolstadt?) supported by a wild man and woman. The flattened cover with band of facets. Finial corresponds to the stem. Bowl and cover with gilt rim.

See cat. no. 154 and its footnote.

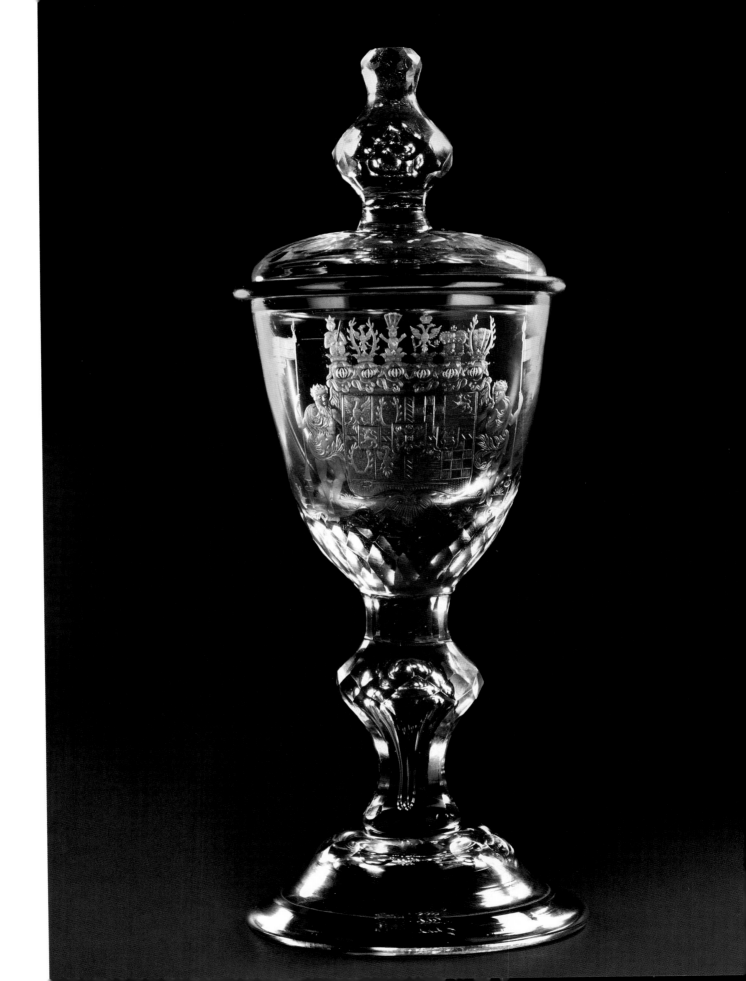

## 156 PAIR OF MONOGRAMMED COVERED GOBLETS

Lauenstein or Hesse, about 1770–1790

Height: a) 33.3 cm (with cover), 24.6 cm (without cover); diameter at rim: 10.5 cm;
b) 33.1 cm (with cover), 24.8 cm (without cover); diameter at rim: 11 cm
thickness of glass: a) and b) about 3 mm (bowl and cover)

Colorless glass with cutting, matt, and polished wheel engraving and gilding. Pontil mark polished out. Bowl and cover with hair cracks and cloudy film (early stages of crizzling).

Bell-shaped foot with wide folded rim and band of polished circlets around the domed section. Muscular baluster stem with enclosed air tear. Stem and base of the ovoid bowl cut with facets. Solid base of bowl enclosing a further tear. Sides with a rococo cartouche enclosing the monogram "CG" flanked by flags and trophies, a) surmounted by a princes's crown, b) with a crown without struts. Flattened cover with band of facets, finial in keeping with the stem. Bowl and cover with gilt rim.

The monogram "CG" possibly refers to Prince Christian Günther von Schwarzburg-Sondershausen (1758–1794).
See also cat. nos. 154 and 155.

Netherlands, last quarter 17th century

Height: 25.2 cm; diameter at rim: 14.8 cm; thickness of glass: 1–1.5 mm

Light-green, tinted glass with diamond-point engraving. Unpolished pontil mark. Star crack in the bowl.

High, conical spun foot supporting a hollow, cylindrical section with four rows of applied, raspberry prunts, at the shoulder an applied, milled ring. Ovoid bowl with a continuous scene on a checkered base: the birthing room with mother in bed, to one side the nurse and midwife at the bath, on the other side, by the cradle, a further scene with seven men at a large table drinking the health of those concerned, as well as the women visitors around the mother, surmounted by the inscription: "De Gesontheijt vande Kraam Vrou."

As opposed to the examples mentioned below, all from the eighteenth century, up until now there had been no recorded examples of a seventeenth-century glass decorated with this subject, and the Wolf Collection roemer must now be seen as the earliest recorded example.

The subject of the lying-in first really became popular in decoration on Netherlands glasses towards the middle of the eighteenth century, and particularly engraved scenes on a type of beaker with bell bowl and everted foot known as a "Hogarth glass." See examples in: Schmidt 1927, p. 39, pl. 75 ; Auction cat. no. 439, Dorotheum, Vienna, 27–29 February 1936, no. 629, pl. XII; Klesse 1965, no. 332, ill. ( Sotheby's Krug I, lot. no. 146, ill.); Baumgärtner 1971, no. 104, ill.; Sotheby's Krug IV, lot no. 668, ill.

## 167 FLASK WITH CALLIGRAPHIC INSCRIPTION

Netherlands, last quarter 17th century

Height: 25 cm;
thickness of glass: (at the thickened rim)
about 5–7 mm

Colorless glass with diamond-point engraving.
Unpolished pontil mark. Neck ring damaged.

Depressed, globular body with kick to base, extended, tapering neck with neck ring, the body encircled with a diamond-engraved calligraphic inscription (in Italian script): "Drink wyn met maat, na Paulus raad."

This type of flask was often used for calligraphic inscriptions by the best-known diamond engraver Willem van Heemskerk (J. G. van Gelder, "Willem Jacobsz. van Heemskerk," in: *Oud Holland 57*, 1940, pp. 181–191; *idem* 1955, pl. XXIII, no. 4), as well as Bastiaan Boers among others (Van Gelder 1955, pl. XXIV, no. 4; Ritsema van Eck 1982, figs. 4, 6, 10 and 11). On account of the somewhat lax symmetry of the calligraphic scrolls, it is not possible to make an attribution to one of the known metics.

For a discussion of the type of script ("Italian script"), see footnote to cat. no. 168.

## 168 ROEMER WITH CALLIGRAPHIC INSCRIPTION

Netherlands, Warmond, Bastiaan Boers, signed and dated 1699

Height: 24.9 cm; diameter at rim: 10.5 cm; thickness of glass: about 1 mm

Light, blue-green glass with diamond-point engraving. Unpolished pontil mark (at the base of the hollow stem).

High, conical, spun foot. Hollow cylindrical stem with kick to base decorated with three rows of applied prunts and milled trail round the shoulder below the ovoid bowl. Sides with an encircling calligraphic inscription (in Italian script): "Heden vrolyk morgen Sorgen." Base of bowl (at the beginning of the inscription) with diamond-engraved signature "B. Boers 1699 / 20. Juni."

The concept of Italian script or lettering derives from calligraphic instruction manuals of the sixteenth and seventeenth century (for this see Pieter C. Ritsema van Eck, 1982, no. 2, pp. 51–56, particularly p. 54, note 19).

In P. C. Ritsema van Eck's monograph on the oeuvre of Bastiaan Boers, published in 1982, the Wolf roemer is not included. According to Ritsema van Eck, Bastiaan Boers (1650–1713) ran a French school (*Franse Kostschool*) in Warmond near Leiden, as teacher and calligraphy-master, later taken over and run by his son Maarten. A thirty-seven page calligraphic pattern book complete with exercises by Bastiaan and Maarten Boers has survived from this period. Calligraphy with the diamond on glass on the other hand, in view of the relatively few remaining glasses by him to have survived, seems in his case to have been something of a casual hobby. Of the six hitherto recorded signed works by him, all done between 1687 and 1699, there is only one roemer, among five flasks, which is in the Boymans-van-Beuningen Museum in Rotterdam (Van Gelder 1955, pl. XXIV, no. 5; Ritsema van Eck 1982, p. 56, fig. 8). The form of the roemer is very similar to that of the Wolf example, except that it is slightly more convex in profile, and the prunts are larger and applied in four more tightly-packed rows. The exact same type of script has been used for the inscription ("Deliciae patrum sobotes") so that the overall impression is very similar (see also above, p. 113, fig. 212).

## 175   GOBLET WITH CUPID WITH BOW

Glass: England, third quarter 18<sup>th</sup> century
Engraving: Netherlands, about 1775

Height: 17.8 cm; diameter at rim: 7.3 cm;
thickness of glass: about 1 mm

Colorless to pale blue-tinted glass with cutting and
diamond stippling. Pontil mark polished out.

Provenance: Marianne Pelliot Collection, Paris.


Plain flat foot and facet-cut stem with shoulder, central, and basal knops. Conical bowl finely stippled
with the infant Cupid, kneeling on a cloud, his quiver
over his shoulder, and taking aim with his bow and arrow.

Marianne Pelliot attributes this glass to David Wolff
himself (1936, p. 92). The only possible glass by David
Wolff which could be compared with this one in an-
imation and richness of stippled contrasts is his earliest known glass in the Museum de Lakenhal in Leiden (E. Pelinck, Stedelijk Museum *De Lakenhal*, Leiden 1951, fig. 26; Tait 1968, pp. 99–108, fig. 2; see
above, p. 118, fig. 226). The delicate modeling on the
Wolff glass, however, is not only of different proportions, but it is also composed of subtler modulations
than on this one accepted early work by Wolff, so that
one must think once more in terms of a contemporary
artist, the so-called *Doppelgänger* or "alias" whose
technique is indeed superior to that of Wolff.

Lit.: Pelliot 1936, pp. 90–92, figs. 11 and 12.

## 176   GOBLET WITH PUTTI

Glass: England, Newcastle upon Tyne,
third quarter 18th century
Engraving: Netherlands, about 1770

Height: 17.6 cm; diameter at rim: 7.3 cm;
thickness of glass: about 1.5 mm

Colorless glass with diamond stippling and small areas
of line engraving. Unpolished pontil mark.

Conical foot and light-baluster stem with beaded
swelling and flattened knops. Conical bowl with very
delicate, at times almost misty, stippled engraving:
above dense cloud balls are three frolicking putti, one
with a bunch of grapes, another holds up a bowl, while
the third holds out its hand. The children's hair emphasized with fine engraved lines.

Stylistic elements in the decoration on this glass are
quite distinct from that of David Wolff, particularly
the treatment of the children, the strong contrast of
light and shade, and the gradations of strongly
stippled areas, placing it within a group of glasses,
Buckley's "group C," which are distinguished by a
richness of nuances which outstrips the work of Wolff.
This extremely accomplished contemporary of Wolff,
already identified by Schmidt (1914), Hudig (1926)
and Buckley (1935), has not as yet been identified, and
is simply known as *Doppelgänger* or "alias" (see Smit
1982, p. 2623, figs. 7 and 8).

## 177  ARMORIAL WINEGLASS FOR WILLIAM V OF ORANGE

Glass: England, about 1775
Engraving: Netherlands, about 1775

Height: 17.6 cm; diameter at rim: 7.8 cm;
thickness of glass: about 1 mm

Colorless glass with cutting and diamond stipple and line engraving. Pontil mark polished out.


Conical foot and facet-cut stem with basal, central, and shoulder swellings. Conical bowl decorated with the arms of William V of Orange within the ribbon of the Order of the Garter inscribed "HONI SOIT QUI MAL Y PENSE" flanked by floral sprays and scrolls on which are placed the lion supporters.

The stippling is only interrupted in some of the armorials by the use of diamond-point line engraving. The delicate pointillist contrasts place the glass within a group which was dealt with by Buckley in a discussion of David Wolff (Buckley 1935, pp. 24 onwards, pl. 15, 15 A; for Wolff's *Doppelgänger* see also: Smit 1982, p. 2624, fig. 9).
For the armorials the closest parallels are in: The Art Institute, Chicago (formerly Mühsam Collection: Schmidt 1914, pl. 6, no. 45); Gemeentemuseum, the Hague (with different stem form: Van Gelder 1955, pl. XXXI, 5; Jansen 1962, no. 236, ill.); formerly in the Snouck Hurgronje Collection, the Hague (with different stem form: Auction cat. 1931, lot no. 629, ill.); Victoria and Albert Museum, Buckley Collection (with identical stem form: Schmidt 1927, pl. 77B).
Further parallels with the arms of William V of Orange, alone, flanked by lion supporters, are usually placed within a rococo scrolling shield rather than, as in this case, an oval one. See for example: Pazaurek 1902, pl. 39c; Schmidt 1914, pl. 9, no. 32; Buckley 1935, pl. 17; Exhibition cat. *A Decade of Glass Collecting, Selections from the Melvin Billups Collection*, the Corning Museum of Glass, Corning 1962, no. 57, ill.; Klesse 1965, no. 322, ill. (Sotheby's Krug IV, lot no. 673); Saldern 1968, no. 132, ill.; Baumgärtner 1971, no. 105, ill.; Auction cat. The Bradford Collection, Christie's, London, 4 June 1985, lot no. 6, ill.

## 178 GOBLET WITH ARMS OF ORANGE AND PRUSSIA

Glass: England or Netherlands, last quarter 18<sup>th</sup> century
Engraving: Netherlands, possibly David Wolff, about 1780–1795

Height: 16.2 cm; diameter at rim: 7.6 cm; thickness of rim: about 1.8 mm

Colorless glass with cutting and stipple engraving.

Provenance: Fritz and Mary Biemann Collection, Zurich; previously Friedrich Neuburg Collection, Dresden/Leitmeritz.

Conical foot and facet-cut stem. Ovoid bowl stippled with the arms of William V of Orange within the ribbon of the Order of the Garter, and those of his wife Frederika Sophie Wilhelmina of Prussia *acolée*, flanked by the relevant supporters: a lion (for Orange) and a wild man (for Prussia).

This combination of Orange and Prussian supporters has not been found so far on any other examples.
In this respect compare other glasses with this marriage alliance (with lion or putto supporters) in: Gemeentemuseum, the Hague (with putti supporters: Jansen 1962, no. 237, ill.); Kunstmuseum, Düsseldorf (with lion supporters: Heinemeyer 1966, no. 410, ill.; Saldern 1968 D, no. 41, ill.); Kunstgewerbemuseum, Cologne (with putti supporters: Cologne 1963, no. 367, ill., as well as 1973, no. 435, ill.); Nordböhmisches Museum, Liberec (with lion supporters: Pazaurek 1902, pl. 39b); Victoria and Albert Museum, London. Buckley Collection (lion supporters: Schmidt 1927, pl. 77C; Buckley 1935, pl. 15; Honey 1946, pl. 59B).
Although the marriage between William V of Orange and the Prussian princess had already taken place in 1767, the glass cannot be dated earlier than 1780.
The physiognomy of the wild man supporter, as well as the regular and coarse-grained diamond stippling is connected with David Wolff's later work, so that his authorship here can be assumed in view of comparable glasses, definitively attributed to him, from the 1780s (with portraits or arms of the prince and his wife).

Lit.: Schmidt Ms 1931, p. 98, no. 90 ("probably the work of D. Wolff, about 1767"); Lempertz auction cat., Cologne, 22–27 May 1957, lot 697, pl. 25; Weinmüller auction cat., Munich, 5–6 October 1960, lot no. 228, pl. 19; Fritz Biemann, "Die holländischen Gläser des 17. und 18. Jahrhunderts der Sammlung Fritz Biemann, Zürich," in: *Alte und Moderne Kunst* 12, no. 101, November/December 1968, p. 18, fig. 7; Klesse/Saldern 1978, no. 87, ill.; Sotheby's Biemann, lot no. 167, ill.

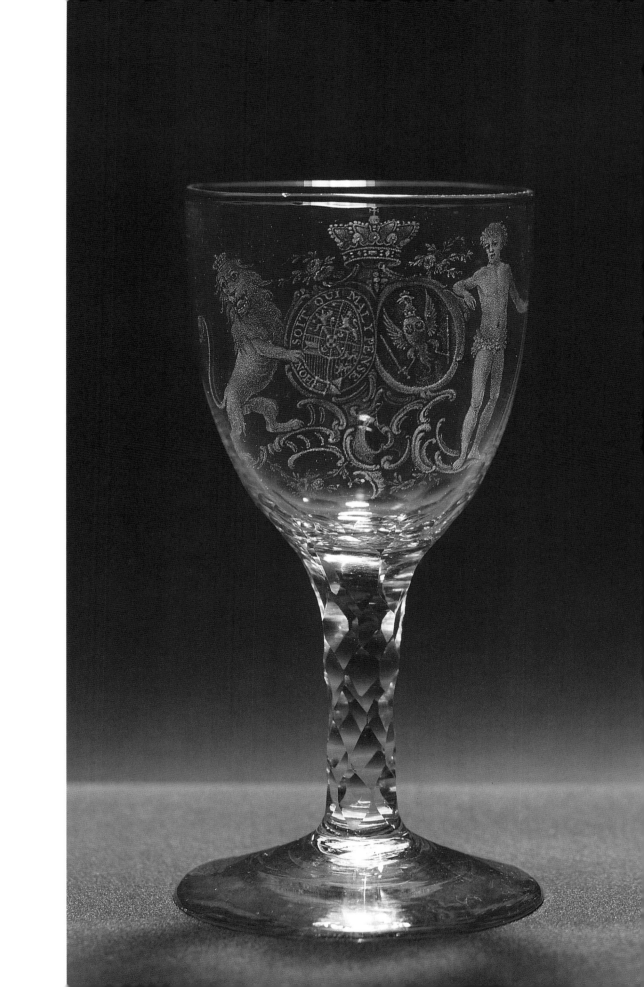

## 179 GOBLET WITH ALLEGORY OF FRIENDSHIP

Glass: England, Newcastle upon Tyne, third quarter 18th century
Engraving: Netherlands, possibly David Wolff, about 1770

Height: 18.2 cm; diameter at rim: 7.4 cm; thickness of glass: about 2 mm

Colorless glass with diamond stippling and small areas of line engraving. Unpolished pontil mark. Foot rim chipped.

Conical foot and light baluster stem with beaded swelling and flattened knops. Conical bowl decorated with two putti on a grassy mount, the one on the left seated with a sash over his shoulder, offering a glass to the one standing on the right, his arm stretched out to accept it, above them a ribbon inscribed in Roman capitals "VRIENDSCHAP." The children's hair, their wings and parts of the foliage are line-drawn with the diamond.

A glass in the Rijksmuseum, Amsterdam (Inv. N. M. 10754: 79) almost identical, except that the composition is reversed, and the children are clothed, is dated 1770 (Buckley 1935, pl. 14). It is certainly by the same hand as the Wolf glass, and possibly an early work of David Wolff (see above, p. 118, figs. 227 and 228).
For further variants with "VRIENDSCHAP" inscription, above two children in slightly different attitudes (on grassy mounts or clouds) see: one in the former Krug Collection, Baden-Baden (Klesse 1965, no. 323, ill.; Sotheby's, Krug IV, lot no. 672, ill.); and another in the Gemeentemuseum, the Hague (Jansen 1962, no. 227, ill.).
There is a late version of this subject signed "D. Wolff 1788" in the Gemeentemuseum, the Hague, stippled with wingless putti holding hands (without glass), and with the inscribed ribbon placed below the grassy base (Jansen 1962, no. 220, ill.). The slimmer proportions of the children and the regularity of stippling must be seen as particular characteristics of the later work of David Wolff; however, in view of the poor quality of engraving, an attribution to another member of the Wolff family would seem more likely, perhaps Daniel Wolff, as Smit (1982) has suggested (see above, p. 118).
Among the many allegories of Friendship symbolized by two children in period costume, the closest to the Wolf glass is one in the Metropolitan Museum, New York (formerly Mühsam Collection, Schmidt 1914, pl. 5, no. 36), on which the two children are portrayed standing beside a table and toasting one another.

## 183 PORTRAIT GLASS
## OF FREDERIKA SOPHIE WILHELMINA
## OF ORANGE-NASSAU

Glass: England or Netherlands, about 1780
Engraving: Netherlands, the Hague, David Wolff, about 1780

Height: 17.3 cm; diameter at rim: 7.4 cm; thickness of glass: about 2 mm

Colorless glass with cutting and diamond stippling. Unpolished pontil mark.

Provenance: Friedrich Neuburg Collection, Dresden/Leitmeritz.

Conical foot and faceted stem supporting the ovoid bowl decorated within an oval, bead-and-rail frame with a bust portrait of the wife of William V of Orange, three-quarters to dexter, her dress décolleté, her hair fashionably dressed and powdered and set with a diadem. The medallion flanked by pendant floral sprays and surmounted by a ribbon inscribed in Roman capitals "FREDERICA SOPHIA WILHELMINA / PRINCESSE VAN ORANIE EN NASSAU."

Frederika Sophie Wilhelmina, Princess of Prussia, married Prince William V of Orange and Nassau in 1767. The engraved source, from which this portrait would definitely have been taken, has not as yet been identified.
Robert Schmidt identified the engraver of this glass as definitely Wolff's work in 1931, at the same time suggesting a "a late date, somewhere around 1780," (see also above, p. 120, fig. 234).

Lit.: Schmidt Ms 1931, p. 98, no. 91.

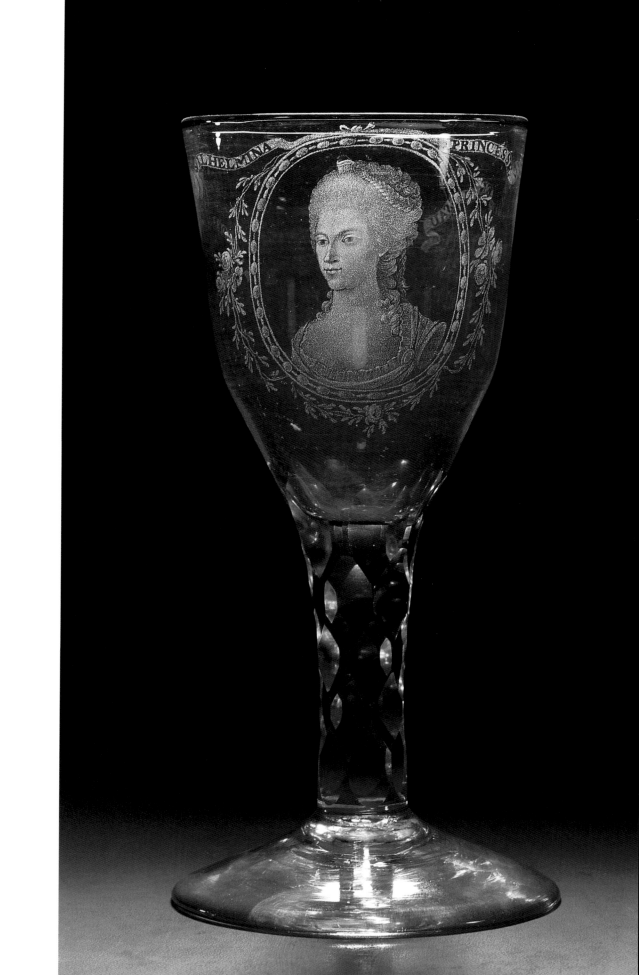

## 184 PORTRAIT GLASS OF BURGERMEESTER TEMMINCK

Glass: England or Netherlands, about 1780
Engraving: Netherlands, the Hague, David Wolff, about 1780

Height: 14.6 cm; diameter at rim: 6.8 cm; thickness of glass: about 2 mm

Colorless glass with cutting and diamond stippling. Unpolished pontil mark.

Provenance: Marianne Pelliot Collection, Paris.

Conical foot and facet-cut stem, the cutting extending onto the base of the ovoid bowl. Sides stippled with a bust portrait of the mayor of Amsterdam, de Vry Temminck, in collar and wig, three-quarters to sinister within an oval medallion, inscribed under the rim in Roman capitals "Mr. B. DE VRY TEMMINCK, BURGEMEESTER EN RAAD DER STAD AMSTERDAM."

According to information kindly provided by B. Haak, Director of the Amsterdam Historical Museum, Mr. Egbert de Vry Temminck (1700–1785), incorrectly inscribed "B" on the glass, was one of the best known and important political personalities in Amsterdam in the eighteenth century, filling many offices and honors (in a letter of 30 July 1984). Between 1749 and 1784 alone, he held the office of mayor twenty-three times. His marriage with Margarethe Temminck (1707–1750), daughter of Jacob and Aletta de Wacker, which took place in 1729, remained childless.
According to A. W. Gerlagh of the Gemeentearchief, Amsterdam (information kindly provided by letter, 18 February 1985), the source for the portrait could have been an etching by Reinier Vinkeles (1741–1816) after a drawing by Jacob Buys (1724–1801), which was in its turn based on a portrait of 1758 by Jan Wandelaar (1690–1759). The etching first appeared in 1780, which gives a clue as to the date of this glass (see above, p. 121, fig. 237).
The rather dry stippled effects and the modeling conincides with David Wolff's style as seen on his later signed and dated portraits (see for example Buckley 1935, pl. 1–4, 10).
For another portrait of Burgemeister Temminck see a very similar glass in the Kunstmuseum, Düsseldorf, which is also stippled by Wolff (Heinemeyer 1966, no. 415, ill.; Helmut Ricke, *Glas, ausgewählte Werke, Kunstmuseum Düsseldorf* V, Düsseldorf 1976, V-19). The softer lines around Temminck's face on the Düsseldorf glass suggest that it is at least a decade earlier than the portrait on the Wolf glass, on which the features are in a harder and more mature mold. The portrait on the Düsseldorf glass is therefore possibly after the drawing by Buys.

Lit.: Pelliot 1930, p. 324, fig. 12.

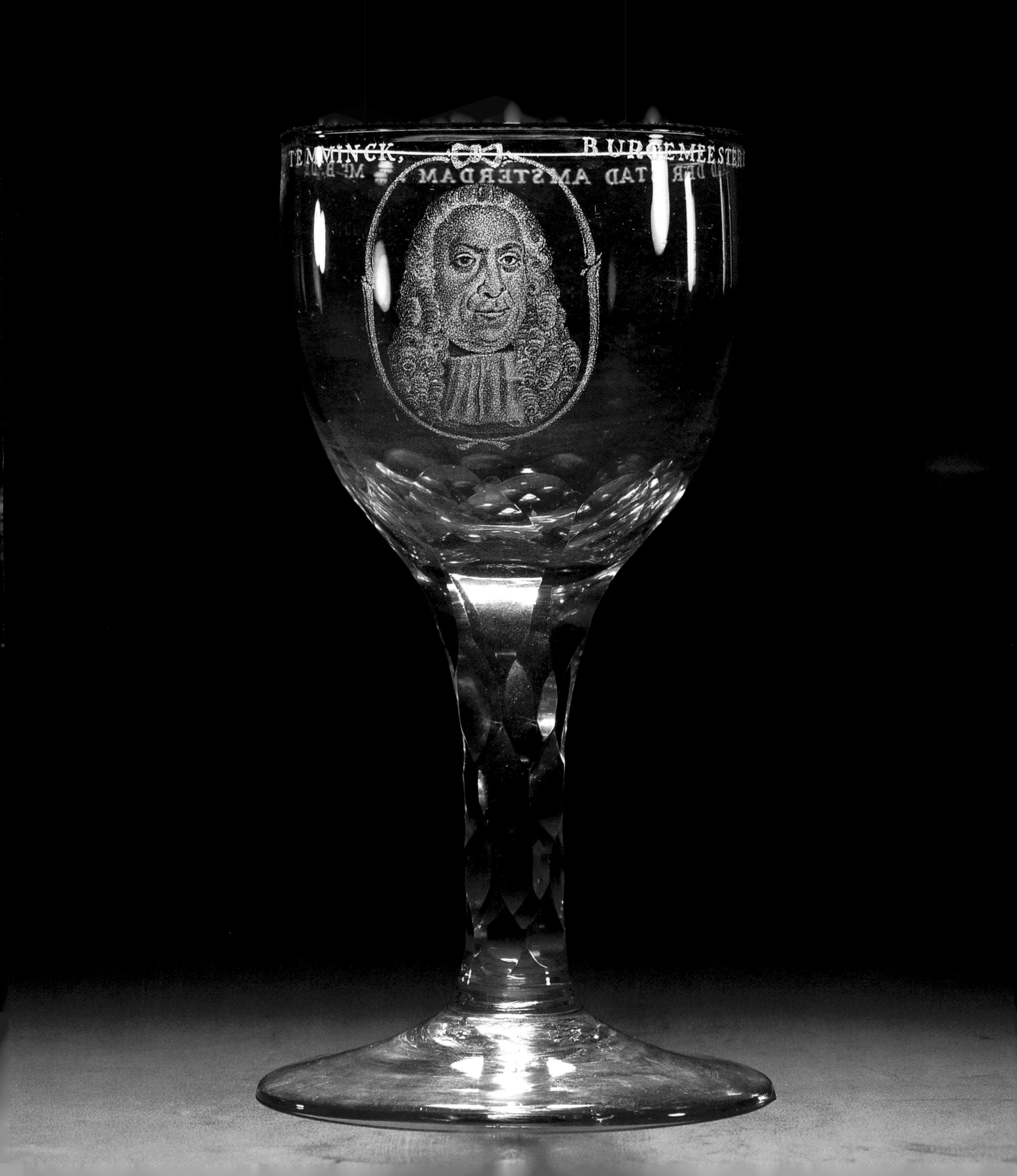
TEMMINCK,
BURGEMEESTER

## 185 COVERED GOBLET DECORATED WITH GOURDS

Netherlands, about 1680–1690

Height: 28.2 cm (with cover), 18.2 cm (without cover);
diameter at rim: 9.5 cm;
thickness of glass: about 2–2.5 mm (bowl and cover)

Colorless glass with wheel engraving, with a few polished details. Unpolished pontil mark.

Wide foot with folded rim. Stem with compressed, hollow, inverted baluster flanked by collars. Cylindrical bowl decorated with a continuous circlet of large leaves, gourds, flowers, and fruit, as well as fine details of veining covering the entire surface of the leaves. Flattened cover engraved with polished, radial lines on a matt ground to represent the upper portion of a gourd. Finial with flattened knops and ball terminal.

This glass belongs to a group of goblets of similar form, all possibly decorated by the same hand, or at least originating from the same workshop. A preference for large vegetable motifs is noticeable, among which the vine and gourd wreaths with delicately-veined leaves are foremost. The Wolf goblet is closest to one formerly in the Krug Collection, Baden-Baden (Klesse 1965, no. 324, ill.; Sotheby's Krug IV, lot no. 667, ill.; see also above, p. 123, fig. 240).
For the shape see footnote to cat. no. 162.

A goblet in the Rijksmuseum, Amsterdam (see above, p. 123, fig. 241) with the arms of the Province of Holland embellished with heraldic oak and orange branches, as well as fruiting vine, forms a link with other related armorial goblets grouped together by P. C. Ritsema van Eck (1984, pp. 95–97, figs. 27–29, 31–34). Their dating is pinpointed by a glass in the Willet-Holthuysen Museum, Amsterdam, commemorating perhaps the coronation of William III as English King in 1689 (Ritsema van Eck 1984, p. 96, fig. 29), and narrowing their decoration to the decade between 1680 and 1690. Compare also with an English goblet with decoration of birds among fruiting vine, of poorer quality, in the Fitzwilliam Museum, Cambridge, which is obviously linked with this group (Cambridge 1978, no. 189, ill.).

## 186 COVERED GOBLET WITH IMPERIAL AND ELECTOR'S ARMS

Glass: Low Countries, possibly Liège, late 17th century
Engraving: Germany, possibly Nuremberg, about 1694–1705

Height: 46.4 cm (with cover), 33 cm (without cover); diameter at rim: 14.2 cm;
thickness of glass: about 2–2.5 mm (bowl and cover)

Colorless glass with matt and polished wheel engraving. Unpolished pontil mark. Bowl in the earliest stages of crizzling (hairline cracks in places).

Wide foot with folded rim, decorated on the upper side with finely engraved wreath of crossed laurel fronds. Stem composed of two quatralobed hollow knops separated by collars. Base of the conical bowl and upper section of the low cover with nipped molded ribs ("nipt-diamond-waies"). One side decorated with the crowned Imperial Eagle with outstretched wings, sword and orb in its talons, and on its breast an oval shield with the arms of Austria and Spain within the collar of the Golden Fleece. The other side decorated with a genealogical "tree" in the form of symmetrical scrolls linking shields of the Electors of the Empire, all with electors' caps: in the center Pfalz, to the left the three spiritual Electorates of Trier, Mainz, and Cologne flanked by crosier and bishop's staff, to the right the three temporal Electorates of Bavaria, Brandenburg, and Saxony. Above the everted rim of the cover a foliate meander. On the upper part of the cover, within the molded area, a finely-engraved "G," and in another a diamond-engraved, illegible monogram. Cover finial in the form of a large ring set on a ribbed cyst and collars.

With regard to the dating of this goblet the genealogist Jürgen Arndt, Berlin (Heraldic commissioner of German Armorial Rolls) makes an important observation: "... Most important are the arms of the three spiritual electors, that is Trier, Mainz with the arms of the Counts of Schönborn and Cologne with the Wittelsbach arms. The date can thus be established from the reigns of the Bishops of Mainz and Cologne. In Mainz the electors from the House of Schönborn were Johann

Philipp von Schönborn (1647–1673) and Lothar Franziskus von Schönborn (1694–1729). The Wittelsbachs who were electors in Cologne were ... Max Heinrich von Bayern (1643–1688) and Joseph Clemens von Bayern (1688–1723) ... As the Imperial arms still include the castle of Castile, they can only be the arms of Leopold I (1658–1705) (or just possibly the last years of the Emperor Ferdinand III (1637–1657), who were both still within the succession to the Spanish throne, a situation which changed at the end of the War of the Spanish Succession (1701–1714)." (by letter 26 March 1985).

With reference to the group of related glasses mentioned below, a date before 1673, and the reign of the first Elector of Mainz from the Schönborn family, cannot be considered. On the other hand, Lothar Franz von Schönborn's reign began only in 1694, so that this year could be seen as the earliest date the glass could have been made, and 1705, the year of Leopold I's death, the latest date.

R. J. Charleston has suggested, on good grounds, a South Netherlandish origin for this group, possibly the Bonhommes Glasshouse at Liège (1957, pp. 234–237).

For the shape compare with parallels among others in: Rijksmuseum, Amsterdam (Charleston 1957, fig. 8 and notes p. 236); The Corning Museum of Glass, Corning (Strauss 1955, no. 235); The National Museum and Rosenborg Castle, Copenhagen (Charleston 1957, notes p. 236); British Museum, London (Slade Bequest: Thorpe 1929, pl. 31, 1); Victoria and Albert Museum, London, Buckley Collection (Schmidt 1927, pl. 63); and anonymous collection (A. Churchill, *Glass Notes* 10, Dec. 1950, frontispiece).

The engraving is of German character, possibly originating in Nuremberg. See cat. nos. 71, 73, and 84, 85.

## 187 GOBLET WITH ENGRAVED LAMBREQUIN BORDER

Glass: possibly England, second quarter 18th century
Engraving: Netherlands, second quarter 18th century

Height: 24.2 cm; diameter at rim: 10.5 cm;
thickness of glass: about 1 mm

Colorless glass with wheel engraving and polished details. Unpolished pontil mark.

Conical foot with folded rim. Light-baluster stem with air-beaded shoulder knop. Conical bowl decorated with a wide, continuous, decorative border below the rim: on both sides a male and a female bust surmounted by a lambrequin baldequin flanked by camel-like grotesques framed by scrollwork, as well as a seated allegorical female figure, also framed by straps and scrolls.

The broad, decorative border has elements, particularly the grotesques and scrollwork, which are based on ornament engravings of Jean Berain I. Around the middle of the eighteenth century this type of border was particularly popular on glasses in England and the Netherlands.

The engraving is also strongly reminiscent of German decoration on glass, particularly Saxon-Thuringian examples, and could have been executed by an immigrant German metic, who, like the Sang, Schröder, and Orban families (see cat. no. 190) found a temporary or permanent home among the expatriate community. A signed glass by J. Sang with a similar border is in the Gemeentemuseum, the Hague.

## 188  GOBLET ENGRAVED WITH THE FIGURE OF MERCURY

Glass: England, Newcastle upon Tyne, about 1760
Engraving: Netherlands, Amsterdam. Jacob Sang, signed and dated 1762

Height: 18.4 cm; diameter at rim: 6.9 cm;
thickness of glass: about 2 mm

Colorless glass with matt and polished wheel engraving. Unpolished pontil mark.


Conical foot and light-baluster stem with air-bead swelling. Conical bowl decorated with the figure of Mercury, standing on a socle, in "antique" dress with herald's staff (*kerykeion*) in his right hand and money bag in the other, behind him a sack and a barrel on which a cockerel perches. Rim inscribed in Roman capitals "DE ALGEMEENE WELVAERD." Pontil with diamond-engraved signature: "J : Sang fec. / 1762."


As protector of travelers and patron deity of commerce and trade, two of the mainstays of the United Provinces, Mercury was a particularly appropriate symbol of "de algemeene Welvaerd" (general prosperity) (see for instance the David Wolff example, cat. no. 181).
See also another glass engraved with this subject, and corresponding in many details, which, thirty years ago, was in the Collection of Jhr. mr. v. Kinschot, Leiden (Van Gelder 1958 I, p. 15, no. 6, fig. 23; see also above p. 124).

## 189 GOBLET ENGRAVED WITH THE MERCHANTMAN VIGILANTIE

Glass: England, mid 18$^{th}$ century
Engraving: Netherlands, Amsterdam, Jacob Sang, signed and dated 1763

Height: 21.9 cm; diameter at rim: 10.1 cm; thickness of glass: about 2 mm

Colorless glass with matt and polished wheel engraving. Unpolished pontil mark.

Conical foot and double-knopped, multi-spiral, air-twist stem. Bell bowl engraved on one side with a two-masted sailing ship on a base of regularly-delineated waves. The rim on the reverse inscribed in Roman capitals "T'. WELVAREN. VAN T'. SCHIP DE VIGILANTIE." Foot diamond-engraved with the signature: "Jacob Sang, inv: et Fec: Amsterdam, 1763."

See glasses with comparable shipping scenes by Jacob Sang in: the Maritime Museum, Rotterdam (signed and dated 1755: Van Gelder 1958 I, p. 15 with inscription "'t Welvaaren van't Schip de Resolutie"); 1976 in the German antiques trade, Heide Hübner, Wurzburg (signed and dated 1761); 1985 in the English art market (signed and dated 1762: Auction cat. Christie's, London, 4 June 1985, lot no. 57, ill.). See also the last dated work of this master depicting the ship "Overijssel," within a rococo cartouche in the Boymans-van Beunigen Museum, Rotterdam (signed and dated 1783: Van Gelder, "Een merkwaardig Sang-glas," in: *Bull. Museum Boymans*, Rotterdam 1957, part VIII, 2, pp. 74–79; idem 1958 I, p. 16, fig. 22; Isings 1966, fig. 111).
Unfortunately, the Nederlands Scheepvaart Museum, Rijksmuseum, Amsterdam, was unable to identify the "Vigilantie," as it was found that between 1758 and 1792, a considerable number of ships were recorded under that name.

## 192   VAN LIMBURG PORTRAIT GOBLET

Glass: England, Newcastle upon Tyne,
about 1760–1765
Engraving: Netherlands, about 1760–1770

Height: 20.3 cm; diameter at rim: 8.2 cm;
thickness of glass: about 2 mm

Colorless glass with matt and polished wheel en-
graving. Unpolished pontil mark. Foot rim chipped.
Base of foot with label printed in green "STEUBEN
COLLECTION ANTIQUE."

Provenance: Steuben Glass, Antiques Collection,
New York.

Conical foot and light-baluster stem with air bead
swelling and flattened knops. One side of the conical
bowl decorated with a rococo cartouche enclosing a
gentleman in contemporary dress, standing at a writing table, a quill in his hand, above, the inscription in
polished Roman lettering on matt ground: "IONAS ·
VAN · LIMBURG · ZECRETARIS." The reverse engraved with a fire-fighters' pump and the polished inscription: "2 – W-YK," flanked by two buckets of water inscribed with the letter "R" within a rococo cartouche, and above the inscription "T = WELVAAREN
= VAN = HET = BRANT = SPUYT = MEESTERS =
GILDE."

As the surname Limburg is very common in a number
of the provinces of the Netherlands, it has not been
possible as yet to discover the person and firemans'
guild commemorated on this glass.

See also a glass engraved with a fire-fighters' pump,
armorials and inscription "Jacob van Lunteren Als
Brandt Meester van de Wijk 28 A° 1726," at one time
in the Snouck Hurgronje Collection, the Hague (Auction cat. Snouck Hurgronje 1931, lot no. 699).

## 193 COVERED GOBLET WITH DOUBLE PORTRAIT OF WILLIAM V OF ORANGE AND HIS WIFE

Glass: Netherlands or possibly Saxony (Glücksburg), about 1765
Engraving: Netherlands, Delft, in the manner of Christoffel G. Schröder, about 1767–1770

Height: 44.5 cm (with cover), 32.9 cm (without cover); diameter at rim: 14.8 cm;
thickness of glass: about 3 mm (bowl and cover)

Colorless to light yellow-green, tinted glass with cutting, mainly matt wheel engraving with small polished details. Unpolished pontil mark. Cover rim and finial knop lightly chipped.

Conical foot with scalloped rim. Knopped and facet-cut stem supporting the large bell-shaped bowl, cut with tulip-shaped blazes round the base. Sides decorated with two large oval medallions *acolée* enclosing half-length portraits of the Stadtholder and his wife, in three-quarter profile facing each other, the youthful William V with ermine cape over his shoulder, wearing the sash of the Order of the Garter, and grasping the regent's baton, and Friederike Sophie Wilhelmine of Prussia with floral *decolleté*, pearl choker, and flowers in her hair, one frame inscribed "WILLEM DE V. PRINS VAN ORANIE ERFSTADHOUDER DER VEREENIGDE NEDERLANDEN," the other "FREDERIQUE SOPHIE WILHELMINE PRINCESSE DE PRUSSE," all embellished with floral scrolls and dentilate border round the rim. Low cover with faceted knopped finial embellished with minute sprigs.

William V of Orange (1748–1806) married Princess Frederika Sophie Wilhelmina, sister of Fredrick William II of Prussia in 1767. The youthful appearance of the prince, who was nineteen at his marriage, suggests that this glass was engraved at the time of, or very close to their marriage. The engraved sources for the portraits would suggest this as well: an engraving after a painting by Daniel Chodowiecki of 1767 of the princess, and a print by J. Houbraken after a drawing of the Prince by Aert Schouman, based on a painting by T. P. C. Haag (see above, p. 126, figs. 250 and 249).

Stylistically, the engraved portraits, with effective polished details, are reminiscent of the work of the German glass engravers Christiaen and Christoffel Gottlieb Schröder based in Delft, whose very similar portraits were first discussed by H. E. van Gelder (1958 III, pp. 148–154). The age of the Dutch ruler and his wife would suggest that this glass is a product of the workshop of the younger Schröder, possibly by an apprentice, as the technique is not of the quality normally associated with Schröder himself.

For shape and decoration, comparison should be made with a very similar goblet, engraved by the same hand with reversed portrait of William V alone, at one time in the German art trade (1983–1987, Brunnarius, Obershagen; see above, p. 126, fig. 252).

## 194 GOBLET WITH INSET MEDALLIONS IN TRANSPARENT COLORS

North Bohemia, about 1720

Height: 21.3 cm; diameter at rim: 9.8 cm; thickness of glass: about 2 mm

Colorless glass with thread inclusions, wheel engraving, polished circlets, polychrome transparent decoration and gilding. Pontil polished out.

Wide foot with polished rosette on the base. Stem with wrythen baluster and flattened knop enclosing gold and red threads, flanked by collars. Deep conical bowl cut with flutes and blazes on the base. Sides decorated with three inset oval medallions painted in transparent colors with emblematic scenes, all within narrow gilt frames and strapwork scrolls: Cupid with his eyes bound, Cupid forging a heart on his anvil, and Cupid appeasing an angry Mars, all in red, yellow, brown, blue, and green, and surrounded by symmetrical foliate scrolls.

The emblematic motifs are based on the anonymously compiled *Devises et Emblemes / Anciennes & Modernes / tirées des plus celebres Auteurs / Oder: / Emblematische / Gemüths-Vergnügung / Bey Betrachtung ... der curieusesten und ergötzlichen / Sinn-Bildern / Mit ihren zuständigen / Teutsch=Lateinisch=Frantzösisch=/ und Italienischen Beyschrifften*, which already in 1703 (the date of the copy most used in Berlin!) was in its fifth edition, edited by Lorentz Kroniger and Gottlieb Göbels Seel, Erben in Augsburg. According to Henkel/Schöne (1976, p. LXVI, no. 338) the first German edition of Daniel de La Feuille's emblem book, published in Amsterdam in 1691, first came out anonymously in 1693.

The medallions are based on the following emblems from the fifth edition in which only the German inscriptions are quoted here: Page 8, Emblem no. 3: "Ein Cupido ohne Köcher, Pfeil und Bogen, aber mit verbundenen Augen: ... 'Augen schöner Jungfrauen seynd meine Pfeile'" (a Cupid without quiver, bow or arrow, but with bound eyes: ... The eyes of young maidens are my arrows); Page 50, Emblem no. 9: "Ein Cupido schmidet ein Hertz auf einem Amboß: ... 'Nur für euch allein'" (a cupid forges a heard on an anvil: ...'For you alone'); Page 9, Emblem no. 8: "Ein ergrimmter Mars, welcher von der Liebe bezäumet wird: ...'Bezwinget den Zorn'" (An enraged Mars being calmed by Love: ... 'Conquer Anger'), (see above, p. 130, figs. 255–257).

For the extremely rare use of the technique of transparent colors on glass in the eighteenth century see various parallels and variations in: The Corning Museum of Glass, Corning (formerly Strauss Collection: Strauss 1955, no. 271); Museum für Kunsthandwerk, Frankfurt a. M. (Ohm 1973, no. 452, ill.); the Toledo Museum of Art, Toledo, Ohio (Inv. no. 50, 15, gift of Edward Drummond Libbey, 1950; formerly in the F. Neuburg Collection, Schmidt Ms 1931, no. 374); Schloss Favorite near Rastatt (Rudolf Sillib, *Schloß Favorite und die Eremitagen der Markgräfin Franziska Sibylla Augusta von Baden-Baden*, Heidelberg 1914, p. 96).

The large service of beakers and goblets (see above, p. 129, fig. 258a and b) at Schloss Favorite near Rastatt, which was built as a summer residence for the Margravine Franziska Sibylla Augusta of Baden-Baden, was probably commissioned as part of the first wave of the furnishing of that residence, which was more or less complete by 1720 (for this see also cat. no. for a discussion of dates; see also above, p. 128, footnote 16). As a daughter of the Duke of Sachsen-Lauenburg, she spent her youth at the North Bohemian castle of Schlackenwerth, and she based her new residence in Baden on it, as well as ordering all the glassware from her Bohemian homeland. Thus the stylistic and technical similarities between these glasses and the Wolf glass and its related variants in Corning and Ohio make possible a point of reference for date of manufacture and place of origin.

## 195 COVERED GOBLET WITH INSET GILT MEDALLION

Bohemia, about 1720–1725

Height: 27.6 cm (with cover), 18 cm (without cover); diameter at rim: 9 cm; thickness of glass: about 1–1.5 mm (bowl and cover)

Colorless glass with colored thread inclusions, wheel engraving, and polished circlets and an engraved and gilt medallion. Small, unpolished pontil mark; small crack in medallion.

Wide foot engraved on the upper side with foliate scrolls. Wrythen baluster stem enclosing twisted red and gold threads, all flanked by collars. Deep, conical bowl with central inset medallion engraved and gilt with a leaping stag within a scrollwork cartouche (coat-of-arms?) within a plain, gilt border and engraved scroll cartouche punctuated with polished circlets, and flanked by symmetrical scrolls with pendant, floral sprays. Flattened cover with everted rim and engraved scrolls matching the foot. Wrythen finial with gold-thread inclusions.

For the relatively rare technique of the inset engraved and gilt medallion see variants in: formerly Krug Collection, Baden-Baden (with arms of Lüttichau: Klesse 1973, no. 699, ill.; Sotheby's, Krug II, lot no. 395, col. ill.; Rückert 1982, II, p. 247, Notes to no. 755); The Art Institute, Chicago (formerly Mühsam Collection with arms of the Nuremberg families of Imhoff and Muffel von Eschenau, 1720–1734: Schmidt 1914, no. 328, pl. 34; Rückert 1982, II, p. 247, notes to no. 755); an example at one time in the Friedrich Neuburg Collection, Dresden/Leitmeritz (with bunch of flowers: Schmidt Ms. 1931, no. 373) Bayerisches Nationalmuseum, Munich (with small Bavarian Elector's coat-of-arms, probably for the Elector Max Emanuel (1679–1726): Rückert 1982, II, no. 755, pl. 218); one formerly in the Philipp Schwarz Collection, Stuttgart (with mirror monogram "CA": Auction cat. Helbing, Munich, 25 October 1916, no. 299, pl. XI).
This group is distinguished by the inset medallion and the shallow wheel engraving (cartouche frames with polished circlets and scrolls). Although mainly combined with wrythen baluster stems with thread inclusions, they are also found with faceted and molded pedestal stems, so that, besides a possible Bohemian origin, perhaps the Bohemian forest as suggested by Schmidt (1914 notes to no. 328) and Rückert (1982, II, notes to 755); a Thuringian and Saxon one must be taken into consideration.

Lit.: Rückert 1982, II, p. 247, no. 755 (few of the examples mentioned here have actual medallions with gilt, engraved decoration, being mostly examples with *Zwischengold* medallions.)

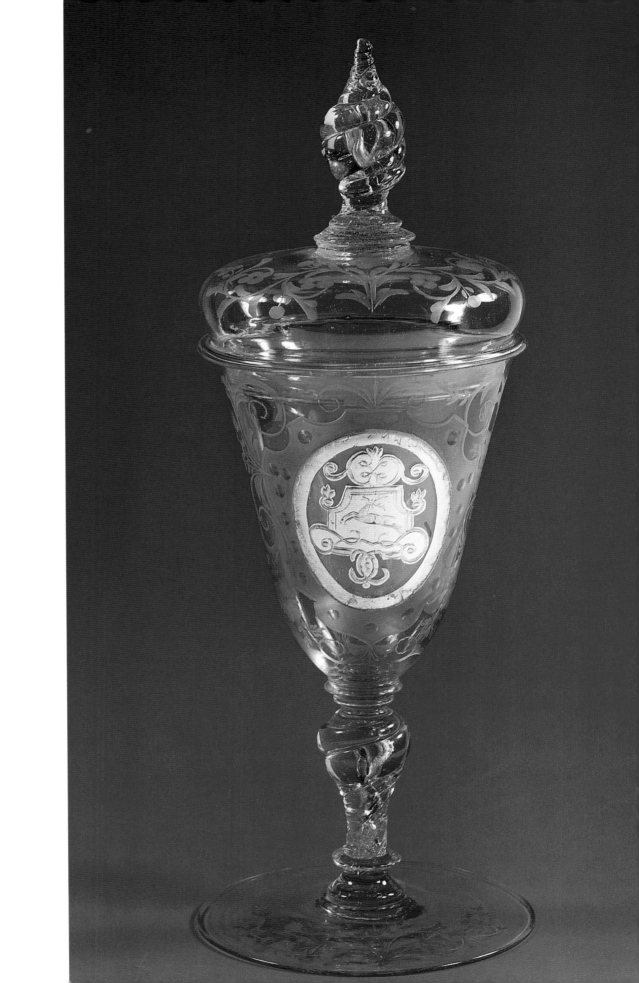

## 196 TWO COVERED GOBLETS WITH ZWISCHENGOLD MEDALLIONS

Bohemia, about 1720–1725

Height: a) 33.6 cm (with cover), 22.5 cm (without cover); diameter at rim: 10 cm;
b) 33 cm (with cover), 22.7 cm (without cover);
diameter at rim: 10.2 cm;
thickness of glass: a) and b) 2–2.5 mm (bowl),
1.5 mm (cover)

Colorless glass with colored thread inclusions, wheel engraving, and polished circlets, *Zwischengold* medallion and red lacquer. Pontil mark unpolished on both glasses.

Conical foot with engraved symmetrical foliate scrolls. Stem with wrythen baluster shaft and shoulder knop enclosing red and gold threads, flanked by collars. Deep, conical bowl decorated with inset *Zwischengold* medallions on red lacquer ground; on one goblet a crowned eagle, on the other a hunter shooting a stag, both medallions surrounded by a flat, matt scrolling frame punctuated by polished circlets and embellished with floral scrolls. Rim with matt line border. Low cover with everted rim and engraving matching the foot, wrythen knopped finial matching the stem.

For similar goblets of the same origin with identical or funnel-shaped bowl and *Zwischengold* medallions (some without red lacquer ground) see: one formerly in the Krug Collection, Baden-Baden (Klesse 1965, no. 374, ill; idem 1973, no. 698, ill.; Sotheby's, Krug IV, lot no. 747, ill. and lot no. 749, col. ill.); The Art Institute, Chicago (formerly Mühsam Collection: Schmidt 1914, nos. 315–317, ill. p. 67); Heine Collection, Karlsruhe (Baumgärtner 1971, no. 52, ill.); Kunstgewerbemuseum, Cologne (Cologne 1963, no. 374, ill., and 1973, no. 439, ill.); at one time in the Philipp Schwarz Collection, Stuttgart (Auction cat. Helbing, Munich, 25 October 1916, lot. no. 300; Schwarz 1916, p. 121, ill. p. 123, no. 145); Österreichisches Museum für angewandte Kunst (Bucher 1888, pl. VIII, 4164).

The use of the wrythen baluster stem with red and gold threads in most of the examples in this group would seem to confirm their Bohemian origin. The stylistic connection with the group of goblets with inset engraved and gilt medallions (see cat. no. 195) is also noticeable.

Lit.: Rückert 1982 II, p. 247, notes to no. 755.

## 197 GOBLET WITH ZWISCHENGOLD PANELS

Bohemia, about 1720

Height: 16.2 cm; diameter at rim: 7.7 cm;

thickness of glass: about 3–3.5 mm

Colorless glass with cutting, wheel engraving, imbricated *Zwischengold* section and red lacquer. Unpolished pontil mark; rim chipped; *Zwischengold* panels with small spots of moisture deterioration, one completely restored.

Base of conical foot with polished rosette; faceted baluster stem flanked by collars; deep, decagonal faceted funnel bowl. Vertical panels alternately decorated with engraved foliate scrolls and oblong *Zwischengold* panels, each with a rich foliate scroll surmounted by an emblem of love (two burning hearts, a burning heart beneath a sunflower and shining sun, and a crowned heart).

No parallel example of this unusual form of *Zwischengold* decoration has as yet been recorded.

## 201 COVERED GOBLET WITH ENGRAVED ZWISCHENGOLD DECORATION

Bohemia, about 1720–25

Height: 23 cm (with cover), 16.3 cm (without cover); diameter at rim: 7.4 cm;

thickness of glass: 2.5–3 mm

Colorless, partly double-walled glass with cutting, gilt engraving, colored lacquered painting, and imbricated *Zwischengold* decoration. Pontil mark polished out; rim of goblet chipped and with small crack.

Wide foot with polished rosette on the underside. Faceted baluster stem flanked by collars. Double-walled bowl with nineteen vertical facets, base with gilt, imbricated acanthus rosette, and gilt acanthus frieze at the double-wall joint. The exterior of the inner wall decorated with gilt engraving and red and green lacquer painting: on both sides a bird perched on calligraphic scrolls as well as pendant flower spray beneath opposed foliate scrolls, and flanked by further symmetrical scrolls. Low, faceted cover with fourteen cut facets with central, double-walled section including a *Zwischengold* medallion decorated with a flowerhead within foliate scrolls. Faceted spire finial.

Compare with similar glasses (with slightly differing decoration) in: Staatliche Kunstsammlungen, Kassel (with replaced foot, no inv. no.); Kunstgewerbemuseum, Prague (with dancing dwarfs between foliate scrolls, Inv. no. 16460); the E. Hickisch Collection, Glasmuseum, Rheinbach.

Together with cat. nos. 200 and 202, this goblet belongs to a distinct group of glasses, which on the grounds of technical and stylistic similarities may well be products of the same workshop. The fact that the decorative motifs are confined to early strap and scrollwork with typical bunches of fruit and flowers, as well as calligraphic scrolls (for this see Pazaurek 1902, pp. 12–13, figs. 10 and 11) with figural motifs playing a minor role in between, suggests a date around 1720 to 1725, within the early period of *Zwischengold* production. This applies to the engraving as well, which is found for instance on dice tumblers (see cat. no. 199), as well as similar types of *Zwischengold*

tumblers (see cat. no. 198). The various types of goblets encountered within this group so far are of the classic Bohemian forms of the first quarter of the eighteenth century.

## 202 ENGRAVED COVERED ZWISCHENGOLD GOBLET DECORATED WITH THE FOUR SEASONS

Bohemia, about 1720–1725

Height: 26 cm (with cover), 18 cm (without cover); diameter at rim: 8 cm; thickness of glass: about 2.5–4 mm (bowl and cover)

Colorless glass, partly double-walled, with cutting, gilt engraving, polychrome lacquer painting, and imbricated *Zwischengold* decoration. Pontil mark polished out. Decoration with areas of moisture discoloration. Rim and finial chipped.

Underside of foot with polished rosette. Faceted baluster and shoulder knop flanked by collars. Double-walled, conical bowl faceted at the base, the remainder with vertical facets. Base of bowl with gilt, imbricated, acanthus-leaf medallion and gilt, scalloped border at the double-wall joint. The remainder decorated on the exterior of the internal wall with gilt engraving, and red, dark green, and dark brown (possibly originally only red and green) lacquer painting: calligraphic socles surmounted by symbols of the Four Seasons as children with basket of flowers for Spring, sheaf of corn for Summer, basket of fruit for Autumn, and faggots for Winter, all four separated by bunches of flowers and scrollwork. Low, faceted cover with central double-walled *Zwischengold* medallion with acanthus rosette within wavy scrolls with red and green lacquer contours. Finial with faceted knop and spire finial.

The graphic source for the motifs of the Four Seasons is taken from those on the title page of the engraved works of André Félibien, based on the designs for a series of gobelins tapestries by Charles Lebrun for Louis XIV *Les Quatres Élémens* ... originally published in 1665 and reissued in a German/French edition by Johann Ulrich Krauss in Augsburg in 1687. (Title for the Augsburg edition: *Tapisseries du Roy, où sont representez les quatre elemens et les quatre saisons ... Königlich Französische Tapezereyen ... in welchen die Vier Elemente samt den vier Jahr-Zeiten ... vorgestellet werden ... an den Tag gegeben und verlegt durch Johan Ulrich Krauss, Kupferstecher in Augsburg ... 1687,*

from Henkel/Schöne 1976, p. LXI, no. 300). See above, p. 69, fig. 117, and p. 131, fig. 259 a–d).

As opposed to the scantily-clothed children in the engraved source material, the figures on the glass are all wearing blouses and knee-length skirts. While this may have been intended to increase the scope for the use of color, it may also have been intended to remove any unseemly or erotic elements, which are also not found on standard *Zwischengold* glasses (see most recently Rückert 1982 II, p. 246). Such an artistic interpretation applied to this distinct group of glasses could strengthen the possibility that they are the products of a monastic workshop (see footnote to cat. no. 206). Of interest in this respect are the drawings of typical *Zwischengold* motifs and incomplete *Zwischengold* glasses, said by tradition to have been found at the Cistercian monastery of Hohenfurth on the Moldau, on the occasion of rebuilding the monks' cells (Rückert 1982 II, p. 246).

Compare also a late nineteenth-century goblet with only two of the Four Seasons; one of the them after the "Spring" on the Wolf goblet, probably executed for the firm of Lobmeyr, in the Österreichisches Museum für angewandte Kunst, Vienna (Neustifter 1978, I, p. 323).

## 203  GOBLET WITH FOUR SEASONS IN ENGRAVED ZWISCHENGOLD

Bohemia, about 1720–1725

Height: 18 cm; diameter at rim: 7.9 cm;
thickness of glass: about 3 mm

Colorless, partly double-walled glass with cutting, gilt engraving, polychrome lacquer painting, and *Zwischengold* decoration. Pontil polished out. Discoloration from moisture.

Provenance: Friedrich Neuburg Collection, Dresden/Leitmeritz; previously Consul Rosenberg Collection, Cologne.


Underside of foot with polished rosette. Faceted baluster shaft and shoulder knop. Double-walled, faceted bowl, in the base gilt imbricated acanthus medallion and gilt, scalloped border at the double-wall join. In between, a continuous frieze of gilt engraving and red and green lacquer painting on the exterior of the inner wall, with symbols of the Four Seasons in the form of children with respective attributes, (similar to cat. no. 202), and also infilled with floral sprays.

The symbolic figures are taken from the same engraved source as cat. no. 202, and show the same modified stylization. See respective footnote.

Lit.: Auction cat. Consul Rosenberg Collection, 1919, lot no. 666; Schmidt Ms 1931, pp. 330–331, no. 364 (here he describes the allegorical figures as "male").

## 204 BEAKER WITH FOUR SEASONS ALLEGORY IN ENGRAVED ZWISCHENGOLD

Bohemia, second quarter 18th century

Height: 8.7 cm; diameter: 6.9 cm; thickness of glass: about 5 mm

Colorless, double-walled glass with cutting, gilt engraving, polychrome lacquer painting, and imbricated *Zwischengold* decoration. Base with patches of moisture deterioration; rim chipped.

Flat base with small, inset *Zwischengold* medallion, with etched basket of flowers on red lacquer ground. Double-walled, conical body with cut, vertical facets decorated at the join with a gilt, scalloped border and round the base with gilt, acanthus-leaf border. In between a frieze of gilt engraved decoration with red, dark green, and (discolored?) brown lacquer painted details: above a foliate circlet on a thin base line the Allegory of the Four Seasons in the form of a woman with flower spray as Spring, a harvester as Summer, a woman with basket of fruit as Autumn, and man with bobble cap beside a fire as Winter. Due to the thickness of the sides the inner side of the rim is chamfered.

Compare the allegorical decoration (same technique but after different engraved sources) with a goblet in a German private collection (Saldern 1968, no. 265, ill.).

For further examples with the Four Seasons (after different engraved sources) see variants in pure *Zwischengold* technique in: Museés Royaux d'Art et d'Histoire, Brussels (Berryer 1957, p. 39, pl. XIX; *Trois Millénaires* 1958, no. 678, ill.); British Museum, London (goblet: London 1968, no. 200, ill.); The Metropolitan Museum of Art, New York (formerly Mühsam Collection; goblet: Schmidt 1926, no. 250, pl. 33; Kunstgewerbemuseum, Prague (tumbler: Prague 1970, no. 177, ill.).
See also variants in polychrome *Zwischengold*; as well as silver examples, in: formerly Krug Collection, Baden-Baden (after the same engraved originals but reversed: Klesse 1965, no. 363, ill.; Sotheby's, Krug IV, lot no. 758, col. ill.); The Metropolitan Museum of Art, New York (formerly Mühsam Collection: Schmidt 1914, no. 283, pl. 34).

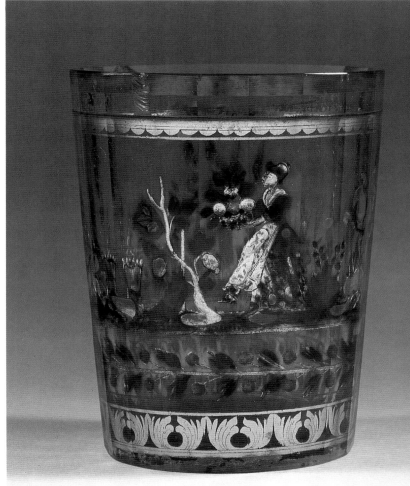

## 205 ENGRAVED ZWISCHENGOLD GOBLET WITH BEAR-HUNTING SCENE

Bohemia, about 1720–1730

Height: 18.1 cm; diameter at rim: 7.7 cm; thickness of glass: about 2.5 mm

Colorless, partly double-walled glass with cutting, gilt and silvered engraving, polychrome colors, and imbricated *Zwischengold* decoration. Pontil polished out. Patches of moisture deterioration overall. Lip chipped.

Provenance: Friedrich Neuburg Collection, Dresden/Leitmeritz.

Underside of foot with polished rosette. Faceted baluster stem with cut shoulder knop flanked by collars. Double-walled, conical bowl, the outer wall cut with eighteen vertical facets, and decorated with gilt, imbricated decoration: an acanthus-leaf medallion at the base below a gilt line border, at the join, below the rim a small leaf border. Central section with gilt and silvered engraving with red, green, as well as (discolored?) brown(?) and black(?) glazes on the exterior of the inner wall: above a broad band of foliate scrolls a continuous landscape, a huntsman standing among the trees while his hounds chase a bear, all gilt except for three silvered hounds.

This glass belongs to the same group as cat. nos. 200–204. See corresponding footnotes.

Lit.: Schmidt Ms 1931, pp. 330–331, no. 363 (as "Bohemian, about 1730").

## 206 COVERED ZWISCHENGOLD TUMBLER WITH PREACHING SCENE

North Bohemia, about 1730–1740

Height: 17.3 cm (with cover), 10.3 cm (without cover); diameter at rim: 8 cm; thickness of glass: about 3 mm

Colorless double-walled glass with cutting, imbricated *Zwischengold* decoration and red lacquer. Patches of moisture deterioration at the base. Cover finial with small chips. Cover possibly not original.

Provenance: Friedrich Neuburg Collection, Dresden/ Leitmeritz: previously Offermann Collection, Cologne (1894, according to Pazaurek 1902, p. 24).

Flat base with inset *Zwischengold* medallion with im- bricated Holy Initials "IHS" flanked by heart and cross in an oval frame supported by angels, on a red lacquer ground. Double-walled body with conical sides cut with twenty-one facets and decorated with *Zwischengold* frieze: above an acanthus leaf border a view of a church interior with a preacher in a baroque pulpit, from his mouth emerging the inscription "KOMMET AVF GERVSALEM," below him a stand- ing congregation. Beneath the pulpit a ribbon inscrib- ed in Roman capitals "P. PACIFICVS / KLIEGEL." Reverse with the fourteen Stations of the Cross with miniature scenes in oval frames in horizontal rows, each with inscribed number and description on rib- bons:

"DIE 1 STATION – IESV / WIRD ZVM / TOD / VERVR / VRTEIL"
"DIE 2 STATION – IESVS NIMT DAS / CREVTZ / AVF / SEINE SCHVL"
"DIE 3 STATION – IESVS VELD / DAS 1 MAHL VN / TERN CREVTZ"
"DIE 4 STATION – IESVS BEGENET / SEINER MVT / TER"
"DIE 5 STATION – IESVS BE / KOMMET ZV / EINER HILF / SIMON"
"DIE 6 STATION – IESVS WIRD / VON VERONI / CA EINSCH T GER"
"DIE 7 STATION – IESVS VELD / DAS 2 VNT / CREV"

"DIE 8 STATION – IESVS TROE / STET DIE / WW"
"DIE 9 STATION – IESVS VELDT / DAS 3 MAL VN / TERN"
"DIE 10 STATION – IESVS WIRD ENT / BLOEST MIT SC / VND GAL / GETREN"
"DIE 11 STATION – IESVS WIRDT / AN DAS CREVZ / GENAGELT"
"DIE 12 SATION – IESVS WIRDT / AM CREVTZ IN / DIE HOE ER / HOEBT"
"DIE 13 STATION – IESVS IN DIE / SCHOSEINER / MVT G"
"DIE 14 STATO – IESVS WIRDT / INS GRAB GE / LOEGET"

At the double-wall join simple gilt line border. Low cover with fifteen facets, and with central *Zwischengold* medallion with a lozenge within calligraphic scrolls and bunches of fruit. Finial with faceted flattened knop and spire finial.

Pazaurek's assumption that the label "P. Pacificus Kliegel" was an artist's signature (1898, pp. 53 onwards; 1902, p. 24), an opinion briefly held by J. Brožová (1973, pp. 61 onwards), was not supported by Robert Schmidt in his unpublished manuscript of the Neuburg Collection (Ms 1931, pp. 328–329). A far more likely explanation is that it is a label identifying the preacher as Father Pacificus, who must obviously have been a beloved sermonizer.
Thanks to Jarmila Brožová we know quite a lot about his life (1973, pp. 60–84): Kliegel (1687–1746). He came from Hassitz in the canton of Glatz, and entered the Franciscan Order on the 14 October 1710 at the Leobschütz Monastery in Silesia, receiving in the same year the minor orders in the cathedral at Breslau and became sub-deacon. From 1712 he was deacon in the Church of St. Martin, and was promoted to presbyter in 1713 and preacher in 1717. After a period at the Silesian monastery of Oppau (1722–1724) and Goldberg (1725–1729), he moved to the monastery of Arnau in Bohemia, and after three years moved again, this time to the monastery of Haindorf (1733–1735), where he remained until his death. On his annual tithe-collecting trips he would have covered the whole area embracing the North Bohemian glassmaking centers. It is therefore highly likely that the Wolf tumbler would have come from this area, and it would have been made during the time he was at Arnau and Haindorf (for closest examples see above, p. 132, fig. 260). There are three further tumblers possibly by the same hand as the Kliegel tumbler with views of the Haindorf monastery and the Madonna of Mercy there, one in The Art Institute, Chicago (Schmidt 1914, no. 307), Museum für Kunsthandwerk, Frankfurt a. M. (Ohm 1973, no. 444, ill.), and Kunstgewerbemuseum, Prague (Brožová 1973, ill. p. 83).

Lit.: G. E. Pazaurek, "Die Heimat der Zwischengoldgläser," in: *Mitteilungen des Nordböhmischen Gewerbemuseums XVI*, 1898, pp. 53 onwards; idem 1902, p. 24; idem in: *Belvedere I*, 1922, p. 188; Schmidt Ms. 1931, pp. 328–329, no. 345; J. Brožová, "Das böhmische Doppelwandglas und seine Hersteller," in: *Acta UPM VIII*, Kunstgewerbemuseum, Prague 1973, pp. 61–66, 71–72, 167–168; Charleston 1977, p. 41; O. Drahotová, in: Exhibition catalogue of *Czechoslovakian Glass* 1350–1980, The Corning Museum of Glass, Corning N. Y. 1981, p. 29; J. Brožová, "Jagdmotive auf böhmischem Doppelwandglas," in: *Tschechoslowakische Glasrevue XXXVI*, 1981, part 8, p. 17; Drahotová 1982, p. 139; O. Drahotová, "Neuer Blick auf die Tradition des böhmischen Glases," in: *Tschechoslowakische Glasrevue XXXIX*, 1984, part 12, p. 6.

KOMMET AVF GERVSALEM

P. PACIFICVS
...REGNI...

DIE 1 STATION   DIE 2 STATION

IESVS WIRD ZVM
TODT VERVR
THEILT

IESVS NIMBT DAS
CREVTZ AVF
SEINE...

DIE 8 STATION   DIE 9 STATION   DIE 10 STAT

IESVS TROST
DIE...

IESVS FVELT
DAS 3 MAL VN
TERM...

DIE 7 STATION   DIE 10 STATION

IESVS FVELT
DAS 2 MAHL VN
TERM CREVTZ

IESVS BEGEGNET
SEINER MVT
TER

DIE 10 STATION   DIE 11 STATION

IESVS WIRDT
REDE STAMPFET
WIRDT...

IESVS WIRDT
AN DAS CREV
GENA...

DIE 6 STATION   DIE 7 STATION

IESVS WIRD
VON VERONI
TIGET

IESVS FVELT
DAS ZVM
CREVTZ

DIE 13 STATION   DIE 14 STAT

IESVS VND IE
SCHOS SEINER
MVT...

IESVS WIRD
INS GRABE
GELOEGT

## 207 ZWISCHENGOLD COVERED GOBLET WITH PRUSSIAN ROYAL PORTRAIT

Bohemia, about 1740

Height: 26.8 cm (with cover), 19.3 cm (without cover);
diameter at rim: 8.3 cm;
thickness of glass: about 4 mm (bowl),
and 2 mm (cover)

Colorless, partly double-walled glass with cutting and *Zwischengold* decoration. Pontil mark polished out. Patches of moisture deterioration at the join. Rim chipped.

Provenance: possibly the Collection of the Dukes of Anhalt-Dessau, Schloss Dessau.

Underside of foot with polished rosette. Faceted baluster stem with cut, flattened shoulder knop flanked by collars. Double-walled bowl, the conical sides cut with twenty-one vertical facets. In the base an acanthus-leaf rosette; on the sides a portrait bust in profile to dexter of the King of Prussia (probably Frederick the Great) within an oval cartouche with soldier supporters and weapon trophies. Join embellished with gilt-line border. Low fifteen-faceted cover with central *Zwischengold* medallion with acanthus-leaf rosette within scrolls and bunches of fruit. Finial matches the stem.

As there is no monogram or other form of identification, and considering the difficulty of identifying a sitter from a profile, the portrait could be cautiously identified as either Frederick the Great (reigned 1740–1786) or his father, Frederick William I (reigned 1713–1740). The soldier supporters could be a reference to the Royal Prussian Life Guards or "Langen Kerls," founded by the latter, but particularly prominant in the reign of his son.
Compare with a very similar goblet in: the Württembergisches Landesmuseum, Stuttgart (Inv. no. G 27, 98, with a substitute cover).

## 208 ZWISCHENGOLD COVERED GOBLET WITH INSCRIPTION

Bohemia, second quarter 18<sup>th</sup> century

Height: 23.5 cm (with cover), 17.2 cm (without cover); thickness of glass: about 2–2.5 mm (bowl), 3–3.5 mm (cover)

Colorless, partly double-walled glass with cutting and imbricated, *Zwischengold* decoration. Pontil mark polished out. Underside of foot with number "74" and ducal crown in sealing wax red.

Provenance: Collection of the Dukes of Anhalt-Dessau, Schloss Dessau.

Underside of foot with polished rosette. Faceted baluster stem with cut shoulder knop. Double-walled, conical bowl cut with twenty-two vertical facets and decorated with imbricated, *Zwischengold* frieze: in the base, a clover rosette, on the sides acanthus scrolls below a short section of landscape with a town besieged by cannon, above the four-part inscription: "GOtt BeSCHItZE DAS LAND BRAVE BLANNE / BURG VND SEGNE VNSER WAFFEN. / SO KOeNNeN MIR IN RVh / VND FRIeDeN SChLAFFeN," on the reverse symmetrical scrolls. Join embellished with giltline border. Low faceted cover with central *Zwischengold* medallion with lozenge and acanthus scrolls, double vollute, and circlet of flowers. Faceted spire finial.

A note by Alfred Wolf points out the possibility that the inscription refers to Brandenburg ("BLANNE-BVRG").

## 209 ZWISCHENGOLD COVERED GOBLET WITH DINING SCENE

Bohemia, about 1730–1740

Height: 24.8 cm (with cover), 18 cm (without cover);
diameter at rim: 8 cm;
thickness of rim: about 3 mm (bowl), 2–4 mm (cover)

Colorless, partly double-walled glass with cutting and imbricated *Zwischengold* decoration. Pontil mark polished out. Inner rim of cover and finial with small chips.

Underside of foot with polished rosette. Faceted baluster stem flanked by collars. Deep, conical, double-walled bowl cut with eighteen facets and decorated with *Zwischengold* frieze: in the base an acanthus rosette below a circlet of acanthus-leaf scrolls and bunches of fruit. Above this a continuous gilt line and convivial scene of gentlemen seated round a table, smoking and playing cards, to one side two standing with dog and cat, as well as a maid carrying a jug. Double-wall join with gilt scalloped border. Low, faceted cover with central *Zwischengold* medallion with large sunflower within acanthus scrolls.

See a goblet with very similar frieze in The Art Institute, Chicago (formerly Mühsam Collection: Schmidt 1914, no. 294, pl. 33).

## 210  ZWISCHENGOLD TUMBLER WITH GALLANT SCENE

Bohemia, about 1730–1740

Height: 8.2 cm; diameter: 6.6 cm;
thickness of glass: about 3.5 mm

Colorless, double-walled glass with cutting, imbricated *Zwischengold* and silver decoration as well as red lacquer. Basal medallion with moisture stains.

Flat base inset with *Zwischengold* medallion with an emblem of Love: a prone heart, above it one in flight with inscription in Roman capitals "VNTER DESSEN VNVOR GESSEN." Double-walled, conical body cut with sixteen vertical facets and *Zwischengold* frieze flanked by basal, stiff-leaf, acanthus border and smaller, acanthus-leaf border at the join. Continuous *Zwischengold* scene with park landscape, in the foreground two gentlemen seated at a table blowing hunting horns, the reverse with a dancing and a courting couple, and a dog among the trees.

For examples with almost identical decoration see one: formerly in the Krug Collection (Klesse 1965, no. 373, ill.; Sotheby's, Krug II, lot no. 397, col. ill.); and in The Metropolitan Museum of Art (formerly Mühsam Collection: Schmidt 1914, no. 264 and 265 pl. 31).
See also variants with similar gallant scenes in: the Art Institute, Chicago (formerly Mühsam Collection: Schmidt 1914, no. 293, pl. 30); Kunstmuseum, Düsseldorf (Jantzen 1960, no. 119, pl. 59; Heinemeyer 1966, no. 428, ill.); Huelsmann Collection, Hamburg (Saldern 1968, no. 260); K. H. Heine Collection, Karlsruhe (Baumgärtner 1971, no. 118, col. pl.); the Nordböhmisches Gewerbemuseum, Liberec (Reichenberg), (Pazaurek 1902, pl. 35c).

## 211 ZWISCHENGOLD COVERED GOBLET WITH HUNTING SCENE

Bohemia, second quarter 18th century
Height: 23.8 cm (with cover), 16.4 cm (without cover);
diameter at rim: 7.7 cm;
thickness of glass: about 2.5 mm

Colorless, partly double-walled glass with cutting and imbricated *Zwischengold* decoration. Pontil mark polished out. Inner rim of cover with small chips.

Plain foot and faceted baluster and flattened shoulder knop between collars. Double-walled, conical bowl cut with sixteen vertical facets and decorated with *Zwischengold* frieze: basal florette and scroll border below a continuous forest and mountain scene with four hunters pursuing chamois and ibex, an assistant already removing the dead animals, in the background a castle. Double-wall join with gilt acanthus-leaf border. Low sixteen-faceted cover with central *Zwischengold* medallion with acanthus scrolls. Cut acorn finial.

The hunting scenes were perhaps inspired by Matthäus Merian's large chamois and ibex hunting scene of 1616 (see Wüthrich 1966, I, no. 410, fig. 191).
Compare with other glasses decorated with chamois and ibex in: formerly Krug Collection, Baden-Baden (*Zwischengold* tumbler: Klesse 1973, no. 690, ill.; Sotheby's, Krug I, lot no. 167, col. pl.); The Metropolitan Museum of Art, New York (formerly Mühsam Collection: in polychrome, glazed on a silver ground: Schmidt 1914, no. 256, pl. 33).

## 212 TWO ZWISCHENGOLD BEAKERS WITH HARE- AND BEAR-HUNTING SCENES

Bohemia, about 1725–1740

Height: a) 7.5 cm; b) 7.3 cm;
diameter: a) and b) 6.7 cm;
thickness of glass: a) and b) about 3–3.5 mm

Colorless, double-walled glass with cutting and imbricated *Zwischengold* and red lacquer decoration. b) the basal medallion missing and small chips on lip and foot rim.

Provenance: b) possibly Friedrich Neuburg Collection, Dresden/Leitmeritz.

Flat base inset with *Zwischengold* medallion with leaping stag on red lacquer ground. Double-walled, conical sides cut with eighteen vertical facets and decorated with *Zwischengold* frieze. Both with lower, silver, acanthus-leaf border below a continuous forest scene with huntsman on foot shooting two hares, while on the reverse another huntsman on foot and a mounted huntsman with smoking pistols and pack of hounds are bringing down a bear. The same scenes on both tumblers with only slight variations as to hounds and trees. Double wall join with silver, scrolling, acanthus-leaf border (a), and acanthus, stiff-leaf border (b).

Compare with other examples with almost identical hunting scenes and decorative borders (as on b) in: Kestner Museum, Hannover (Mosel 1957, no. 257, ill; 1979, no. 282, ill.; Savage, 1965, fig. 70); and James A. de Rothschild Collection, Waddesdon Manor (Charleston 1977, pp. 253–255, no. 73, ill.).
Compare also with a variant in: Museum für Kunsthandwerk, Frankfurt a. M. (Ohm 1973, no. 439, ill.).

Both tumblers are by the same hand. The huntsmen are almost in caricature, with their exaggerated tricorn hats and double-clouds of smoke (issuing from barrel and lock) and are found on other *Zwischengold* glasses. See for example a flask with similar bear hunt in The Metropolitan Museum of Art, New York (former Mühsam Collection: Schmidt 1914, no. 301, pl. 34),

as well as a tumbler in the Kestner Museum, Hannover (with reduced rim: Mosel 1957, no. 258; 1979, no. 283, ill.), and a tumbler in the Kunstgewerbemuseum, Prague (Brožová 1981, p. 16, fig. 6). Perhaps they are all products of the same workshop (see above, p. 133, fig. 261).

Lit.: (b): Lempertz auction 447, Cologne, 15 May 1957, lot no. 631, pl. 26; Schmidt Ms 1931, no. 336.

## 213 ZWISCHENGOLD FLASK WITH DANCING PEASANTS

Bohemia, about 1730–1740

Height: 11.7 cm (with stopper), 9.6 cm (without stopper); diameter at base: 6.9 cm; thickness of glass: about 5 mm

Colorless, double-walled glass with cutting and imbricated *Zwischengold* decoration. Patches of moisture deterioration on the shoulder. Stopper replaced.

Provenance: Friedrich Neuburg, Dresden/Leitmeritz.

Flat base with polished rosette. Double-walled, tapering body cut with sixteen exterior vertical facets terminating at the rounded shoulder, on which is a single-walled, plain, cylindrical, short neck. Fitted stopper with cut wafer finial. Sides decorated with a continuous *Zwischengold* scene above a clover-leaf border of a peasant with drum and his lady with flute, playing for three dancing couples. Shoulder decorated with acanthus-leaf scrolling frieze.

The engraved sources for the dancing peasants may have derived from prints in the manner of Pieter Nolpe.

On the technique of this type of flask see Neustifter 1978, I, p. 321, fig. 13 and 15.
For similar flasks (with differing *Zwischengold* decoration) see examples in: formerly Krug Collection, Baden-Baden (one with hare- and one with stag-hunting scenes: Klesse 1965, no. 366 and 367, ill.; Sotheby's, Krug IV, lot no. 743, ill and 763, col. ill.); The Art Institute, Chicago (formerly Mühsam Collection, with arms of the Austrian families of Moser, Plankenheim and Thannhausen (?): Schmidt 1914, no. 274, pl. 34; with stag hunt; idem 1926, no. 238, pl. 34); The Metropolitan Museum of Art, New York (formerly Mühsam Collection, with bear hunt: Schmidt 1914, no. 301, pl. 34) Kunstgewerbemuseum, Prague (with arms of Franz-Gregor Giannini, 1722–1730, prelate in Olmütz and Breslau: exhibition cat. *Le Baroque en Bohême*, Grand Palais, Paris 1981, p. 197, no. 195, ill.); Österreichisches Museum für angewandte Kunst, Vienna (with same arms as on Chicago flask: Neustifter 1978 I, p. 321, fig. 15).
For the rare theme of the peasant dance see a *Zwischengold* goblet in The Metropolitan Museum of Art, New York (formerly Mühsam Collection: Schmidt 1926, no. 249, pl. 33).

Lit.: Schmidt Ms 1931, no. 348.

## 214 ZWISCHENGOLD GOBLET WITH POLYCHROME TROPHIES AND FLOWERS

Bohemia, about 1740–1745

Height: 15.6 cm; diameter at rim: 7.3 cm; thickness of glass: about 3.5 mm

Colorless, partly double-walled glass with cutting, imbricated *Zwischengold* and silver foil decoration as well as colored glazes. Pontil mark polished out. Small chips on rim.

Underside of foot with polished rosette. Faceted baluster stem flanked by collars. Double-walled, conical bowl cut with nineteen vertical facets and with imbricated *Zwischengold* decoration: in the base a leafy medallion below an acanthus-leaf, scrolling border; sides decorated with opposed silver trophies and a vase with large flower arrangement, overglazed in red, green, yellow, and brown. Double-wall join with gilt line borders.

The bowl with ogee basal section is very rare in examples decorated with *Zwischengold*. See parallels (with *Zwischengold* decoration) in: The Art Institute, Chicago (formerly Mühsam Collection: Schmidt 1914, no. 276, ill. and no. 309, pl. 30); Museum für Kunsthandwerk, Frankfurt a. M. (Ohm 1973, no. 447, ill.).

## 215 ZWISCHENGOLD BEAKER WITH POLYCHROME DUELING SCENE

Bohemia, second quarter 18th century

Height: 8.5 cm; diameter: 6.6 cm;
thickness of glass: about 3.5–4 mm

Colorless, double-walled glass with cutting, imbricated *Zwischengold* and silver decoration, as well as colored glazes. Patches of moisture deterioration in basal medallion and at the upper joint; rim chipped.

Flat base with inset *Zwischengold* medallion with flower spray on red lacquer ground. Double-walled, conical body cut on the exterior with twenty-two vertical facets, and decorated with imbricated frieze; above a gilt, acanthus-leaf border a continuous scene imbricated on silver foil, embellished with red, yellow, green, brown, and black glazes, of two skirmishes between pairs of horsemen, one with Turkish turban and scimitar, another already struck down and lying in front of a tent. Upper join with gilt line border.

Compared with the more common dueling scenes with pistols (see Schmidt 1914, no. 279 and 280, pl. 34; idem 1926, no. 254, pl. 34; Klesse 1965, no. 357, ill.; Sotheby's, Krug I, lot no. 166, col. pl.) dueling scenes with sabers and scimitars are rarer. See for example a tumbler in the Kunstmuseum, Düsseldorf (Heinemeyer 1966, no. 424, ill. ) and, in the same technique as the Wolf tumbler, one in The Art Institute, Chicago (formerly Mühsam Collection: Schmidt 1926, no. 255, pl. 34).

## 216 BEAKER WITH POLYCHROME STAG HUNT

Bohemia, second quarter 18th century

Height: 10 cm; diameter: 8.1 cm;
thickness of glass: about 3–4.5 mm

Colorless, double-walled glass with cutting, imbricated *Zwischengold* and silver decoration, as well as colored glazes. Base with stains from moisture.

Flat base with imbricated, silver, inset medallion with a hound pursuing a hare on a red-lacquer ground. Double-walled, conical body cut on the exterior with twenty vertical facets and decorated in imbricated foil with: a continuous forest scene with two horsemen, one with whip, the other firing a pistol, above a simple line border and large, acanthus-leaf border, on a silver foil frieze with glazes in red, green, brown, and black: on the reverse two hunters with hounds hunting a stag, one firing his gun. Simple, gilt-line border at the upper join.

## 217 ZWISCHENGOLD BEAKER WITH POLYCHROME FLORAL DECORATION

Bohemia, about 1720–1730

Height: 8.5 cm; diameter: 7.4 cm;
thickness of glass: about 3 mm

Colorless, double-walled glass with cutting, *Zwischengold* and silver decoration as well as polychrome glazes. Foot rim damaged; vertical crack in the outer wall; some moisture stains on the painted decoration.

Provenance: Friedrich Neuburg Collection, Dresden/Leitmeritz.


Flat base with inset *Zwischengold* medallion with red-painted rose spray on a silvered ground. Double-walled, conical body with twenty vertical facets cut on the outer wall and with overall silver-foil base. Upper and lower rims with simple, scalloped, gilt borders, flanking continuous scattered flower sprays, including rose, dianthus, tulip, lily, and narcissus in red, brown, yellow, and green. Upper join on the rim.

The colored painted glazes on solid rather than imbricated silver ground is a technical variant seldom encountered (see also above, p. 133).
See a parallel tumbler in the Kunstgewerbemuseum, Prague (Lanna Collection 890 as well as 362) as well as a variant in The Metropolitan Museum of Art, New York (formerly Mühsam Collection; in place of the flowers a horseman and townscape on silver ground: Schmidt 1926, no. 257).

Lit.: Schmidt Ms 1931, p. 331, no. 367 (as "Bohemia, about 1730").

## 218 FÜRNBERG PORTRAIT BEAKER

Lower Austria, Gutenbrunn, Johann Joseph Mildner, signed and dated 1791

Height: 10.7 cm; diameter: 7.6 cm; thickness of glass: about 4 mm

Colorless glass with cutting, *Zwischengold* medallion and colored, miniature portrait. Upper rim reduced; small chip on foot rim.

Provenance: Friedrich Neuburg Collection, Dresden/Leitmeritz; previously Bertha Kurtz Collection, Vienna.

Cylindrical body with flat base. Foot rim with applied inset border with a gilt, imbricated, guilloche border on red ground flanked by dot-and-reel borders. Wall set with central inset medallion with gilt-imbricated, oval, stiff-leaf frame within outer polished ovals, and enclosing a bust portrait of Friedrich Joseph Weber, Edler von Fürnberg, in profile to dexter, dressed in white frock coat with red velvet collar, jabot, and bag wig, on a green ground. On the gilt reverse of the medallion the imbricated inscription "Verfertiget / zu Gutenbrunn / im Fürnbergischen Großen / Weinspergwald / 1791. / Von Mildner."

As is well known, the Gutenbrunn glasshouse of Saggraben belonged to the Edler von Fürnberg (1742–1799) until 1795, where Johann Joseph Mildner (1765–1808) as well as his father Franz Xaver Mildner (1739–1802), and his brothers Franz (born 1767) and Johann (born 1778) were artisans officially described as "glass cutters." It was there that Mildner executed a considerable number of portrait glasses for the lord of the manor.

Compare with other identical Fürnberg portraits within different frames on beakers dated between 1788 and 1799 (in chronological order) in: The Corning Museum of Glass, Corning (formerly, Jerome Strauss Collection; formerly Friedrich Neuburg Collection, Dresden/Leitmeritz; formerly Ferdinand Oser Collection, Krems: 1788, single portrait to sinister: Vienna 1922, no. 3; Pazaurek 1923, p. 322; Strauss 1955, no. 280, ill.; Österreichisches Museum für angewandte Kunst, Vienna (1789: Vienna 1922, no. 7, fig. 1; Pazaurek 1923 p. 322; Pazaurek/Philippovich 1976, p. 301); Museum für Kunst und Gewerbe, Hamburg (1789: Pazaurek 1923, p. 323; Pazaurek/Philippovich 1976, p. 301); formerly Dr. Köhler Collection, Vienna (1790: Auction cat. at C. J. Wawra, Vienna, 1917, lot no. 673; Pazaurek 1923, p. 323; Pazaurek/Philippovich 1976, pp. 301–302); Kunstgewerbemuseum, Prague (1791: Inv. no. 24689 as well as further undated examples without no.); in a private collection (1791: Baumgärtner 1981, p. 104, col. pl. 152, incorrectly dated 1799); The Metropolitan Museum of Art, New York (formerly Mühsam Collection: 1792: Schmidt 1914, no. 336, pl. 35; Pazaurek 1923, p. 324; Pazaurek/Philippovich 1976, p. 304); Mahler Collection, Neenah, Wisconsin (previously Bertha Kurtz Collection, Vienna; 1792: Vienna 1922, no. 25; Pazaurek 1923, p. 324; Pazaurek/Philippovich 1976, p. 304; Strasser 1979, no. 89, col. ill.); Österreichisches Museum für angewandte Kunst, Vienna (1798: Vienna 1922, no. 55, fig. 6; Pazaurek 1923, pp. 322, 331–332, fig. 286; Pazaurek/Philippovich 1976, pp. 301, 310; Neustifter 1978 II, p. 1159, fig. 20); private collection, Vienna (1799: Prager 1976, ill. p. 28; Baumgärtner 1981, p. 104, col. pl. 151, incorrectly dated 1791; Prager 1983, p. 2933, fig. 4).

Lit.: Pazaurek 1923, p. 324 (at that time still in the Bertha Kurtz Collection, Vienna, and still with its upper rim border, Pazaurek/Philippovich 1976, p. 303); Schmidt Ms 1931, p. 142, no. 128.

## 219 BEAKER WITH ARMS
## OF THE WIRTH FAMILY

Lower Austria, Gutenbrunn, Johann Joseph Mildner, signed and dated 1795

Height: 10.8 cm; diameter 7.3 cm;
thickness of glass: about 3.5 mm

Colorless, double-walled glass with imbricated *Zwischengold* and silver decoration. Small patches of moisture deterioration on the frame of the medallion.

Provenance: Friedrich Neuburg Collection, Dresden/ Leitmeritz; before that Major Hetzner Collection, Dresden; before that Dr. Spitzner Collection, Dresden (according to Pazaurek; but not in auction cat. Spitzner Collection, 1918).

Cylindrical body with flat base and exterior and interior *Zwischengold* decoration. Interior of base with star cutting, exterior with *Zwischengold* on red ground with imbricated inscription "Verfertiget / zu Gutenbrunn, im / von Fürnbergischen grohsen / Weinspergwald / 1795 / Mildner," all within a stiff-leaf circular frame. Side with inset oval medallion with the gilt, imbricated arms of the family of Wirth (gate with two towers) and the inscription "ARMA WIRTH" on a red-lacquer ground within silver dot border, the medallion surmounted by pendant, laurel garlands below a silver dot border beneath the rim with laurel swags.

The arms were possibly for the Viennese court medallist Johann Nepomuk Wirth, whom Mildner could have known personally as Mildner executed a glass with a portrait of the Emperor Franz I of Austria, based on a medal by Wirth. (Baumgärtner 1981, p. 106, figs. 142 and 143).
For comparisons with the very few other completely double-walled beakers by Mildner, see one with similar laurel garlands and signature (dated 1794: in place of the coat-of-arms a crowned mirror monogram "CF") in the John Nelson Bergstrom Art Center and Mahler Glass Museum, Gift of Mrs. Ernst Mahler, Neenah, Wisconsin, (formerly Bertha Kurtz Collection), Vienna: Pazaurek 1923, pp. 326–327, fig. 283; Pazau-rek/ Philippovich 1976, pp. 306–307; JGS 22, 1980, p. 93, fig. 24).

Lit.: Pazaurek 1923, p. 328; Schmidt Ms 1931, p. 143, no. 130.

Verfertiget
zu Gutenbrunn, im
von Fürnbergischen großen
Weinspergwald,
1795.
Mildner.

ARMA WIRTH.

## 220 BEAKER WITH MONOGRAM AND PORTRAIT SILHOUETTES

Lower Austria, Gutenbrunn, Johann Joseph Mildner, signed and dated 1797

Height: 11.7 cm; diameter at rim: 7.6 cm; thickness of glass: about 3 mm

Colorless, partly double-walled glass with partial *Zwischengold* and silver decoration, colored and black painting and diamond engraving.

Provenance: Friedrich Neuburg Collection, Dresden/Leitmeritz.

Cylindrical body with flat base. Inside of basal medallion with three youthful silhouettes, one male and two female, in black on silver foil ground, framed by gilt scrolls on red lacquer ground; underside of basal medallion with gilt, eight-pointed star on silver ground, in the center the imbricated inscription within a circlet of stars: "Verfertiget / zu Gutenbrunn / von Mildner / 1797." Upper and lower rims with applied inset bands with silver stars and gilt lines on red lacquer ground. Sides embellished with opposed inset oval medallions, one with the monogram "ILD" and the other "WFJ" (or "FJW") in gilt on a black ground within a circlet of roses and forget-me-nots and outer frame of silver stars and gilt lines on red lacquer ground. On the silvered, reverse sides of the medallions a six-part imbricated inscription: "Freundschaft / ist das schönste Band, / Was nur je ein Mensch erfand, / Drum, dich Freundin, bitte ich / Dencke nur recht oft / an mich" and "Wahre Freundschaft / macht Vergnügen / Was die Falschheit nie gewährt / Diese, thut sie dan besiegen; / Weil sie wahre / Freunde ehrt." The gilt ground of the inside of the lip band is also inscribed: "Wein, erheitert das Gemüthe, macht uns fröhlich hier auf Erden, wenn, gewirzt durch Freundschafts-Gütte, solcher kañ getruncken werden." Medallions framed by diamond-engraved, forget-me-not chains held by ribbons at the top, and flanked by three floral swags.

Compare with similar richly-decorated variants in: formerly Dr. B. Růžička Collection, Budweis i. B. (dated 1797, with similar Friendship verses and silhouettes in the basal medallion: Pazaurek 1923, p. 331, fig. 285; Pazaurek/Philippovich 1976, p. 310); and one formerly in the Dr. Karl Ruhmann Collection, Vienna (Schlosser 1965, p. 302, col. pl. XIII).

Lit.: Schmidt Ms 1931, pp. 143–144, no. 135, see also above, p. 134.

# TABLE OF CONTENTS